CARE MANAGEME[N]
HEALTH CARE OF
PEOPLE

THE DARLINGTON COMMUNITY CARE
PROJECT

Care Management and Health Care of Older People

The Darlington Community Care Project

David Challis, Robin Darton, Lynne Johnson, Malcolm Stone and Karen Traske

PSSRU
UNIVERSITY OF KENT
AT CANTERBURY ■■■■

First published in Great Britain in 1995

Arena
Ashgate Publishing Ltd
Gower House
Croft Road
Aldershot
Hants GU11 3HR
England

Ashgate Publishing Company
Old Post Road
Brookfield
Vermont
U.S.A.

British Library Cataloguing in Publication Data
Challis, David
    Care Management and Health Care of Older
    People: Darlington Community Care Project
    I. Title
    362.60942863
    ISBN 1–85742–184–1

Library of Congress Cataloging-in-Publication Data
Care management and health care of older people:
    the Darlington community care project / David Challis ... [et al.]
        p. cm
    Includes bibliographical references and index.
    ISBN 1–85742–184–1 (hbk): $54.95 (est.)
    ISBN 1–85742–190–6 (pbk): $29.95 (est.)
    1. Frail elderly – Care – Great Britain. 2. Frail elderly – Home care –
    Great Britain. I. Challis, David, 1948- .
    HV1481.G52C354   1994   94–35859
    362.6′09428′63--dc20   CIP

Typeset by Jane Dennett at the PSSRU, University of Kent at Canterbury
Printed in Great Britain by Hartnolls Ltd, Bodmin, Cornwall

Contents

List of Boxes, Figures and Tables

Tables

Preface

This has been an exciting venture which has examined the benefits of a closer relationship between community care and geriatric services. The study has focused upon care management in the setting of a geriatric multidisciplinary team and the provision of care through community support staff with wide-ranging roles. Such a study of an innovative approach to community care would not have been possible without a great deal of assistance and cooperation, and there are many people to whom we are grateful for their contribution to this study. Although we cannot mention all who have helped us in a variety of ways, we thank them for their kindness. There are several who must be mentioned specifically.

The Joseph Rowntree Foundation (then the Joseph Rowntree Memorial Trust), which generously saw the value of the Darlington initiative and provided their support for the local research worker. Janet Lewis, on behalf of the Foundation, was a source of much support and encouragement throughout.

The Department of Health has supported PSSRU in the programme of studies of care management, without which this study would not have been possible. The interest and advice of several liaison officers — Hazel Canter, Sue Moylan, Jenny Griffin and Ruth Chadwick — were greatly valued.

We should like to thank the Unit Director, Professor Bleddyn Davies, for his support and infectious enthusiasm. Our external advisers — Professor J. Grimley Evans, Miss E.M. Goldberg, Professor Peter Huxley and Mr Ken Wright — were all invaluable sources of advice and encouragement.

Numerous staff in Darlington and Durham Health Authorities and Durham County Council Social Services Department generously gave their time to assist us and provide information. Of particular mention are the four consultants, Doctors Peter Carr, Philip Earnshaw, Paul Suri and Irene Wandless; the care managers from the original project, Eileen Peart, Clare Walker and Chris Timson; the service managers of the domiciliary care service, Jill Bywater and Carol Meaney, and their manager, John Browne; the home care assistants; and finally the project physiotherapist, Ceri Kent, and occupational therapist, Sally Anne Kelly. Mr Oliver Coles, then of the Research Department of Durham Social Services Department, kindly helped us in gathering information about the local service system. The General Manager of the Health Authority, Mr Geoff Nichol, the Director of Social Services, Mr Peter Kemp, the Darlington Social Services District Controller, Mr Alan Barton, and Mr David Flett, then the Director of Nursing Services, all did their best to facilitate the study for us. Dr Sushma Acquilla provided much help and friendly advice in setting up the study. Darlington Museum provided valuable advice on sources of information about the historical background of the area.

At the PSSRU, Barbara Wall assisted in setting up the database and undertook some of the initial analyses, and Andrew Fenyo also assisted in some of the data analysis. Glenys Harrison typed the drafts of the chapters with unfailing accuracy and good humour, and Nick Brawn prepared the map in Chapter 3.

The manuscript has been set by Jane Dennett at the PSSRU with her usual care and efficiency and it has benefited from her many helpful suggestions.

Finally, our particular debt is to the elderly people and their carers in the project, the locality and the comparison hospitals, who were so willing to help us and provide information.

Notwithstanding the kindness of all of these people, the responsibility for any final errors of the manuscript must lie with the authors alone.

David Challis, Reader in Social Work and Social Care,
   and Assistant Director, PSSRU.

Robin Darton, Research Fellow, PSSRU.

Lynne Johnson, Community Care Training and Development Officer,
   South Tyneside Health Care Trust. Formerly, Research Fellow, PSSRU,
   and Research Officer, Darlington Community Care Project.

Malcolm Stone, Senior Lecturer, New College, Durham, and
   Social Worker, North Yorkshire County Council Social Services Department.
   Formerly, Project Manager, Darlington Community Care Project.

Karen Traske, Research Officer, PSSRU.

1 Community Care for Older People

Dramatic and wide-ranging developments in community-based and long-term care for the elderly are occurring in many countries (Challis et al., 1994), and some broadly similar trends can be discerned. In their study of emerging patterns of change in services for elderly people in the Netherlands, Sweden and the United Kingdom, Kraan and colleagues (1991) noted a move away from institution-based care, made possible by the enhancement of home-based care and the development of the mechanisms of coordination and care management to achieve this. In the care of elderly people in many other countries — such as the United States, Canada, Australia and Japan — a similar trend can also be observed (Challis, 1992a,b). These patterns of change are designed to produce, at least at the margin, a degree of downward substitution in the provision of care, from high-cost to lower-cost solutions, from restrictive to less restrictive environments, and from institution-based to home-based care. Underlying this is a major debate about the extent to which community services complement or substitute for institutional care: one of the key questions addressed in this book. The role of care management, one of the mechanisms of change in organising packages of care to meet the needs of individual clients, was endorsed by Sir Roy Griffiths in his report *Community Care: Agenda for Action* (1988), and the 1989 White Paper *Caring for People* described assessment and case management as the cornerstones of the new policy, specifically citing the Darlington Community Care Project and the earlier Kent and Gateshead projects as demonstrations of the successful use of care management (Cm 849, 1989, para. 3.3.3).

The Darlington Community Care Project was designed to provide a community-based alternative to long-stay hospital care for physically frail elderly people. It sought to extend the care management approach of the Kent and Gateshead studies (Challis and Davies, 1986; Challis et al., 1990) into a geriatric multidisciplinary team. The care managers had devolved budgets and were responsible for multipurpose workers (home care assistants), whose role was to reduce overlap between personnel in providing hands-on care (Challis et al., 1989, 1991a,b). The project was one of 28 pilot projects funded by the Department of Health and Social Security under the Care in the Community Initiative (DHSS, 1983). The central funding lasted for three years from 1985 to 1988, and the project was then incorporated, in a modified form, into the local mainstream service system.

The project was designed to establish a care system for the very frail which would reduce duplication of tasks, provide more coordinated care by using the skills of a range of professional staff to optimum effect, and improve collaboration between key agencies. The referral, assessment and review of clients were undertaken by the geriatric multidisciplinary team, and the project team (consisting of a project manager and three care managers) was responsible for ensuring that the core tasks of care management were undertaken for the clients. The project developed enhanced home care for frail elderly people by combining the functions of a home help, an auxiliary nurse and aides to various professional staff into the activities of one person: the home care assistant. According to the differing needs of their frail elderly clients, the home care assistants acted as aides to, and were instructed by, several different health and social services personnel. The aim was both to extend the range of services and to reduce the number of hands-on staff involved in providing care to individual elderly people. Interagency collaboration was mediated through a joint coordinating group of senior managers and clinicians. Thus, the project employed the principles of care management both in the process of providing care to individual elderly people and, at the system level, in coordinating the activities of the key agencies.

This chapter provides an outline of some of the policy and practice influences in the development of community care, sets the project within this context and introduces the book as a whole.

Developments in community and long-term care for the elderly

Community care for priority groups

Since legislation such as the 1959 Mental Health Act and the White Paper *Health and Welfare: The Development of Community Care* (Cmnd 1973) in 1963, community care has been a long-standing policy objective in the United Kingdom for all client groups. Particular stress was laid upon the needs of the priority groups, of whom four were identified: elderly people, especially the most vulnerable and frail; mentally ill people; mentally handicapped people; and physically and sensorily handicapped people (DHSS, 1981a). During the 1970s and early 1980s, community care initiatives were mainly focused upon influencing the degree of coordination between health and social care through planning processes, financial transfers and financial incentives (Webb and Wistow, 1986). During 1980-81, the Department of Health and Social Security undertook a series of studies of national policies relating to the National Health Service and personal social services provision, covering the acute sector, the care of elderly hospital patients and community care. The study of community care concentrated on two areas: first, on the extent to which there had been a shift in the balance of care away from long-term hospital or residential provision for people on the boundary between institutional and other forms of care; and, second, on the contribution of the voluntary sector (DHSS, 1981c). It concluded that the appropriate pattern of community care needed to vary according to the client group, but that a package of services rather than a single service would have to be created for each individual to enable them to be cared for in the community. The provision of packages of services was seen to depend upon collaboration between health authorities and social services departments, both in planning services and in their provision to individual clients. Stress was also laid upon the role of the voluntary sector, and particularly of informal carers, in making community care feasible and cost-effective for individuals on the boundary between institutional and other forms of care. This represented a greater policy focus upon client-level activities.

For people with a mental handicap and people with a mental illness, the policy of reducing hospital provision and replacing it with community-based packages of care provided by health and local authorities was set out in the White Papers *Better Services for the Mentally Handicapped* (Cmnd 4683, 1971) and *Better Services for the Mentally Ill* (Cmnd 6233, 1975). For those people discharged from long-stay hospitals, the provision of a range of alternative accommodation, from ordinary housing to residential accommodation, located within the community was seen as an essential part of the package of care. In this case, community care appeared to be defined principally as 'non-hospital care' (Sinclair et al., 1990).

For elderly people generally, policies about levels of hospital provision were influenced by the projected increase in the number of very elderly people in the population. Between 1981 and 2001, the total number of people aged 65 and over in England and Wales was projected to increase by about 5 per cent, while the number of people aged 75 and over was projected to increase by nearly 30 per cent (OPCS, 1984b). The Government's policy to constrain public expenditure, combined with the change in the structure of the elderly population, was reflected in the emphasis in the 1981 White Paper *Growing Older* that the primary sources of support and care for elderly people were informal and voluntary. The White Paper stated that 'Care *in* the community must increasingly mean care *by* the community' (Cmnd 8173, 1981, p.3). Although Government policy remained 'to enable elderly people to live independent lives in their own homes wherever possible' (Cmnd 8173, 1981, p.6), it was necessary to make sufficient provision in the acute sector to deal with the increasing number of elderly patients, and to provide long-term hospital or residential care for the minority of elderly people requiring such care (DHSS, 1981a). The White Paper indicated that the policy of enabling people to live independent lives in their own homes accorded with the preferences of people themselves (Salvage, 1986; Tinker, 1992), although this had to be set in the context of low expectations and little knowledge of other forms of care (Goldberg and Connelly, 1982).

Despite a commitment to community-based care at the policy level, rapid growth of the private and voluntary residential and nursing home sectors occurred during the 1980s, supported by social security funds. The effects of this shift in expenditure were analysed by the Audit Commission in an influential report in 1986, which identified the 'perverse incentives' created by such a system of funding and criticised the organisational fragmentation and failure to match resources to need in community care. The Government appointed Sir Roy Griffiths as a special adviser to report upon possible solutions for community care, and his report was published in early 1988. He recommended a more coordinated approach to the funding and management of care, placing the responsibility for allocation of funds, assessment of need and coordination of care with the local authority social services department, and proposed care management to ensure a more effective use of resources.

The majority of these recommendations were accepted by the Government in the 1989 policy document *Caring for People* (Cm 849). This document had six key objectives for service delivery (para. 1.11):

- To promote the development of domiciliary, day and respite services to enable people to live in their own homes wherever feasible and sensible.
- To ensure that service providers make practical support for carers a high priority.
- To make proper assessment of need and good case management [subsequently care management, SSI/SWSG, 1991a] the cornerstone of high quality care.
- To promote the development of a flourishing independent sector alongside good quality public services.
- To clarify the responsibilities of agencies and so to make it easier to hold them to account for their performance.
- To secure better value for taxpayers' money by introducing a new funding structure for social care.

Much greater coherence and specificity has been given to the policy, compared with previous developments, by the detailed guidance on different aspects of implementation and specification of critical path activities and tasks issued to social services and health authorities (SSI/SWSG, 1991a,b).

Health care developments: geriatric and psychogeriatric services

The specialty of geriatric medicine developed from the pioneering work of Dr Marjory Warren in the 1930s, who demonstrated that rehabilitative treatment for patients in wards for the chronic sick could enable many patients to be discharged from hospital (Clark, 1983). The specialty itself was founded in 1947, and clinicians working in the specialty became aware that elderly people often suffered from a combination of physical, psychological and social problems, and that a comprehensive assessment of these was required in order to prepare an appropriate treatment plan (Isaacs, 1981). Although elderly people in the 65-74 age group use more services than younger adults, the combination of several problems becomes increasingly common for elderly people over the age of 75 (DHSS, 1981d; Horrocks, 1983). Although the introduction of rehabilitation had enabled patients to be discharged from hospital, a continual problem was the shortage of long-stay hospital beds, leading to the occupancy of acute beds by patients requiring only nursing care, or 'bed blocking' (Rubin and Davies, 1975). In the 'traditional' model of geriatric care (Evans, 1983; Irvine, 1983), the geriatric department received patients referred by general practitioners or by consultants in other specialties, following hospital treatment. However, this model became less popular once the specialty became established because it did not enable acute care to be provided by clinicians working in the specialty (McArdle et al., 1977; Royal College of Physicians, 1977). Two other models of geriatric care, the 'age-defined' or 'age-related' model, in which the geriatric department provides all care for patients above a defined age, for example, 75 years (Bagnall et al., 1977), and the 'integrated' or 'Newcastle' model, in which physicians with special interests share the facilities of the general medical department, have been developed (Evans, 1983; Irvine, 1983) to enable physicians in geriatric medicine to become involved in treating patients in the early, acute phase of disease. The age-related model of geriatric care requires the department of geriatric medicine to have sufficient resources, particularly beds in the district general hospital, while the integrated model overcomes the problem of insufficient geriatric beds in the district general hospital by integrating geriatric and other medical beds into a single pool (Evans, 1983; Irvine, 1983).

The Department of Health and Social Security report (1981c) on national policies relating to the care of elderly patients observed that during the 1970s the number of patients treated and discharged had grown substantially and the average length of stay had been reduced, while the number of available geriatric beds had been reduced slightly and the balance between long-stay beds and acute beds had shifted towards the latter. However, there was still a substantial proportion of health districts which had no geriatric beds located in general hospitals, and the problem of blocked beds continued to restrict the availability of acute care (McAlpine, 1979; Coid and Crome, 1986; Maguire et al., 1986), although improvements were being made (Seymour and Pringle, 1982; Gibbins, 1984). Although the number of beds in geriatric hospitals in

England declined slightly during the 1970s, the number in England and Wales remained stable during the first half of the 1980s, and then began to decline, from 61,000 beds in 1985 to 55,000 in 1990 (Darton and Wright, 1993). As a result of the reduction in beds, the level of disability among the remaining long-stay patients tended to increase, and these patients were more difficult to place in alternative forms of care (Jenkinson et al., 1992).

For elderly people suffering from mental infirmity or illnesses such as depression, there was less change in the pattern of services than had been recommended in the 1975 White Paper (DHSS, 1981c). The development of a comprehensive, integrated service (Health Advisory Service, 1982) was the aim of Government policy for elderly people suffering from mental illness, as well as for younger people. The Health Advisory Service report, *The Rising Tide* (1982), proposed that a psychogeriatric department, or department for the psychiatry of old age, would provide hospital care for elderly patients suffering from functional or organic psychiatric disorders. Such a department would provide a parallel psychiatric service to that provided by the geriatric department, and thus promote close working relationships between the two departments or possibly the development of a combined department. The main purpose of the psychogeriatric department would be to provide treatment or hospital care for the most seriously ill people, while the great majority of elderly people suffering from mental illness lived at home and received care from their general practitioner and from local authority services (Jolley and Arie, 1978). The growth of psychogeriatric services subsequently has been substantial (Wattis, 1988; Murphy and Bannerjee, 1993). However, the provision of support, advice and temporary relief to families and primary health and social services was regarded as essential by the report. The Department of Health and Social Security recognised the need to provide sufficient residential and inpatient care for elderly mentally infirm people (DHSS, 1981a), and also raised the question of whether elderly mentally infirm people in hospital could be provided with alternative forms of care (DHSS, 1981b).

Residential and nursing home care

During the 1970s, there was a significant increase in the level of provision of community-based services, such as home helps, district nurses, and day centre and day hospital places, whereas the proportion of elderly people in long-term residential and hospital care had remained fairly constant. Approximately 5 per cent of elderly people lived in hospital or a residential home, but consumed a considerable proportion of health and personal social services resources (DHSS, 1981c). However, although there appeared to have been little overall movement away from long-term residential or hospital care, the age on admission to residential care had increased and dependency among those admitted to residential care also appeared to have increased (Darton, 1986). A majority of residents had been living alone prior to admission

(Darton, 1984, 1986; Booth, undated). One interpretation of these changes could be that community care policies were successful in maintaining people in their own homes for longer or in matching admission more closely to individual needs, although improvements in health and increases in the number of elderly people living on their own could also have resulted in increases in the average age of admission (DHSS, 1981c).

During the 1980s, the total number of places available increased substantially as a result of the increase in private residential and nursing homes. The overall number of individuals supported by local authorities declined slightly, and local authorities reduced their use of private and voluntary homes (DHSS, undated(b)). However, the use of social security funds, provided purely according to financial need, to support people in independent, mainly private, residential and nursing homes, created 'perverse incentives' for residential rather than community care (Audit Commission, 1986). Hence there was a serious distortion in policy which between 1979 and 1989 led to the number of places in private residential homes in England rising by 323 per cent, from 32,000 to 135,000, despite a policy commitment to community care (Department of Health, undated). The cost to the public purse for the increased residential and nursing home provision in the non-statutory sector rose from £10 million in 1980 to £1,000 million in 1989 (Cm 849, 1989). However, in relation to the total number of elderly people aged 75 and over who form the majority of new admissions (Darton, 1986; Larder et al., 1986), and who tend to suffer from multiple problems, as noted above, the relative number of places in local authority, voluntary and private residential homes remained fairly constant up to 1983, at approximately 70 places per thousand, before increasing to 79 places per thousand in 1986 and to 85 places per thousand in 1990 (Darton and Wright, 1993).

Domiciliary and day care services: flexibility and substitution

Despite growth in the provision of domiciliary and day care services, after allowing for increased levels of need, the increase in the number of people receiving services was achieved by reducing the amount of service provided to each person (Bebbington, 1979). Reviews of studies of services have stressed the lack of intensity of provision, the lack of flexibility of services, the lack of integration with other services and inadequate support to carers (Goldberg and Connelly, 1982; Sinclair et al., 1990). In order to achieve a move away from long-term hospital care, changes in the balance of resources between hospital inpatient and community-based services were required, both within the National Health Service and between the National Health Service and local authority personal social services (DHSS, 1981c). A study by the Social Services Inspectorate in 1986 indicated that, although the authorities investigated were developing policies for more flexible and intensive personal care services for people who would otherwise require institutional care, the home help service largely remained a domestic care service (SSI, 1987). Although it was recognised (DHSS, 1981c) that a package of services would have to be created for each individual to enable them to remain in the community, Plank's (1977) observation that the 'care system' consisted of an uncoordinated set of different activities and that the care received by an individual depended largely on the service contacted initially was confirmed by later studies (Goldberg and Connelly, 1982; Sinclair et al., 1990). Creating packages of community-based services to maintain elderly people in their own homes would entail giving higher priority to such clients and to the services employed (DHSS, 1981c). Services provided by nursing auxiliaries and home helps appeared to overlap, and more of the care of patients discharged from hospital could be undertaken by less qualified nurses, with the benefit of allowing district nurses to spend more time on the tasks for which they were trained (DHSS, 1981c). However, the development of community-based services might be hindered by labour supply, and competition between, and demands on, health and social services exacerbated by demographic changes (Goldberg, 1983).

Although frailty and disability are important factors in leading to admission to residential care (Bland and Bland, 1985), many studies of residential care have shown that a substantial minority of residents are fairly fit (Bessell, 1984; Booth, 1985), and that other factors are important. These include the absence of carers or supportive relationships, a lack of material and financial resources, and inadequacies in support received from the community or domiciliary services (Neill et al., 1988; Sinclair et al., 1988, 1990; Booth, undated).

The report of the Department of Health and Social Security study of community care emphasised the importance of informal care in maintaining elderly people in their own homes, and noted the role of services in substituting for, rather than complementing and supporting, informal care (Bergmann et al., 1978; Bebbington, 1979; Neill et al., 1988). Subsequently, the need to support carers has become an important theme for the success of community care. The White Paper *Growing Older* (Cmnd 8173, 1981) stressed the role of public services in sustaining and developing but never displacing informal care. The Griffiths Report (1988) recommended that carers' views and needs should be taken into consideration, and the White Paper *Caring for People* (Cm 849, 1989) affirmed that practical support for carers should be one of the key objectives for services. Underlying this view of the importance of informal care is a perception that public support for carers represents a long-term investment. Evidence of the effects of services upon carers suggests that the provision of domiciliary services could benefit the mental health of those caring for confused elderly people and also play some part in delaying admission to residential care (Levin et al., 1985, 1989). However, the role of carers as resources or clients in the caring process has, at times, been ambiguous (Twigg, 1989; Twigg and Atkin, 1994).

Intensive home care services: substitution

The perceived inflexibility and lack of intensity of standard domiciliary services has led to concerns as to whether they would be able to meet the increasing and more complex needs of elderly people, or offer a realistic alternative to institutional care (Goldberg and Connelly, 1982; Davies et al., 1990; Sinclair et al., 1990; Jamieson, 1991). A number of initiatives to provide intensive community-based care were developed to address these concerns. Examples include the Coventry Project (Latto, 1982), in which the amount of home help within one area of the city was doubled, and the intensive domiciliary service in Hove, East Sussex (Dunnachie, 1979), which established a team of home care assistants to undertake home help and personal care tasks, and demonstrated that frail elderly people could be maintained in their own homes and thus reduce demand for residential care. Similarly, intensive home nursing schemes, such as the scheme in North Tees Health District (Gibbins et al., 1982; Gibbins, 1984), reduced the number of patients occupying continuing care rehabilitation beds in hospitals and thus reduced the problem of blocked beds. The North Tees scheme combined the provision of intensive home nursing with an augmented home help service provided by the local authority social services department. A more specifically carer-focused specialised unit designed to provide support for elderly mentally infirm people and their carers — offering respite, evening care and occasional residential care — was also developed in the North-East (Donaldson and Gregson, 1989). Although the costs appeared markedly higher than traditional community services, there appeared to be a reduction in admissions to long-stay hospital beds. Some concerns have been expressed about whether the costing of all these initiatives was sufficiently complete to indicate whether they were necessarily cost-effective alternatives to institutional care (Wright et al., 1981; Salvage, 1985; Challis, 1992a). Nevertheless, the growth in the costs of providing care and constraints on public expenditure (DHSS, 1976) had created a focus on innovatory approaches to care and ways of increasing the efficiency and effectiveness of services (Ferlie et al., 1989).

Care management and coordination

Where policy is designed to reduce the unnecessary utilisation of institutional care, not only the enhancement of home care but also improved coordination and care management are necessary. Some of the earliest studies of care management for elderly people in the United Kingdom were the Kent and Gateshead schemes (Challis and Davies, 1986; Davies and Challis, 1986; Challis et al., 1988a, 1990, 1992), the effects of which were evaluated in comparision with the provision of the usual range of services. Replications of the original Kent scheme have also been undertaken in other areas of Kent, within the mainstream of service provision (Chesterman et al., 1994). Initially these studies were focused upon care management in social care. A later initiative, in Gateshead, involved joint agency care management in a general practice setting. The model of care management which was developed was designed to ensure that improved performance of the core tasks of care management could contribute towards more effective and efficient long-term care. The devolution of control of resources — within an overall cost framework of two-thirds of the cost of a place in a residential home — to individual social workers acting as care managers, was designed to permit more flexible responses to needs and the integration of fragmented services into a more coherent package of care, so as to provide a realistic alternative to institutional care.

The studies of care management in social care (Challis and Davies, 1985, 1986; Challis et al., 1988a, 1990, 1992) indicated that social workers with greater budgetary flexibility, acting as care managers, were able to respond more effectively than is usually the case. The care provided was more individually varied, and control of a budget meant that assessments became more wide-ranging and problem-focused. Consequently, a number of problems often associated with the breakdown of community care — such as severe stress on carers, confusional states and risk of falling — were more effectively managed at home than in the comparison groups. It was found that this approach significantly reduced the need for institutional care for vulnerable elderly people. In both Kent and Gateshead, over 60 per cent of those receiving these care management schemes were still at home after one year, compared with far fewer members of the comparison groups, who were receiving the usual services. There were marked improvements in the levels of satisfaction and wellbeing of elderly people and their carers, and these were achieved at no greater cost to the social services, the National Health Service or society as a whole than was expended upon the comparison groups. Similar findings were observed in the primary care service initiative in Gateshead, where a full-time nurse and part of the time of a doctor and a physiotherapist were added to a small team of social worker care managers, with a flexible budget split equally between health and social services (Challis et al., 1990, 1992).

The Care in the Community Initiative

Joint finance, introduced in 1976, had been designed as a mechanism to improve interagency collaboration in community care using National Health Service funds for community-based services. However, the potential of joint finance was not realised due to a variety of legal, administrative and financial obstacles, particularly the long-term revenue consequences for social services. A consultative document on the implications of transferring people from hospital to community care was published in July 1981 (DHSS, 1981b). This document noted that personal social services and primary health and acute geriatric services had to be developed if elderly people were to be enabled, as far as possible, to live in the community. Following the consultative document, the Government decided to make changes to joint finance arrangements to encourage the Care in the Community Initiative (DHSS, 1983). As part of the initiative, a programme of pilot projects was announced, 'to explore and evaluate different approaches to moving people and resources into community care' (DHSS, 1983, para. 11). Each project selected would be funded for three years, with funding being made available on the understanding that it would continue with local funding after the three-year pilot period. The continuation of projects beyond the pilot phase was important if the necessary developmental work to enable innovatory experiments to be incorporated into routine practice, identified by Goldberg (1983) as generally lacking, was to be undertaken.

The programme of pilot projects established under the Care in the Community Initiative was undertaken between 1984 and 1988, and included 28 projects, three of which, including the Darlington Project, were for physically frail elderly people, and four of which were for elderly mentally infirm people. Thirteen projects were funded for the three years 1984 to 1987, and fifteen for 1985 to 1988. The Darlington Project was one of the second round of projects, funded from 1985 to 1988. In April 1988 the project was incorporated, in a modified form, into the local mainstream service system, funded by the closure of two long-stay wards. However, as noted above, policies towards changes in hospital provision were influenced by the projected increase in the number of very elderly people, and although some of the seven projects for elderly people were designed to contribute to hospital closure strategies, their policy relevance lay more in the testing of alternative methods of providing community-based support (Renshaw et al., 1988; Knapp et al., 1992). The Personal Social Services Research Unit (PSSRU) was commissioned by the Department of Health and Social Security to monitor and evaluate the programme of pilot projects (Renshaw et al., 1988; Knapp et al., 1992). Additional funding provided by the Joseph Rowntree Memorial Trust, now the Joseph Rowntree Foundation, made possible a more detailed evaluation of the Darlington Project.

The Darlington Project

The first formulation of the issues which underlay the Darlington Project originated at a joint conference of health and social services staff held in Darlington in 1984. At this local conference the possibility was considered of combining the functions of a home help and an auxiliary nurse in one worker, termed a home care assistant, to reduce the overlap and duplication of tasks and provide more coordinated care to individual elderly people. The role of the home care assistant was subsequently developed to include tasks designated by professional staff, and preparatory discussions relating to the programme of pilot projects led to the incorporation of care management principles.

The shortcomings in the local care system that were influential in the development of ideas for the project were also evident at the national level. It is interesting to summarise these as they indicate how local concerns and frustrations about services related to broader national policy debates. There were four areas: issues of choice for elderly people; the multi-faceted nature of need; overlap and duplication of services; and the lack of flexibility in service provision. These are discussed below.

Lack of choice for and control by frail elderly people

It was felt that most older people, if given the realistic choice of an appropriate level of support, would prefer to remain in their own homes (Cmnd 8173, 1981; Salvage, 1985). However, people who lack a sense of control over their own lives can deteriorate psychologically and functionally, with consequent helplessness, depression, apathy and poor functional performance (Seligman, 1975; Goldberg and Connelly, 1982; Baltes, 1986). In resource terms, the lack of real choice was reflected in the considerable difference between the level of resources normally available for home support, and the level of resources devoted to people in residential or hospital care. Despite efforts to improve levels of provision, particularly of basic personal care, a key element in maintaining frail people in their own homes (Currie et al., 1979), the home help service, to a very large extent, remained a domestic care service (SSI, 1987).

Needs are multi-faceted

The needs of frail elderly people are complex, spanning the provision of different agencies. The services provided by different agencies appeared unlikely to combine to achieve an efficient and effective level and type of care for each individual person, without being carefully integrated and coordinated at the level of the individual person (Goldberg and Connelly, 1982). It was not clearly anyone's role to undertake such coordination.

Overlap and duplication of services

It appeared that different service providers could, and did, perform very similar tasks in assisting elderly people, with the result that gaps in service provision could occur, and boundary and territorial disputes arise. The roles of district nurses, physiotherapists and occupational therapists seemed to overlap to a considerable degree, and a number of different personnel could be involved in providing basic personal care such as washing and dressing, including home helps, district nurses and nursing auxiliaries (DHSS, 1973, 1981a). The need, wherever possible, to reduce the number of actors performing care tasks for an individual elderly person has been recognised (Clarke, 1976, 1979; Mowat and Morgan, 1982), and schemes have demonstrated that it is possible to recruit and deploy staff who span these boundaries, reducing the number of individuals in contact with the elderly person (Latto, 1982; Oxfordshire Social Services Department and Oxford Health Authority, 1982) and hence the likelihood of boundary disputes.

Inflexible patterns of service delivery

Patterns of organisation and provision of services have tended to render services inflexible and unresponsive to the changing needs of dependent people and their carers. These problems could be seen in the demarcation of legitimate and non-legitimate tasks for different types of employee, the lack of variety of ways in which care was provided, and the restricted times at which help was available (Dexter and Harbert, 1983; Challis and Davies, 1986). Often flexibility was restricted by conditions of service, contracts of employment, boundary disputes between occupational groups, health and safety regulations and the like. Indeed, the structures surrounding service systems may themselves impede the kind of necessary change required (Challis and Ferlie, 1986, 1987).

The split between agencies which adopt different criteria for providing services and different levels of service has further restricted effective care. As a consequence, people may have to move between settings rather than the levels of care being adapted to meet their changing needs. This could involve elderly people in moves from their own homes, where they may receive insufficient home help and community nursing, to residential care, and later perhaps moving from there to long-stay hospital care as their dependency increased. Indeed, at the time of planning the Darlington Project, there were 23 elderly people on the long-stay wards who had made just this series of moves as a result of functional deterioration. The structure of incentives to the agencies, despite the considerable investment in joint finance and joint planning, had failed to overcome this separation of provision, which frequently led to inappropriate and unsatisfactory responses for elderly people, and to inappropriate allocation of scarce resources (Webb and Wistow, 1986).

The project response

These key concerns, which formed the background for the local planning of the Darlington Project, have also been concerns at a national level. During the life of the project, these were more fully articulated in the work of the Audit Commission (1986), policy documents such as the Griffiths Report (1988) and the White Paper *Caring for People* (Cm 849, 1989). Underlying these concerns was the need to improve the content of services (what kind of care and how it is provided) and to develop the process of service delivery with care management (more effective individual care planning and coordination). The Darlington Project aimed both to improve the content of services through its own home care assistants undertaking a wide range of caring tasks, and to improve coordination through the care management function undertaken by the project care managers.

The project built on the care management models developed previously in Kent and Gateshead (Challis and Davies, 1986; Davies and Challis, 1986; Challis et al., 1988a, 1990), and it extended these into a joint health and social services model of provision, based upon a geriatric multidisciplinary team and using multipurpose care workers. As in the Kent and Gateshead schemes, the package of care provided to individual clients was limited to a budget of two-thirds of the cost of alternative institutional provision, in this case a long-stay hospital bed. Brief descriptions of the project and the key findings were published previously (Challis et al., 1989, 1991a,b), and a comparison of the main results of the Kent, Gateshead and Darlington projects was presented in Challis et al. (1993a).

The development of community care policy from the 1960s to the 1990s (with the implementation of the National Health Service and Community Care Act) can be characterised in broad terms as a movement from exhortation to specification, from a sole concern with 'top-down' pressures of implementation to a focus both upon 'bottom-up' aspects of practice and 'top-down' policy (Barrett and Fudge, 1981), and influence through specific directives and incentives. The Darlington Project played a significant role in the development of ideas about care management and can be seen as a valuable model for linking care management and secondary health care services.

Structure of the book

There are three major elements in this book. First, it describes the implementation of the Darlington Project and the role of intensive care management for frail elderly people located in a geriatric multidisciplinary team. Second, the book discusses the results of the evaluation of the effects of the project on the elderly people and their carers, and examines the costs of the project and the factors associated with variations in the cost of providing the project service to clients with differing characteristics. Third, the book describes the absorption of the project into the mainstream service system and considers the development of care management. Following this introduction, Chapter 2 examines care management and the implementation of the model of care management in Darlington, and Chapter 3 presents a description of health and social services provision in Darlington and a brief history of the town, and describes the design of the evaluative research. Chapters 4, 5 and 6 are concerned with aspects of the process of care provision: care management in practice; the characteristics of the home care assistants and their role in the project; and aspects of organisation and multidisciplinary working. Chapters 7, 8 and 9 are concerned with the costs and outcomes of the project. Chapter 7 describes the project clients and the members of the comparison group, and considers the outcomes of care for the two groups. Chapter 8 examines the effects of the project on the carers of project clients, in comparison with the carers of the patients in hospital and with the carers of elderly people receiving traditional services in the locality. Chapter 9 examines the costs of the project in comparison with the costs of hospital-based care, and examines the factors associated with variations in costs for clients with different characteristics. Finally, Chapter 10 examines the process of absorption of the project into the local service system and identifies changes which occurred in the service following the project phase, and Chapter 11 discusses the key findings of the evaluation of the project and develops significant themes highlighted by the study which are relevant for the wider implementation of care management.

2 The Darlington Care Management Model

In the new community care system, assessment and case management have been identified as the cornerstones of the new policy (Cm 849, 1989). As noted in Chapter 1, this is indicative of the extent to which policy-making, as a top-down process, has increasingly taken account of both the top-down perspective of funding and guidance, and the necessary practice-level mechanisms required to achieve effective policy change. The focus upon assessment and care management is also evident elsewhere. In Australia, a very clear role has been designed for geriatric assessment in community care, and this is discussed further in Chapter 11 in the light of the findings of this study. Reflecting the need for simultaneous change at different levels, the Darlington Project was designed to increase and improve collaboration and coordination of care, both within and between agencies, in the home care of frail elderly people who would otherwise have remained in hospital. The aim was to design a care system which could reduce the duplication of tasks and to provide more coordinated care, using the skills of a range of different professionals to optimum effect, and thereby improve collaboration between key agencies. However, it is evident that the way care management is interpreted varies in different contexts. In the early phase of community care in the United Kingdom, staff undertaking the care management role appear to have been given a variety of titles, to work with broader or more narrowly defined client groups and to have predominantly assessment roles on the one hand, or continuing responsibility for activities from assessment to review on the other (Department of Health, 1994).

Faced with such variety of interpretation, the first part of this chapter attempts to distil the essential characteristics of care management from the United Kingdom and international experiences. The remainder of the chapter elaborates an understanding of the features of the model of care management implemented in Darlington, relates the specific features of that model to the dimensions by which care management may vary (Challis, 1994a,b) and considers some factors that appear to be associated with more or less effective implementation. In this way an attempt is made to set the particular model of care management implemented in Darlington in the broad context of care management systems overall.

Care management

Care management and case management

The definition of care management is far from easy: definitions abound and even terminology changes. Thus the Griffiths Report (Griffiths, 1988) talked of care management, and the subsequent White Paper (Cm 849, 1989) used the term case management. Later the Department of Health guidelines published for managers and practitioners referred to care management, justifying this in terms of the fact that it is the care which is being managed and that the word case may be perceived as demeaning (SSI/SWSG, 1991a,b). A similar point is made in the United States in the Care Management Standards of the National Institute on Community-Based Long Term Care (NICBLTC, 1988). This debate about nomenclature occurs elsewhere too (Challis, 1994a). The point is well made in the care management standards documentation in the state of Wisconsin in the United States:

> No amount of discussion will settle the question of what is the best word to use to describe the care management function. 'Case management' is probably the most widely used term. 'Care coordination' and 'service coordination' are often used instead to emphasise the fact that people are not 'cases' and that it is the care or services, not the person, which are being managed (Wisconsin Department of Health and Social Services, 1992, p.3).

What is important is less the precise terms which are used and more the clarity of meaning which is attached to different aspects of the process, since the term 'care management' may obfuscate more than it clarifies (Onyett, 1992). It covers such a wide variety of needs and organisational responses, both a general care process and a specific designated case manager (SSI/SWSG, 1991a,b). Onyett (1992) has suggested that the term case management more helpfully describes the activities undertaken by a specific designated worker. If care management is defined both as a broad process through which most service users will pass and also the use of a designated worker, there is likely to be a need for agencies to differentiate in some way between this generic process and a more intensive response for individuals with chronic and varying problems requiring substantial levels of assistance, whatever the terms chosen. As will be seen from the following discussion, this latter group is commonly described as the recipients or target population of care management. In time it is likely that there will be a need to differentiate more clearly between the process of care management and intensive case management

(Challis, 1994b). A similar distinction has also been employed in mental health services in the United States (McGurrin and Worley, 1993).

In this book we have used the term 'care management': a process implemented by designated workers who are care managers, except where the specific term 'case management' has been used in work cited.

The origins of care management

There has been a long-standing concern to improve coordination in the development of community care policy following two important policy developments: the 1959 Mental Health Act and the 1963 policy document, *Health and Welfare: The Development of Community Care* (Cmnd 1973, 1963). During the 1970s, in the newly developing post-Seebohm personal social services, attempts to improve interagency coordination between health and social care principally took the form of initiatives such as joint care planning and joint financing (Webb and Wistow, 1986; Sinclair et al., 1990). In the mental health field, coordinating activities at the client level were initiated at an earlier stage than for elderly people, particularly regarding discharge of dangerous patients from hospital (Cmnd 5191, 1973; Cmnd 6244, 1975). The more recent implementation of the care programme approach has extended this (Department of Health, 1990). A focus upon specific approaches and organisational techniques to achieve coordination at the client level occurred later in the wider social services field, a bottom-up perspective which complemented the previous top-down initiatives.

Compared with the USA, this focus upon coordination at the client level came considerably later, being less evident in a setting like the United Kingdom where most services were provided by two main agencies (health and social services, albeit separate), than where multiple agencies provided care. Nonetheless, the fragmentation within those agencies experienced by clients rendered the need for coordination equally great (Challis and Davies, 1986). For people with learning disabilities in the USA, discharge from hospital and developing continuity of care have been key themes since the early 1970s, with case management made mandatory to improve coordination of care after discharge (Intagliata, 1982). The rationale for this is cited by Miller, who quotes the conclusion of the US Presidential Commission on Mental Health regarding case management:

> Strategies focused solely on organisations are not enough. A human link is required. A case manager can provide this link and assist in assuring continuity of care and a coordinated program of services (Miller, 1983, pp.5-6).

In general, therefore, the origins of care management lie in the 'need to coordinate delivery of long-term care services to individual clients' (Austin, 1983, p.16). In the United States context, Moxley (1989) cites six factors underlying the development of care management: deinstitutionalisation, the decentralised nature of community services, growing numbers of clients with multiple needs living at home, the fragmentation of care services, a growing awareness of the importance of social supports and the needs of carers, and the need for cost containment. Care management and coordination are thus central to the achievement of the goals of community-based care.

In the United Kingdom and elsewhere, care management is thus in a crucial position in the new care arrangements, as it is the mechanism designed to achieve both the move away from institutional provision and the strengthening of home-based care. Much is dependent upon the coherence, form, style and structure of the care management processes implemented in each service system. Care management brings welfare objectives and resource constraints together, and therefore it has a pivotal role in the integration of social and economic criteria at the level of service provision, where the balancing of needs and resources, scarcity and choice must take place (Challis, 1992b). It should not be seen, however, as a panacea (Hunter et al., 1988; Callahan, 1989; Austin, 1992) for solving the complex problems in providing adequate community care, but rather a mechanism which, dependent upon the manner of its implementation, offers a means to manage some intractable policy and practice dilemmas in the developments in community care in a number of countries (Challis, 1992a).

Key characteristics of care management

Box 2.1 summarises six identifying characteristics which serve to distinguish care management from other service-related activities. It may be distinguished

---

Box 2.1
The key characteristics of care management

Functions — Coordination and linkage of care services
Goals — Providing continuity and integrated care; increased opportunity for home-based care; promote client wellbeing; making better use of resources.
Core tasks — Case-finding and screening; assessment; care planning; monitoring and review; case closure.
Characteristics of recipients — Long-term care needs; multiple service need.
Main features — Intensity of involvement; breadth of services spanned; lengthy duration of involvement.
Multi-level response — Linking practice-level activities with broader resource and agency-level activities.

by its functions, goals, core tasks, the characteristics of those for whom it is designed, its main features, and its systemic response. These are discussed below and in Challis (1994a,b,c).

The functions of care management. The functions of care management are usually identified as the coordination of care arrangements to create a comprehensive response to need (Austin, 1983). The Department of Health Guidance defines care management as 'the process of tailoring services to individual needs' (SSI/SWSG, 1991a, p.11). Moxley defines case management as being undertaken by:

> a dedicated person (or team) who organises, coordinates and sustains a network of formal and informal supports and activities designed to optimise the functioning and wellbeing of people with multiple needs (Moxley, 1989, p.17).

The Wisconsin Community Options Program defines care management as:

> the comprehensive assessment of an individual's long-term care needs, capacities and preferences and the planning, authorising, arranging, coordinating and monitoring of appropriate services and supports to meet those needs (Wisconsin Department of Health and Social Services, 1992, p.3).

The goals of care management. The goals of care management cited usually cover client-level needs, such as improved care and reduced reliance upon institutional care, and system-level goals, such as more efficient use of resources. The Department of Health guidance (SSI/SWSG, 1991a,b) cites ten benefits of care management, ranging from client-level goals, such as a more needs-led approach and continuity of care, to system-level goals, such as more responsive and integrated services both within and between agencies. Moxley (1989) notes three goals of case management: improving client utilisation of support and services; developing the capacity of social networks and services to promote client wellbeing; and promoting service effectiveness and efficiency. These are similar to those cited in the USA by the National Institute for Community-Based Long Term Care (NICBLTC, 1988) which cover both client-centred activities such as enhanced service access, coordinated care, independence and enhanced ability to remain at home, as well as more system-focused goals such as improved service availability, reaching a specified target population and cost containment through use of appropriate community-based services. The potential for goal conflict, for example between client and carer or between cost containment and client responsiveness, was recognised, and mechanisms to resolve such conflicts were identified. These include family meetings, advocacy, case manager peer group support and effective supervision (NICBLTC, 1988).

The core tasks of care management. Care management involves the performance of a series of core tasks in long-term care (Steinberg and Carter, 1983;

SSI/SWSG, 1991a,b). Overall there would seem to be a broad consensus across the literature. These core tasks are case-finding and screening, assessment, care planning, implementing and monitoring the care plan and case closure. Case-finding is concerned with mechanisms to ensure that those defined as suitable for the service receive it: access. Conversely, screening is concerned with en-suring that those defined as inappropriate for the service do not receive it. In much of the medical literature on geriatrics, the term 'screening' corresponds to what has been described here as 'case-finding' (Williamson, 1981). Assess-ment is the means of problem identification and evaluation, or defining needs. This is followed by care planning, which involves the formulation of the problems identified at assessment so that interventions and services may be arranged to meet needs. Monitoring and review involve the evaluation of the effectiveness of the care plan in meeting needs and therefore lead to re-assessment. Case closure may involve the transfer of the client to other care settings without care management, or the death of the elderly person. As such these core tasks may usefully be differentiated from more short-term activities of care providers (Challis et al., 1990).

There is some variation in the precise description of these core tasks; for example, the Department of Health has included 'publishing information', which elsewhere might be considered as part of case-finding. The Province of British Columbia defines case management as:

> a specific set of client-related functions that include intake and screening for eligibility, assessment of functions and needs, mutual service plan-ning and goal-setting, efficient linkage with available resources, quality assurance through ongoing monitoring, review and evaluation, and dis-charge policy (British Columbia Ministry of Health, 1992, p.26).

However, care management is more than a set of processes in long-term care since, in undertaking these tasks, it also involves advocacy and integrating formal and informal care (Capitman et al., 1986). These other more traditional 'casework' activities are critical in discriminating between more 'clinical' and more 'administrative' approaches to care management (Challis, 1994a,b).

The characteristics of recipients of care management services. Another key characteristic of care management is that it is concerned with meeting the needs of a specified group: people with long-term care problems or multiple needs (Steinberg and Carter, 1983; Moxley, 1989). Brody refers to long-term care as:

> one or more services provided on a sustained basis to enable individuals whose functional capacities are chronically impaired to be maintained at their maximum levels of health and wellbeing (Brody, 1977a, p.14).

The definition of this group is not easy. Davies and Challis (1986) characterise long-term care populations as: those involving a high proportion of health and social care expenditure, individuals with multiple and varied needs, and recipients of multiple and inflexible services of which social care is the largest component. Ballew and Mink (1986) describe case management as concerned with people experiencing multiple problems that require multiple sources of help, and who experience difficulty in utilising that help. The role of care management is thus seen as combining brokerage, which is principally third-party service arrangement, with interpersonal skills, since it is focused both 'on the network of services needed by multi-problem clients and the inter-action between members of the network' (Ballew and Mink, 1986, p.8). There-fore, care management is concerned with providing services to a specific target group and need not be seen as the mechanism for providing all forms of care for those who need assistance in coping with everyday living (Kane, 1990). Specificity of target populations is evident in the application of care management to community care developments in a number of countries (Challis, 1992b,c), and is associated with the more successful programmes (Huxley, 1991). The dilemma of the need to identify specific targets and yet the complexity of so doing is reflected in the varying definitions of eligibility for services and levels of assessment evident in different local authority systems in the United Kingdom (Department of Health, 1994b). It is also evident in the United States, where well-validated indicators tend to be more variable when used in non-experimental and less controlled practice environ-ments (Liu and Cornelius, 1991). In the broader international context, the difficulties of estimating eligibility and demand for the long-term care insur-ance law in Israel is an instructive one, since although eligibility and targeting were determined by objective assessment of activities of daily living, actual numbers have been substantially above those expected, indicating the dif-ficulty of estimating the size of target populations (Brodsky et al., 1993; Naon et al., 1993). Similar problems are evident, due to differences in definitions, in the variations in the estimates of the numbers of disabled people in the United Kingdom, as can be seen from the comparisons of the 1985 General Household Survey and the 1985 OPCS Survey of Disability, and of the 1991 General Household Survey and the 1991 Population Census (Charlton et al., 1994).

Main differentiating features of care management. One of the areas of confusion about care management is the extent to which the activities appear to overlap with those of many staff in health and social service agencies. Applebaum and Austin (1990) note that many organisations report that they do care manage-ment and observe that in fact they do undertake some of the relevant activities. In the US context it has been argued that case management is what most social workers do in most fields of practice most of the time (Roberts-DeGennaro, 1987). In the United Kingdom an obvious example of this broad definition in-volves the overlap with the role of the keyworker within multidisciplinary teams. However, there are important differences between these keyworker ap-proaches, which aim to coordinate the work of a single service or team to meet individual needs, often on a short-term basis, and care management, which aims to coordinate multiple services and providers, usually on a long-term basis. This is precisely the content of Ovretveit's (1993) distinction between keyworkers and case managers, which is based upon the locus of coordinatory activity whether within one service or across many. Applebaum and Austin (1990) identify three factors which differentiate care management in long-term care from these keyworker approaches. These are intensity of involvement, reflected in relatively small caseloads; breadth of services spanned, covering more than one service, team or agency; and length or duration of involvement, being a long-term commitment. In the Case Management Standards documentation of the National Institute of Community-Based Long Term Care, a similar distinction is made between single agency coordination and comprehensive case management which is:

> an inclusive look across a person's needs and re- sources, linking him or her to a full range of appropriate services, using all available funding sources and monitoring the care provided over an extended period of time' (NICBLTC, 1988, p.3).

The multilevel organisational response of care management. Most of the defining characteristics have focused upon client-level activities in care management, but effective practice is dependent upon the organisational environment. Care management practice in coordinating services is dependent upon a care management system which links the needs of individuals with service development at a more strategic level. Miller (1983) has observed that a focus on client-level activities is insufficient since it does not address the idea of a care management system. Similarly, O'Connor (1988) makes the distinction between case management practice and case management systems. As Moore (1990) argues, the degree of horizontal integration of services to individuals achieved by case management practice, through coordinating care, needs a degree of vertical integration of client-level work with more strategic concerns at system level in order to be effective. The Department of Health guidance expects this process to occur through the identification of unmet need at the individual level (SSI/SWSG, 1991a, para. 3.20). Kane (1990) links case management practice with system-level activities through the use of comprehensive assessments to provide aggregated information for needs-based planning by agencies. There are two elements to this. First, a more permissive and less procedurally dominated environment is required to produce more lateral and creative responses. Second, and related to this, care management is designed not just to influence care at the individual client level but also at the system level through the aggregation of a myriad of care decisions at the individual client level which exert pressure for changes in patterns of provision themselves. An underlying objective is to make those patterns of services more relevant to individual needs (Austin, 1983; Steinberg and Carter, 1983; Department of Health, 1991b). This is one of the rationales for devolved budgets and micro-level purchasing.

The Darlington model of care management

Having briefly considered the key elements which define care management, an examination is now made of the specific features of the Darlington model. The concept of model implies a degree of deliberate and planned congruence between the goals of the service and the resources, structures and constraints within which practice takes place (Challis, 1994a,b). In this section we first describe briefly the origins of the project in the locality and the objectives which were set for it. We then consider the ways in which the model was designed to improve the coordination and quality of care.

The origins of the project

The proposal of a hybrid worker, combining the roles of a home help and a nursing auxiliary and recognising the overlaps between the two, developed out of a conference of health and social services staff held in Darlington in 1984. At that time there were already examples of extended home help services (Dunnachie, 1979; Gibbins et al., 1982; Goldberg and Connelly, 1982; Latto, 1982, 1984; Gibbins, 1984), and so the idea was not completely new, but there was agreement among the middle managers in both health and social services to explore the development of the role across the traditional boundaries between the two services, where there had been much less experimentation. In this area the most obvious example was the Oxford Community Care Project for the Elderly, which had developed a team of home care assistants undertaking personal and domestic care supervised and coordinated by a project team of a project leader (senior social worker), a social worker, a district nurse and a community psychiatric nurse (Oxfordshire Social Services Department and Oxford Health Authority, 1982).

During early discussions the role of the hybrid worker was expanded to incorporate the work of therapy auxiliaries, such as physiotherapy and occupational therapy helpers, in recognition of the multiple service needs of elderly people and the difficulties often arising in the coordination of these services. A census of patients carried out in the Darlington Memorial Hospital in 1984 provided information on the potential clientele for such a service. Sixty-two physically disabled but mentally alert elderly people in long-stay care were identified as potential recipients of the proposed service. The Government's Care in the Community Initiative (DHSS, 1983) provided the opportunity for funding a domiciliary care service for 60 elderly people who might otherwise have remained in long-stay hospital care, with the expectation that housing would be provided, where necessary, by the local housing department and a housing association. Commitment in principle to provide housing was obtained from the local authority and a local housing association, the latter having plans for a sheltered housing scheme in Darlington which might offer suitable facilities.

In addition to the use of the hybrid workers, consultations relating to the bid for Care in the Community Initiative funding led to the additional formulation of a project team which would manage the implementation of the scheme and have a care management role. The care managers would coordinate the care given to individual people, along the lines adopted in the Kent and Gateshead projects (Challis and Davies, 1986; Challis et al., 1990). Their function was to span the different agencies of health and social care and ensure that the care offered by different professional groups was provided in a coordinated and appropriate fashion. The final scheme therefore had two necessarily interlinked components: to enhance service content through the hybrid workers, termed home care assistants; and to improve coordination through care management for individual elderly people (Challis and Davies, 1986). More generally, it also encompassed the three common elements of community care for elderly people which have been observed in a number of different countries: de-institutionalisation; enhanced home care; and coordination through the mechanism of care management (Kraan et al., 1991).

The objectives of the project

Each of the Care in the Community projects (Renshaw et al., 1988) had to identify a set of objectives for the centrally-funded service. The Darlington Project had five objectives by which at a local level its adequacy and effectiveness were to be judged. These objectives are shown in Box 2.2, and the extent to which these were achieved are examined in this book.

Box 2.2
The objectives of the project

- The maintenance at home of a group of physically handicapped but mentally alert elderly people, who would have otherwise remained in long-stay hospital care.
- In order to reduce the duplication of tasks, trained home care assistants were to carry out both the domestic and the caring tasks required by individual clients, replacing the use of separate helpers working as part of different professional groups.
- The quality of care and the satisfaction of the elderly person and their family were to be enhanced when compared with similar clients receiving the usual forms of care in hospital and in the community.
- The cost of providing home care was to compare favourably with that of long-stay hospital care.
- The creation of the service was to provide an additional level of long-term care in the community for frail elderly people, which had not previously existed in the district.

The model of care: care management and coordination at four levels

As summarised in Box 2.1, a care management approach requires a multilevel response for effective implementation. This is particularly so for interagency and interdisciplinary services. It is possible to define four distinct levels of collaboration and coordination relevant to the Darlington care management model: first, collaboration between agencies at the highest level; second, inter-professional operation; third, coordination of care by an individual worker; and, finally, coordination of a number of discrete activities in the hands of one care provider. Each of these is examined in turn.

Collaboration between agencies. The project was jointly planned by the Durham County Council Social Services Department and Darlington Health Authority. From the joint planning process emerged a joint coordinating group which consisted of senior managers from the two agencies and clinicians. The chairman of this group was the local social services manager. This coordinating group was responsible for determining and monitoring the operational policies of the project, such as defining the target population, clarifying the referral procedure and allocating the budget. It also provided the forum for examining interagency working arrangements. During the project phase the social services

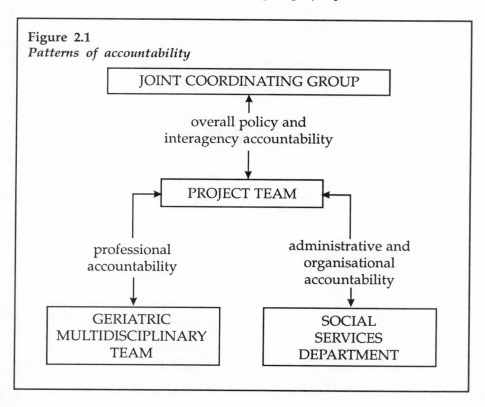

Figure 2.1
Patterns of accountability

JOINT COORDINATING GROUP

overall policy and
interagency accountability

PROJECT TEAM

professional
accountability

administrative and
organisational
accountability

GERIATRIC
MULTIDISCIPLINARY
TEAM

SOCIAL
SERVICES
DEPARTMENT

department employed the staff, except for health service professionals such as an occupational therapist and a physiotherapist, and administratively the project was part of the social services department. The project team was the agent of the joint coordinating group in implementing the service, and consisted of a project manager, three care managers who were termed 'service managers', and home care assistants.

Any service which utilises the resources and budgets of more than one agency requires the patterns of accountability and responsibility to be carefully defined. Figure 2.1 indicates how the different features of accountability were resolved for the Darlington Project. Essentially there were three different forms. For overall policy, interagency accountability and budgetary scrutiny, the project was responsible to the joint coordinating group. In administrative and organisational terms, the project was accountable to the social services department, which employed the project manager, care managers and home care assistants, as well as providing day-to-day management of the budget. The project manager, responsible to the joint coordinating group for the three-year pilot phase of the project, was the senior social caseworker who had been a member of the care planning team. Prior to appointment he had been released from his normal duties to spend time on the preliminary work needed to implement the project. This involved planning the budget, negotiating an assessment and referral procedure with members of the geriatric multidisciplinary team, clarifying the roles of project staff, and promoting the integration of the project into the existing structure of services. He was also responsible for publicising the project and assisting in the evaluation and research. The project National Health Service staff — a physiotherapist and an occupational therapist — were administratively responsible to their respective health service managers. Finally, in professional terms for the day-to-day welfare of elderly people, the project was accountable to the geriatric multidisciplinary team. The definition and separation of the different aspects of accountability were made explicit in order to avoid confusion over areas of responsibility between the different agencies.

Multidisciplinary working and care planning. The referral, assessment and review of the clients who were to receive the service were undertaken by the geriatric multidisciplinary team, comprising a consultant geriatrician and other medical staff, hospital and community nursing staff, social workers, therapy staff and the care managers from the project. Home care assistants also contributed to the review of clients' progress. In identifying patients suitable for the project, the level of dependency and physical impairment, and factors such as personality, motivation, family circumstances and the effects of length of stay in hospital on the individual were taken into account. Thus, some potential clients were deemed to be unsuitable for the project because of factors such as the carer's refusal to accept help, a family unwilling to accept terminal care at home, or poor housing conditions making discharge impossible. Each person identified as suitable for the project was re-assessed in detail using information available from the different professionals, a process coordinated by one of the care managers. The care manager also visited the family and discussed issues concerning discharge, and in about half the cases a home visit was undertaken with the elderly person, so that the physiotherapist, occupational therapist and care manager could assess the suitability of the person's home environment. These procedures usually took place between the first case conference at which a person was identified as potentially suitable for the scheme, and a second conference two weeks later when the additional assessments were considered.

It had been planned that a full medical reassessment and review would take place six months after discharge. However, in practice this could not be organised and subsequent medical review occurred when initiated by the care manager or other professionals, as described later in Chapter 4.

Individual care management and the role of the project team. Care managers were appointed to provide coordinated and individualised care for the recipients of the service. The main function of the project team, and in particular of the care managers, was to ensure that the 'core tasks' of care management — case-finding and screening, assessment, care planning, and monitoring and review (Challis and Davies, 1986) — were undertaken for their clients. These 'core tasks' are used to illustrate the expected roles of the geriatric multidisciplinary team, the care managers and home care assistants in the 'client pathway'. This is shown as Box 2.3. While in some models of care management the care manager is responsible for undertaking all these tasks, in the Darlington Project some of the tasks were performed by others, and it was the responsibility of the care managers to ensure that they were properly undertaken and coordinated. Given the nature of the project, case-finding was a task of the multidisciplinary team as a whole, and the initial task of the care managers was screening, to ensure that only clients eligible for the project were accepted. If the service were to focus on referrals from the community, preventing admission to long-stay settings, the relative importance of the care managers' role in case-finding would certainly increase.

Coordination of activities through one care worker. One of the objectives of the project was to enhance the content of services, in terms of the type and amount of help given and the time when help would be available. This objective is not in itself new, since there are many examples of improved domiciliary care schemes for elderly people (Ferlie, 1982; Salvage, 1985). Most of these services have developed to use home care workers to provide a wider range of services, usually on a more flexible basis.

The Darlington Project developed enhanced home care further by enabling care workers to be instructed and utilised by a variety of different professionals, in an attempt to integrate much of the work of several different 'hands-on' providers into the activities of one single care worker. Thus, the functions of home help, auxiliary nurse or aide to any occupational group,

Box 2.3

The client pathway

GERIATRIC MULTIDISPLINARY TEAM (GMDT)	CARE MANAGERS	HOME CARE ASSISTANTS (HCAS)
Case finding, screening and referral Assessment and consideration of treatments and service options for patients. Referral of suitable patients.	Clarify target criteria with all in geriatric service: frail elderly mentally alert patients requiring long-stay care but wishing to return home. Receive referral.	
Assessment Secondary assessment of referred patients, their support network and home circumstances. Home visit/assessment by occupational therapist and physiotherapist.	Discuss referral with patient and describe the nature of support to be offered. Collate assessment of GMDT. Home visit: assessment, informing, consultation and negotiation with support network. Involve district nursing service. Discuss possible referral with HCAs, and consider suitable HCA for client.	
Care planning and discharge Instruct HCA on the ward in respect of the individual needs of the patient.	Continued liaison with GMDT and acceptance of patient. Construct and finalise care plan. Coordinate formal and informal network, ensuring that each part of the network is aware of the functions of the other parts. Familiarise HCAs with support network, formal and informal. Consult patient and family on adequacy of support. Inform GP.	Visit patient on the ward and receive instruction and advice from members of the GMDT. Meet members of support network.
Home support, monitoring and review Provide treatment and continue to assess needs of client. Monitor performance of HCA in respect of prescribed tasks. Formal review including district nurse at six weeks after discharge and six months.	Progress-chase care plan. Support HCAs, ensuring demands are not too great. Call team meetings of HCAs for mutual support. Monitor adequacy of support network in consultation with client, carers, HCA and professionals. Refer problems back to GMDT. Take responsibility for resolving problems between client, carers and professionals. Act as advocate on behalf of client. Coordinate review. Progress agreed changes in care plan.	Perform prescribed tasks at a time and in a manner convenient to the client. Notify professionals and care managers of problems arising, seeking advice and providing feedback. Monitor client wellbeing and observe changes. Advise informal network of developments. Provide other assistance to client, e.g. contact Department of Social Security. Contribute to review.

were combined in one person. The home care assistant was available to, and could contact, consult and be instructed by, several different health and social services personnel according to the differing needs of elderly people. The aim was to give both an extension of service and a reduction in the number of individuals involved in providing care, since activities such as basic physiotherapy or meal provision, usually carried out by staff from several different agencies, could be provided at home by fewer and less specialised personnel. Acting as a single care worker meant that the home care assistant could make an important contribution to the care management process by their part in early ascertainment of problems, monitoring client wellbeing and providing feedback, and alerting the care managers and health care staff when action was required. This role developed as they become more confident in their work with clients.

The model of care

The attempt to provide coordinated care at these four different levels constituted the model of care which the project sought to develop. The service model is summarised in Figure 2.2, which indicates the relationship between the project team and the professional staff, and the activities which were undertaken by care managers, both in relation to carers and clients, and in relation to home care assistants. The feedback between carers, clients, care assistants, the project team and health staff is indicated by broken lines. It can be seen in Figure 2.2 how the design of the project enabled various health care professionals and the care managers to work either directly with clients and carers, or indirectly through the home care assistants to achieve their goals.

Key features of the Darlington model

A number of elements have been identified which are likely to influence the pattern of implementation of care management. Variation on these dimensions is evident in much of the international literature. The ways in which variation on these dimensions combine together contributes towards the definition of different models of care management. These indicators are: targeting; the distinction between care management and intensive care management; the location of care management; the style of care management; operational aspects of care management, such as caseload size, staff mix and continuity of care; the degree of influence over service providers; management, standards and quality assurance; and the logical coherence of care management arrangements (Challis, 1994a,b).

Precisely where the Darlington model is located on these dimensions is

Figure 2.2
The model of care

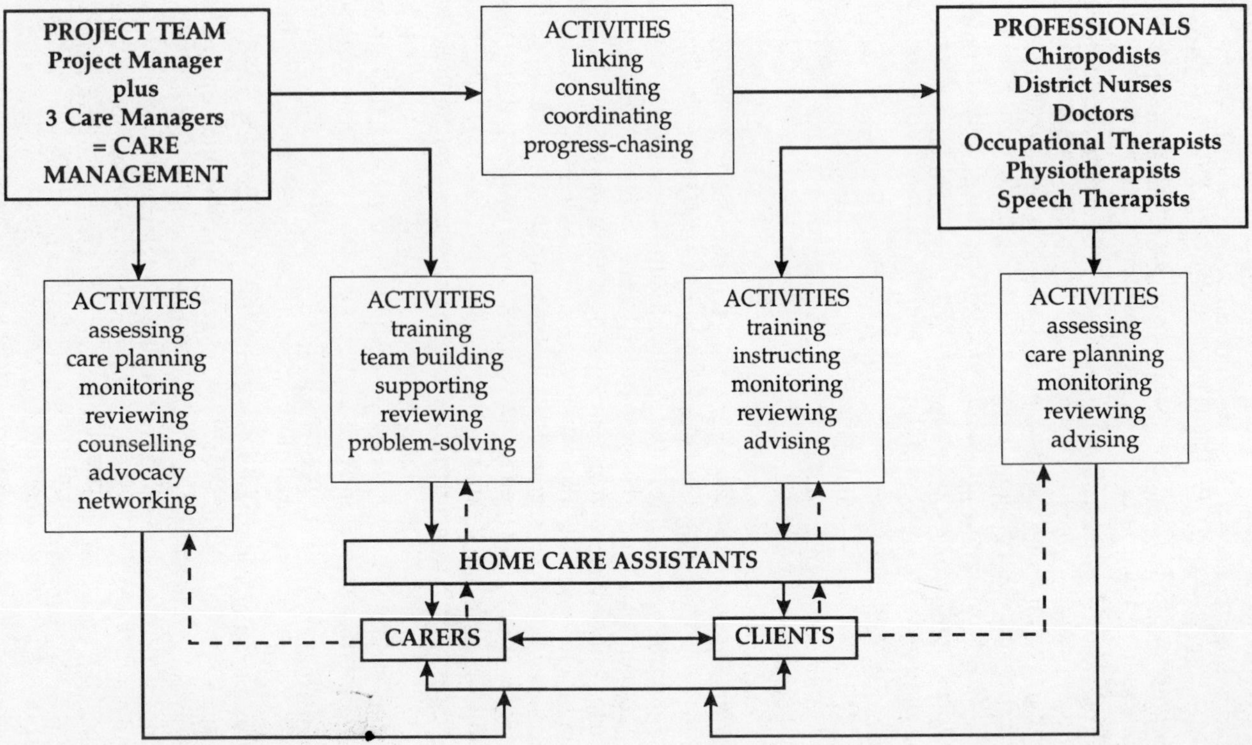

PROJECT TEAM
Project Manager
plus
3 Care Managers
= **CARE**
MANAGEMENT

PROFESSIONALS
Chiropodists
District Nurses
Doctors
Occupational Therapists
Physiotherapists
Speech Therapists

ACTIVITIES
linking
consulting
coordinating
progress-chasing

ACTIVITIES
assessing
care planning
monitoring
reviewing
advising

ACTIVITIES
training
instructing
monitoring
reviewing
advising

ACTIVITIES
training
team building
supporting
reviewing
problem-solving

ACTIVITIES
assessing
care planning
monitoring
reviewing
counselling
advocacy
networking

HOME CARE ASSISTANTS

CLIENTS

CARERS

Box 2.4
Key characteristics of the care management model

Target group — Elderly people at risk of admission to, or receiving, long-stay hospital care.

Intensiveness of care management role — Intensive care management for a high-need group.

Location — Social services department care managers, as members of geriatric multidisciplinary team.

Style of care management — Care managers with responsibility for counselling, advice and social support, as well as arranging and coordinating services.

Operational features:
  Caseload size — small, 20 cases per care manager.
  Staff mix — trained social workers and nursing staff as care managers.
  Continuity of care — Long-term responsiblity; undertaking all core tasks from screening to review.

Influence over providers — Direct control and responsibility for home care assistants; small budget for additional services.

Management: standards and quality assurance — Care management team manager; only limited covering role in client-level work; own assessment, review and costs information system. Home care assistants monitor well-being and contribute to review.

Coherence of arrangements — Project designed to tackle four levels of coordination: interagency, interprofessional, individual care management and the individual worker.

---

shown in Box 2.4. The target group was a physically frail group at risk of admission to, or currently receiving, long-stay care. The care management role was necessarily an intensive one given the extent and potential volatility of the needs of such frail individuals. It required continuity of care with a long-term responsibility for clients, and care managers also had direct responsibility for home care assistant allocation as well as a budget for purchasing additional services. They were trained in social work, nursing or both, and their caseloads were sufficiently small to reflect the intensity of work both in care management, and service development and provision. The care managers were not only responsible for coordinating assessments, arranging and reviewing services, but also had a role in providing support to both clients and carers. There was certainly no rigid separation of purchaser and provider functions at the micro level (Department of Health, 1990), and indeed such ideas did not have common currency in health or social services at the time the project began. In order to facilitate case-finding and to provide access to necessary skills for comprehensive assessment, the care managers were members of the geriatric multidisciplinary team. The project team had its own manager who played a limited role in client-level work, being mainly responsible for supervision, monitoring and dealing with interagency issues. The tasks of supervision and monitoring were made easier since the team had its own system of documenting information about needs and assessment, reviews and service costs at the client level. Finally, the project was designed as a small care management system, tackling issues of coordination at the four levels described earlier: interagency, interprofessional and multidisciplinary, individual care management and the individual 'hands-on' worker.

This was the model of care implemented in the Darlington Project, providing an example of how long-term community-based care could be linked with a geriatric service. The approach was designed to provide enhanced home care and care management, dealing with both client-level and system-level issues. In 1986 it won the *Health Service Journal* Health Management Award. The operation of the project and its outcomes for clients and carers are the focus of this book.

3   The Study: Method and Context

The purpose of this chapter is, first, to set the study in context by describing Darlington and its health and social services system and, second, to describe the aims of the research and the methodology used. The chapter therefore begins with a brief history of Darlington, which is followed by a description of health and social services provision. These sections are followed by a description of the research methodology.

Darlington is a town in the north-east of England, situated in the south-east corner of County Durham (see Figure 3.1). The town is associated in particular with the Stockton and Darlington Railway, which was opened in 1825 and was the first public railway in the world on which a locomotive hauled passengers (Flynn, 1987). Prior to the Local Government Act 1972, Darlington was a county borough, with its own social services department. Following the 1972 Act, which came into force in 1974, Darlington Borough Council and the majority of Darlington Rural District Council became Darlington District Council, one of eight district councils in County Durham, with a population of about 100,000 (OPCS, 1976). A Royal Charter has given Darlington the right still to call itself a Borough and to have a mayor. At the time of the project, social services provision by Durham Social Services Department was administered in eight districts corresponding to the district councils. Recently, two of the administrative districts were amalgamated. Policy development, administrative planning and budgetary control were centralised at county level.

Darlington is the principal town in Darlington Health Authority, and the district general hospital, Darlington Memorial Hospital, is situated in the town. Darlington Health Authority has a population of approximately 125,000 and comprises two district councils, Darlington and Teesdale, which were also coterminous with the administrative districts of Durham Social Services Department at the time of the project. The Darlington District Council area is predominantly urban, surrounded by a small number of villages from which many people commute to Darlington itself or to neighbouring Teesside

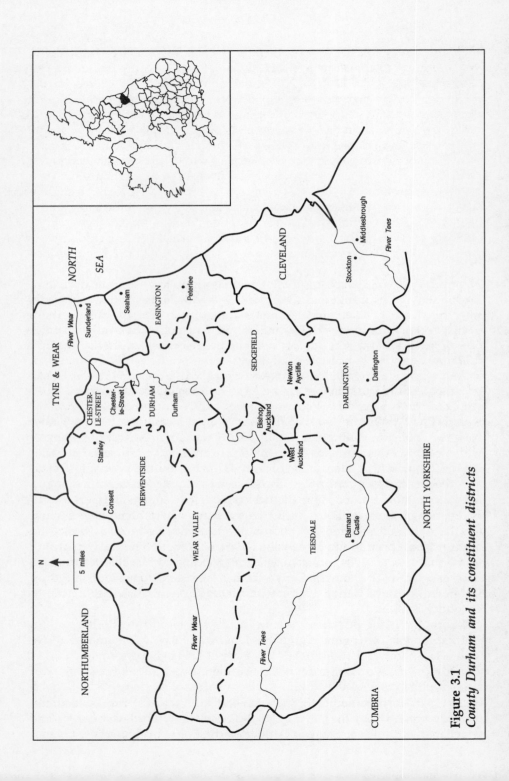

Figure 3.1
County Durham and its constituent districts

in Cleveland to the east. Teesdale, to the west of Darlington, is predominantly rural, with one main centre at Barnard Castle, and has only one-quarter of the population of the Darlington District Council area. The clients for the Darlington Project were drawn from patients in Darlington Memorial Hospital who had been admitted from the Darlington District Council area.

The total population of Darlington and the proportion of elderly people for 1986 are shown later in Table 3.1. Although Darlington had a higher proportion of elderly people than Durham as a whole, 15.5 per cent compared with 15.0 per cent, the proportion of elderly people in Darlington corresponded to the national average, shown later in Table 3.2. However, a slightly higher proportion of elderly people in Darlington was aged 65 to 74, and a slightly lower proportion was aged 75 and over, than in England as a whole; for Darlington the proportions were 9.1 per cent and 6.4 per cent respectively, compared with 8.9 per cent and 6.6 per cent respectively for England as a whole.

Although County Durham had a declining population during the 1980s, the population of Darlington has been relatively static. However, as elsewhere, the proportion of elderly people has increased, particularly among those persons aged 75 or over. The estimated mid-year population in Durham in 1981 was 611,300 (OPCS, 1984a), and projected to fall to 588,300 in 1991 (Durham County Council forecasts). For Darlington the estimated mid-year population was 98,600 in 1981, and the projected figure for 1991 is 97,100, with the proportion of people aged 65 and over rising from 15.2 per cent to 16.1 per cent and the proportion of people aged 75 and over rising from 5.8 per cent to 6.6 per cent (Durham County Council forecasts).

At the time of planning the project, Darlington had relatively high levels of institutional care, provided by the health authority, the social services department and the independent sector, but generally lower levels of community care. Furthermore, the services provided by the district nursing and home help services were fairly inflexible and restricted, despite increases in the average number of hours provided to clients of the home help service. This is discussed in detail below. For England and Wales as a whole, the 1986 report on community care by the Audit Commission noted that, during the period 1974 to 1984, domiciliary services had been unable to do more than keep pace with demographic trends, with the exception of local authority day care during the period 1974 to 1979 (Audit Commission, 1986).

Brief history of Darlington

This brief history of Darlington draws on the books by Flynn (1987) and Sunderland (1972).

The most likely beginning for the town appears to be as a Saxon settlement, probably dating from the period 550-650 AD. The town developed on the west bank of the River Skerne at its first crossing point above its junction with the River Tees. There is some evidence that a Saxon church was built on the site of St Cuthbert's Church, the parish church at the centre of the town, but the earliest surviving documentary record of the town dates from the beginning of the eleventh century. Later in the eleventh century, William I delegated powers to the Bishops of Durham to establish strong government in the area and to oppose the Scots. St Cuthbert's Church was begun at the end of the twelfth century, and the Bishop of Durham built a manor house towards the end of the twelfth century and created a borough and a market in the town, although unfortunately no borough charter survives. Market days on Mondays continue to be an important weekly event. St Cuthbert's, which was extensively restored in the middle of the nineteenth century, is the only ancient building to have survived. The town was not walled or fortified and a fire in 1585 devastated the Tudor town, although the Church, the Deanery and the Bishop's manor house escaped damage. However, the manor house and the Deanery were demolished in the nineteenth century.

Darlington was not included in William I's Domesday Book because the commissioners did not cross to the north of the River Tees, and the Bolden Book, a summary of the Bishop of Durham's lands and his tenants' obligations produced in 1183, provides the first record of the activities of the mediaeval town and its inhabitants. The Bolden Book recorded the existence of a woollen industry, and during the following centuries cloth was sold in the market and exported to Flanders. Although the production of cloth appears to have declined by the beginning of the sixteenth century, the weaving of wool continued, and linen weaving was also introduced.

During the sixteenth and seventeenth centuries, conflicts between the English and the Scots, and political conflicts within England, had serious economic and social effects on the town. Darlington accommodated Henry VIII's administrative Council of the North between 1538 and 1544, and provided a base for the leaders of his army. In 1569 Darlington provided billets for Elizabeth I's army, which was engaged in suppressing the rising of the Earls of Northumberland and Westmorland. During the seventeenth century, Charles I's soldiers were billeted in the town before being defeated by the Scots, and the Scots occupied the town again after the defeat of Charles I's army in the Civil War Battle of Marston Moor in 1644. In 1745, the Duke of Cumberland's army passed through Darlington on the way to the Battle of Culloden, and soldiers were also quartered in the town.

The woollen industry brought Edward Pease of the Quaker Pease family to Darlington in the eighteenth century. Linen manufacture was an important industry in Darlington in the eighteenth century and the town was probably the largest producer in England in the latter part of the century. Members of the Backhouse family, another Quaker family, were engaged in linen manufacturing, but the industry subsequently declined with developments in Leeds. A leather industry had also developed in Darlington, associated with the cattle market, and the town claimed to produce the most leather for its size of any town in England at the beginning of the nineteenth century.

Quakers had used the avenues of commerce and banking to advance, being excluded from universities, Parliament and many of the professions, and, led by the Backhouse and Pease families, Quakers became disproportionately prominent in the affairs of Darlington in the eighteenth and nineteenth centuries.

Darlington was on the route from London to Edinburgh, and during the eighteenth century a number of improvements to the roads were undertaken, financed by the establishment of turnpike trusts, which were authorised to charge tolls. In the middle of the eighteenth century a turnpike trust took control of the road from West Auckland, on which coal was carried from the pits of the South West Durham coalfield to Darlington, Stockton and North Yorkshire, described by Flynn as probably the busiest road in the district. However, the costs of road transport added substantially to the cost of coal, and proposals were made to build a canal from south-west Durham to Stockton via Darlington, but this plan did not materialise due to a lack of subscribers. Further plans to build canals or railways were considered in the early nineteenth century, and led to the issuing of a prospectus in 1818 for a railway from the collieries of Auckland to Darlington, Yarm and Stockton, supported by Edward and Joseph Pease and Jonathan Backhouse. After various setbacks the Stockton and Darlington Railway Bill was given Royal Assent in 1821. The original plan was for haulage to be by 'men or horses or otherwise', but on the day the Bill was approved the engineer George Stephenson met the railway committee and proposed the use of locomotives. The line was formally opened on 27 September 1825, and within two weeks a regular passenger service between Darlington and Stockton was established, although locomotives were used only for bulk mineral haulage, and horses were used to haul passengers and other goods; steam locomotives were not used for all traffic until 1833. Other railway developments followed, including lines linking Darlington with York and Darlington with Newcastle. Amalgamations between the separate railway companies resulted in the formation of the North Eastern Railway in 1854, with which the Stockton and Darlington Railway amalgamated in 1863.

Some small iron foundries operated in Darlington before the completion of the Stockton and Darlington Railway, but substantial development of iron foundries and locomotive engineering works followed the building of the railway. Iron manufacture subsequently ceased when Middlesbrough was developed on Teesside, but heavy engineering continued, particularly related to the requirements of the railway.

The population of Darlington grew substantially during the nineteenth century. In 1821 the population was 5,750, rising to nearly 15,800 in 1861 and to just over 44,500 at the beginning of this century. As a result of the growth in population, both existing buildings and new buildings became overcrowded and deteriorated into slums, while contamination of water supplies also affected public health. Although a local Act of Parliament was obtained in 1823 for paving, lighting, watching and cleansing the town, the Act was not very effective. However, in 1847 a sanitary committee, chaired by John Pease, was established to improve conditions. Greater improvements followed the 1848 Public Health Act, which required towns with a death rate of 23 or more per thousand to appoint a local Board of Health, and permitted other towns to apply to set up a board with the approval of 10 per cent of their ratepayers. A successful petition in 1849 resulted in the establishment of a Board of Health, and Dr Stephen Piper was appointed as Medical Officer. At this time the death rate in the wealthier west end of the town was under 10 per thousand, compared with around 50 per thousand in the slums. Dr Piper held his position for 31 years, and many improvements to public health were introduced during his period of office.

The Pease family held a large block of votes for the Board of Health, and several members of the board were Quakers. The Board of Health gradually acquired more powers and became the effective governing body of the town. The dominance of the Pease family and their associates led to pressure for the town to apply to become a corporate borough with a mayor and elected representatives, which was achieved in 1867. However, the Pease family retained their influence. Seven Board of Health candidates and five members of the Pease family were on the new council, and the first mayor was Henry Fell Pease, who took the place of Joseph Pease who had declined the honour on the grounds of poor health.

As a result of its development as a commercial and industrial centre, a number of small banks were established in Darlington in the eighteenth and nineteenth centuries, two being owned by the Backhouse and Pease families. The Backhouse bank merged with other private Quaker-owned banks at the end of the nineteenth century to form the forerunner of Barclays Bank, but the Pease bank was less successful and was forced into voluntary liquidation at the beginning of the twentieth century. In the middle of the nineteenth century, Darlington also became important as a newspaper-publishing town, using the railway network to distribute newspapers. The country's first half-penny morning paper, *The Northern Echo*, began publication in Darlington on 1 January 1870.

The engineering base of the town declined in the 1960s and 1970s, with the closure of the various railway workshops and other engineering concerns. However, some engineering companies remain and have been augmented by lighter industries and, although Darlington has suffered from unemployment, this has been lower than in other urban areas in the north-east of England (Northern Regional Health Authority, 1985). Darlington itself is not a mining area and there is no evidence of a preponderance of industry-specific diseases. Levels of permanent sickness among adults and standardised mortality ratios are lower in Darlington Health Authority than in other areas in the north-east of England. In Darlington Health Authority in 1981, 2.0 per cent of adults were recorded as permanently sick, compared with 2.5 per cent in the Northern Regional Health Authority area as a whole (Northern Regional Health Authority, 1985). In 1983, standardised mortality ratios were 97 for males and 99 for females for mortality from all causes, compared with 113 for males and 110 for females in the Northern Regional Health Authority area as a whole, and 92 for males and 91 for females for mortality from respiratory diseases, compared with 111 for males and 103 for females in the Northern Regional Health Authority area as a whole (Northern Regional Health Authority, 1985).

Health, social services and housing provision in Darlington

At the time the Darlington Project was introduced, health and social services provision in Darlington combined a relatively high level of institutional care with lower levels of domiciliary support. Table 3.1 presents information on levels of provision of the principal services for elderly people in Darlington, Darlington Health Authority and County Durham, and Table 3.2 presents corresponding information for County Durham, English counties and England as a whole. Table 3.3 presents more detailed information on the characteristics of the home help service in Darlington, County Durham, English counties and England as a whole for 1986-87, using the measures of provision defined by Dexter and Harbert (1983). Prior to the election of the Conservative Government in 1979, national guidelines on levels of provision were produced by the Department of Health and Social Security, and some of the figures shown in Tables 3.1 and 3.2 may be compared with the national guidelines. The guidelines, per thousand population aged 65 and over, were ten beds for geriatric inpatients, 25 beds in residential homes, and 200 meals per week (DHSS, 1977, 1978). For district nurses the national guideline was 0.40 whole-time equivalent staff per thousand total population, although published staffing figures for the years from 1980 onwards are incompatible with those for previous years due to changes in definition (DHSS, 1986a). For home help the national guideline was given in terms of staff, not cases. No guideline was given for nursing homes. In 1980, the Conservative Government reduced the emphasis on national guidelines, other than financial guidelines, in order to allow more flexibility in responding to local needs and circumstances (Cmnd 8086, 1980; DHSS, 1981a).

In 1981, the Department of Health and Social Security indicated that an effective geriatric service could be achieved with three beds per thousand population aged 65 and over for assessment and active treatment in the main district general hospital, a further two beds per thousand elderly population for active rehabilitation, preferably in the district general hospital, or in a general hospital with other acute beds, and up to five longer-stay beds per thousand elderly population, depending on local circumstances (DHSS, 1981d). The report indicated that fewer longer-stay beds would be required in districts with properly equipped and staffed acute geriatric services and adequate primary health care and social services, and that some districts were able to manage with a total of eight beds per thousand elderly population.

Table 3.1

Health and social services provision for elderly people in Darlington, Darlington Health Authority and County Durham

	Date	Darlington	Darlington HA	County Durham
Mid-year population (000s)	1986	100.6	124.5	599.6
Population distribution (%)	1986			
65 & over		15.5	16.1	15.0
65-74		9.1	9.4	9.0
75 & over		6.4	6.6	6.0
Geriatric beds/1,000 pop'n 65+	1984	na	10.7	9.8
District nurses[a]/1,000 pop'n 65+	1984	na	2.3	2.4
Nursing home beds/1,000 pop'n 65+	31/12/85	na	13.2	3.3
Residential home places/1,000 pop'n 65+	31/3/86			
Local authority homes		23.1	21.3	20.6
Voluntary homes		0.0	0.0	1.2
Private homes		8.7	8.4	4.0
Home help cases[b]/1,000 pop'n 65+	1986	68.2	63.0	77.5
Meals/week/1,000 pop'n 65+	1985-86	69.3	68.2	93.4

Sources: CIPFA (1986, 1987, 1988); DHSS (1986b, undated(a)); Durham County Council Social Services Department (1986); Northern Regional Health Authority (1985); OPCS (1988).
  'na' = information not available.
a Whole-time equivalents.
b Point prevalence figure for all clients.

However, although the report stated that the provision of fewer acute and rehabilitation beds could exert severe pressure on other acute medical and surgical services, and increase the need for longer-stay provision, it did not take account of the need to include resources available to elderly people in other medical departments before stating guidelines for levels of provision (Evans, 1983). In the Regional Strategic Plan for the period 1985 to 1994, the Northern Regional Health Authority set an interim target, pending a review of the need for inpatient and day places for elderly people, of 7.5 designated geriatric beds per thousand elderly population (Northern Regional Health Authority, 1985). The review of the need for inpatient and day places for elderly people was intended to take account of the varying roles of voluntary organisations, social services, the private sector, and general and acute hospital services in different health authorities, and the interim target of 7.5

Table 3.2

Health and social services provision for elderly people in County Durham, English county councils and England

	Date	County Durham	English counties	England
Mid-year population (000s)	1986	599.6	29,311.4	47,252.4
Population distribution (%)	1986			
65 & over		15.0	15.7	15.5
65-74		9.0	9.0	8.9
75 & over		6.0	6.7	6.6
Geriatric beds/1,000 pop'n 65+	1984	9.8	na	7.9
District nurses[a]/1,000 pop'n 65+	1984	2.4	na	2.2
Nursing home beds/1,000 pop'n 65+	31/12/85	3.3	5.8[b]	4.7
Residential home places/1,000 pop'n 65+	31/3/86			
Local authority homes		20.6	14.5	15.6
Voluntary homes		1.2	4.1	4.2
Private homes		4.0	15.9	12.6
Home help cases[c]/1,000 pop'n 65+	11/11/85	74.4	72.3	84.9
Meals/week/1,000 pop'n 65+	1985-86	93.4	94.2	117.5

Sources: CIPFA (1986, 1987, 1988); DHSS (1986a, 1986b, undated(a)); Durham County Council Social Services Department (1986); Northern Regional Health Authority (1985); OPCS (1988).

'na' = information not available.

a Whole-time equivalents.

b For health authorities within county boundaries.

c Elderly clients in one week.

beds per thousand elderly population was to be achieved by 1995 at the latest, and preferably by 1990. The Strategic Plan also included the objective of locating at least 30 per cent of geriatric beds in district general hospitals for assessment and short-term rehabilitation, while beds for longer-term care and rehabilitation would be located in community hospitals, NHS nursing homes or other suitable accommodation in local communities. Thus the overall level of provision and the provision of beds for assessment and short-term rehabilitation proposed in the Strategic Plan were lower than the levels of provision suggested in the 1981 report (DHSS, 1981d). In several districts in the Northern Regional Health Authority, although not in Darlington, the provision of geriatric beds in district general hospitals was significantly below the target figure.

In 1984, Darlington Health Authority had 212 geriatric beds, corresponding to 10.7 beds per thousand population aged 65 and over. For the health districts comprising County Durham the corresponding figure was 9.8 beds per thousand population, and for England as a whole the corresponding figure was 7.9 beds. Of the total of 212 beds in Darlington, 120 were in Darlington Memorial Hospital (the district general hospital), 60 were in Greenbank Hospital in Darlington, and 32 were in Richardson Hospital in Barnard Castle; 68 of the beds in Darlington Memorial Hospital were for assessment or rehabilitation, twelve of which were joint assessment beds with psychiatry, and the remaining 52 beds in Darlington Memorial Hospital and the beds in Greenbank Hospital and in Richardson Hospital were long-stay beds (Acquilla, 1986). Following the three-year period of central government funding for the Darlington Project, from 1985 to 1988, funding for the subsequent service was released by the closure of the long-stay beds in two wards in Darlington Memorial Hospital, then containing 54 beds. A total of 146 acute and long-stay geriatric beds remained after the closures, and there were 29 assessment and long-stay beds for elderly mentally ill patients (Ord and Wade, undated). Excluding the provision of places in the domiciliary scheme, the 146 acute and long-stay geriatric beds represented only a slightly lower level of provision than the interim target of 7.5 beds per thousand elderly population set by the Northern Regional Health Authority in the Regional Strategic Plan.

Until 1984, the geriatric service in Darlington Health Authority was headed by a single consultant geriatrician operating the 'traditional' model of geriatric care (Evans, 1983; Irvine, 1983; Acquilla, 1986), in which the geriatric department provides care for elderly patients selected by local general practitioners or referred on by consultants in other specialties following treatment. In 1984, a consultant physician with an interest in the care of the elderly was appointed as the second consultant, and operated the 'integrated' or 'Newcastle' model of geriatric care (Evans, 1983; Irvine, 1983; Acquilla, 1986), in which physicians with different special interests work in teams and share the wards and facilities of the general medical department, in order to increase the effectiveness of care and decrease length of stay.

Independent nursing home provision for elderly people in the Northern Regional Health Authority was concentrated in the Darlington Health Authority (DHSS, 1986b), and Darlington Health Authority had a high level of provision in comparison with the level of provision in the country as a whole. Although parts of Yorkshire Regional Health Authority contained high levels of provision, the adjacent health authority to Darlington in the Yorkshire Region, Northallerton Health Authority, had few nursing homes (DHSS, 1986b), while the area of Cumbria to the west of Darlington Health Authority was very sparsely populated.

Levels of provision of local authority residential care for elderly people were significantly higher in County Durham than for the country as a whole, but independent residential care was less prevalent. In Darlington, both local authority and private residential care were more prevalent than in County Durham as a whole, but, whereas the level of provision of nursing home care was more than twice that for English counties as a whole, the level of provision of private residential home care was approximately half the level in English counties as a whole, and there were no voluntary residential homes in Darlington. As for nursing homes, the adjacent local authority areas in North Yorkshire also had few independent residential homes (Corden, 1992). Although provision of local authority residential care for elderly people in Darlington or County Durham did not reach the national guideline of 25 beds per thousand elderly population, aggregate residential care provision by the local authority and by independent providers in County Durham as a whole slightly exceeded the national guideline, and aggregate residential care provision in Darlington was significantly greater than the national guideline. The level of provision of local authority residential care in Darlington also met a local guideline set by Durham County Council of 56 residential care beds per thousand population aged 75 and over (Durham County Council Social Services Department, 1986), but for County Durham as a whole only the aggregate level of residential care provision met the local guideline.

Housing for elderly people in accommodation supervised by a warden was provided by Darlington District Council, and by housing associations and other organisations in the voluntary sector. The district council provided 28 schemes supervised by a warden living on the premises, containing 826 units of accommodation, and approximately 25 per cent of the total housing stock managed by the district council was available for elderly people. Approximately 200 dwellings and units of accommodation for elderly people were provided by housing associations and other voluntary organisations, and two houses managed by the local Abbeyfield Society provided a further eighteen places.

In contrast to the relatively high overall level of institutional care in Darlington, district nursing provision in Darlington Health Authority was only slightly higher than that for England as a whole, and lower than the national guideline, while levels of provision of home help and meals were lower than for England as a whole, although the average amount of home help received by each client was higher than for England as a whole. Relative to the total population, the number of whole-time equivalent district nurses per thousand population was 0.36 for Darlington Health Authority, 0.34 for County Durham and 0.32 for England (Northern Regional Health Authority, 1985; CIPFA, 1986; DHSS, 1986a; OPCS, 1988), compared with the national guideline of 0.40 per thousand population. However, it should be noted that the national guideline was produced before the definitions used in the published staffing figures for district nurses were changed, as noted above. For home help services, Dexter and Harbert (1983) defined three interrelated measures of provision, as shown in Table 3.3: *level*, which is the average number of hours of home help time available per week per thousand population aged 65 and over; *cover*, which is the average number of cases per week per thousand

Table 3.3
Profiles of resource use in the home help service in Darlington,
County Durham, English county councils and England

	Darlington	County Durham	English counties	England
Date	1986	1986-87	1986-87	1986-87
Level (hours/week/1,000 pop'n 65+)	287	339	246	318
Cover (elderly clients/1,000 pop'n 65+)[a]	68[b]	70	68	88
Intensity (hours/week/client)	4.2	4.3	3.3	3.3

Sources: Social Services Inspectorate (1988); Durham County Council Social Services
Department (1986).
a Definition as in SSI (1988), except for the Darlington figure.
b All clients per 1,000 population aged 65 and over.

elderly population, and is shown in Tables 3.1 and 3.2; and *intensity*, which
is the average number of hours of home help time received per week by each
client. Using these definitions, *level* is equivalent to the product of *cover* and
intensity. However, the information on cover shown for County Durham,
English counties and England as a whole in Tables 3.2 and 3.3 relates to
elderly clients, instead of all clients, and so in Table 3.3 the relationship
between the three measures only applies for the information for Darlington.
The level of provision of home help in Darlington was lower than for County
Durham, while the level of provision of home help in County Durham was
higher than for English counties and for England as a whole. However, for
both Darlington and County Durham the cover of the home help service was
relatively restricted and, conversely, the intensity of the service was
substantially higher than for England as a whole. The level of provision of
meals in Darlington was lower than for County Durham, while for County
Durham the level of provision of meals was similar to that for English counties
as a whole, although lower than for all authorities in England.

District nurses provide physical, psychological, social and rehabilitative
care to patients, and 90 per cent of their time was spent in the care of elderly
people (Ord and Wade, undated). In addition, although they worked mainly
with children, a small amount of the time of health visitors was spent with
elderly people. The community nursing service did not offer comprehensive
24-hour domiciliary support, and the only evening and out-of-hours service
was provided for the administration of controlled drugs. However, although
the community nursing service did not formally include a put-to-bed service,
this was provided for a few people in Darlington. An examination of the
frequency of visits by districts nurses in a four-week period in early 1987
indicated that 62 per cent of elderly patients had received visits monthly or
fortnightly, 18 per cent had received weekly visits, 18 per cent had received

daily visits, and 2 to 3 per cent had received two or more visits per day.

The home help service was predominantly a domestic help service, undertaking fire lighting, housework, the preparation of meals and shopping. A limited incontinence laundry service was also provided. Although the home help service had increased the level of personal care to clients, 90 per cent of whom were elderly, the majority received too few hours of help per week for the service to provide much personal care, despite the relatively high level of intensity of the service noted above. For some clients, a limiting factor in the amount of home help received was the requirement to pay charges for home help. Only 11 per cent of clients in the Darlington District Council area received over six hours of help per week in the period to the end of September 1986 (Ord and Wade, undated). In early 1987, the home help service provided a put-to-bed service for a small number of clients in Darlington, while just over 10 per cent of clients were receiving a weekend service.

In addition to the principal services for elderly people shown in Tables 3.1 and 3.2, elderly people also received day care provided in two day hospitals and by the local authority and voluntary organisations, and care from members of professions allied to medicine, including chiropodists, dieticians, occupational therapists and physiotherapists, and from speech therapy staff. However, as noted in the Regional Strategic Plan, the supply of staff in several professions allied to medicine and in speech therapy had not kept pace with demand during the previous ten years, and would not be able to cope with future requirements without changes in the number of trainees, changes in the pattern of retention and wastage of staff, and changes in the use of helpers to professionally-qualified staff (Northern Regional Health Authority, 1985).

Day hospital provision in Darlington included a separate 25-place day hospital unit for elderly people, and twelve places for elderly mentally ill patients in the district general hospital. The day hospital provided assessment and rehabilitation for patients, most of whom attended for two or three days per week. Twenty-four day care places were provided in eight of the nine local authority residential homes for elderly people in Darlington, and elderly people were also able to attend a handicraft centre run by the social services department. In addition, several day and luncheon clubs, including a stroke club, were provided by voluntary organisations in Darlington between Monday and Saturday each week.

Approximately 80 per cent of the time of the staff of the chiropody department was spent in the care of elderly clients. Chiropody clinics were held in locations across the health authority, and approximately 25 per cent of elderly people in the health authority received care from the chiropody service, although there was a waiting list for assessment, and an estimated need for the chiropody service by a further 15 per cent of elderly people in the authority. To help overcome the shortfall, a policy to employ foot care assistants was being developed in 1987 to expand the service. The chiropody service provided care for housebound or non-mobile clients in their own homes, and care for residents in local authority residential homes and patients in the day hospital, but did not provide care for residents and patients in private residential and private nursing homes, unless they were able to attend the clinics, and only provided an emergency service for elderly mentally ill clients.

The dietetics service was not funded to care specifically for elderly people, and the level of provision for elderly people, both in hospital and in the community, was recognised as inadequate (Ord and Wade, undated). Approximately 50 per cent of the time of the hospital-based staff was spent with elderly patients, including both inpatients and outpatients, but the majority of the inpatient work was undertaken in the acute medical and surgical wards rather than in the geriatric wards. Ten per cent of the time of the community-based dietician was allocated to elderly people, but this included visits to homes for elderly people and training sessions for other staff and agencies, as well as individual contacts with clients.

Occupational therapy was provided for patients in the geriatric wards, the day hospital and for elderly mentally ill patients, and involved the development of individual treatment programmes covering the domestic, personal, physical, psychological and social aspects of the elderly person's life. In order to assist the resettlement of patients in their homes following hospital treatment, the occupational therapists also undertook home assessments. In addition, an occupational therapist was employed by the local authority to make assessments and recommendations for the provision of aids and adaptations for elderly people in their own homes, and the staffing of the Darlington Project included 50 per cent of the time of an occupational therapist.

Physiotherapy was provided each day for patients in the acute geriatric wards and in the day hospital, but only by request for elderly mentally ill patients, while only a very limited service was provided for patients in the long-stay geriatric wards. The staffing of the Darlington Project included 50 per cent of the time of a physiotherapist, and a pilot domiciliary service, which received referrals from general practitioners, was introduced in 1985-86. Eighty per cent of the patients seen by the domiciliary physiotherapy service were elderly and, overall, elderly people received approximately one-quarter of the total time provided by the physiotherapists in the health authority.

Speech therapy was provided in the health authority by two full-time staff, with some assistance from junior staff, for all clients, and was not allocated specifically to elderly people. The speech therapists covered the geriatric wards and the day hospital but, although all patients referred to the speech therapists would be assessed, priority was given to patients who had had a stroke or who had undergone laryngectomy.

Overall, Darlington had a relatively high level of institutional care at the time the project was introduced, although levels of hospital provision were subsequently reduced to the existing national levels. Aggregate levels of residential and nursing home provision were higher than for English counties as a whole, with levels of local authority residential care and independent nursing home care exceeding the national average, while independent residential care was less prevalent than in the country as a whole. Levels of provision of domiciliary services were generally lower than for England as a whole, although the intensity of provision of the home help service exceeded the national average, while levels of provision of district nursing were similar to the national average. Thus, although there were a number of differences between Darlington and the country as a whole in terms of levels of health and social services provision, the differences were not sufficiently extreme for Darlington to be unsuitable as a representative of a health and social services system in England. Furthermore, the relatively high level of institutional provision made Darlington a particularly suitable area for study, given the emphasis on the transfer from institutional to more community-based provision under the National Health Service and Community Care Act 1990.

The research design and method

The Darlington Project was one of the second round of pilot projects funded under the Care in the Community Initiative (DHSS, 1983). The Personal Social Services Research Unit (PSSRU) was commissioned by the Department to monitor and evaluate the initiative (Renshaw et al., 1988; Knapp et al., 1992). Additional funding provided by the Joseph Rowntree Memorial Trust, now the Joseph Rowntree Foundation, made possible a more detailed evaluation of the Darlington Project.

As noted in Chapter 1, 28 projects were centrally funded under the Care in the Community Initiative, each for a period of three years: thirteen from April 1984 and fifteen from April 1985. The projects in the second round were approved by the Department of Health and Social Security in February 1985 (Renshaw et al., 1988). The first clients of the Darlington Project were discharged from hospital in October 1985. The request for additional funding from the Joseph Rowntree Memorial Trust, for a research officer to be based in Darlington, was made during the summer of 1985 and approved by the Trust in September 1985. Interviews for the post of research officer were held in December 1985, and the successful candidate took up her appointment in February 1986. Until the appointment of the research officer, the elderly people being considered for the project were included in the interviews for the monitoring and evaluation of the 28 pilot projects by the PSSRU. Information common to the questionnaires used in both the Care in the Community and the Darlington study was used for both pieces of research. The results of the Care in the Community research, covering all pilot projects, are presented in Knapp et al. (1992).

The evaluation of the Darlington Project used the same methodology as the evaluation of the care management models developed previously in Kent and Gateshead (Challis and Davies, 1986; Davies and Challis, 1986; Challis et al., 1990). However, in Darlington the approach was developed in a multi-agency setting, to discharge people from hospital rather than prevent their admission to long-stay care, with the service deploying its own multipurpose workers, the project home care assistants. Nonetheless, in its use of decentralised budgets and care management undertaken by care managers, many of the principles and practices of the approach remained similar and contribute further to our understanding of long-term care. The underlying theoretical framework for these evaluations is the production of welfare model developed at the PSSRU (Davies and Knapp, 1981; Knapp, 1984), which relates resource inputs (services provided to clients and their informal carers), non-resource inputs (for example, dependency, health and social networks) and outputs (the effects of services provided). Whereas evaluative studies of welfare programmes have often concentrated upon the outcomes of the programme, without examining the resources employed and the costs of these resources (Weiss, 1972; Challis et al., 1988c; Thomas, 1988), the production of welfare model explicitly introduces the costs of inputs into an analysis of the effects of a welfare programme. The production of welfare model provides the framework for examining the research question: 'What were the costs to different parties of the outcomes of care for elderly people in various circumstances, and how were these outcomes achieved?' (Challis and Davies, 1986, p.17). A brief description of the production of welfare model is contained in Challis and Darton (1990).

Research questions

The aim of the research in Darlington, as well as in Kent and Gateshead, was to examine the kinds of care arrangements which are necessary to maintain severely disabled elderly people in their own homes. The study was designed to examine how appropriate this model of community care was for patients with varying degrees of physical and mental frailty; to compare the effects of community care with those of institutional care on family and other informal carers; to compare the relative costs of care at home and long-stay hospital care; and to examine whether health and social services may be effectively integrated at the individual client level. These research questions may be summarised as *care process* and *costs and effectiveness* issues.

The *care process* questions include two key areas. The first concerns the way in which the care managers in the project coordinated care and undertook the activities of care management across agency boundaries. The second concerns the activities of the home care assistants who helped to integrate care for individual clients by undertaking a wide range of domestic, caring and therapeutic tasks.

The *costs and effectiveness* questions concern the relative costs and benefits incurred by different parties following the introduction of the new form of care. In addition, the information collected can help to identify the characteristics of patients for whom discharge from hospital and the provision of non-institutional forms of long-term care are most appropriate and represent the best use of scarce resources.

Research design

A *quasi-experimental* research design (Campbell and Stanley, 1966) was employed to examine the relative effectiveness of the project, compared with
long-stay hospital care. The individuals receiving services from the project
were compared with a group of patients with similar characteristics in the
long-stay wards in hospitals in an adjacent health district. The choice of
research design was determined by the administrative aspects of the project
and by the need to study the project as a system as well as its effects on
individual clients. In medical research the randomised controlled trial (or
RCT), in which a random allocation procedure is used to assign experimental
subjects to the different treatments under examination, has become a powerful
technique for assessing the effectiveness of different treatments. However, in
the evaluation of a service such as the Darlington Project, a number of factors
militate against a random allocation procedure (Goldberg and Connelly, 1982;
Challis and Davies, 1986; Challis and Darton, 1990):

- Service providers may be unwilling to allocate clients to the comparison
  group rather than to the preferred experimental group, and thus may
  sabotage random assignments by deliberately assigning particular cases
  to the experimental group.
- Random assignment of individuals to the experimental and comparison
  groups within a particular health authority or local authority area may be
  politically unacceptable by appearing arbitrary. The introduction of a new
  service in one area, with comparisons made with other areas providing
  the existing services, is likely to be more acceptable.
- Random assignment of individuals to the experimental and comparison
  groups within part of a particular health authority or local authority is
  likely to lead to 'contamination'. For example, the introduction of the
  experimental service may effectively reduce the workload for the practitioners providing the comparison service and enable them to provide an
  improved service for the comparison group.
- The evaluation of the effects of a programme requires the comparison of
  the system of care in the area chosen to receive the experimental treatment
  with the traditional system of care in another, similar area. The choice of
  the area to receive the experimental programme is not usually made randomly, and then the researcher's task is to find a suitable control area to
  match the experimental area.
- A randomised experiment can provide evidence about whether a particular
  input produces a particular change, rather than why the result occurred.
  In a quasi-experimental design, the behaviour of the system may be examined through the collection of a wider range of information relating to care

process questions, as well as the effects of the system on the individual clients.

The research design used for the comparisons of the elderly people in Darlington and in the comparison group was a before-after design or, in the terminology of Campbell and Stanley (1966), a *non-equivalent control group* design. Both groups of elderly people were assessed in hospital and followed up after six months. The elderly people in Darlington were also interviewed about six weeks after discharge from hospital to obtain further information about their social networks. In 'true' experiments, random allocation ensures that differences between the groups result from chance fluctuations only, and so the pre-treatment measurement, corresponding to the initial assessment in hospital, is not essential. The sensitivity of a true experiment to the treatment of interest may be increased by matching the groups on certain key variables, or by making adjustments in the analysis (Moser and Kalton, 1971), and it may be useful for the investigator to know how successful random allocation, with or without matching, had been in equating the groups. Since random allocation is not possible in quasi-experiments, matching and adjustment play a more important role than in true experiments. The interpretation of the results of a quasi-experiment depends on the similarity of the groups, and thus a comparison of the groups requires the inclusion of pre-treatment measurements. Initially it was intended that the elderly people in Darlington and in the comparison group would be matched individually. However, the overall similarity between the two groups, on most variables of interest, led to the use of covariance adjustments to adjust for differences between the two groups in the comparisons presented in later chapters. These points are discussed in more detail in Challis and Darton (1990).

Several health districts in the Northern Regional Health Authority near to Darlington were considered as potential comparison districts for the evaluation of the Darlington Project. Following discussions with senior medical staff in the area in autumn 1985, Durham Health Authority appeared to be the most appropriate comparison district, as it had the most similar geriatric service and was also within the boundaries of County Durham. Agreement to participate in the study followed discussions with the hospital consultants in Durham and approval by the ethical committee of Durham Health Authority. (From 1992, Durham Health Authority and North West Durham Health Authority have been combined as North Durham Health Authority.) There were nine wards with 184 beds in two separate hospitals. The researcher appointed as part of the research team attended ward meetings at the comparison group hospitals and discussed potential cases with senior medical and nursing staff. Knowledge of the characteristics of the clients in the Darlington Project enabled the researcher to focus specifically on particular types of patient and form a comparison group of patients with similar characteristics to those of the Darlington clients. For the Darlington Project, participation in the evaluation of the project was a condition of being funded under the Care in the Community Initiative (DHSS, 1983).

The SPSS package (SPSS Inc., 1990) was used for the analysis of the data collected in the evaluation, supplemented, where appropriate, by a package for the exact probability analysis of contingency tables (StatXact, 1989).

Identification of the potential clientele for the project

As explained in Chapter 2, a census of patients carried out in 1984 provided information on the potential clientele for the project. Information on mobility, orientation, continence, vision and hearing was used to identify 62 physically disabled but mentally alert, elderly people in long-stay care in hospitals in Darlington on 1 March 1984. The results of the 1984 day census, together with the results of a previous day census undertaken in June 1983, are discussed by Acquilla (1986). Further annual day censuses were conducted in July 1985, May 1986 and June 1987, providing a profile of the patients in Darlington and identifying changes in the characteristics of the hospital patients during the period of central government funding for the Darlington Project (Acquilla et al., 1987b,c). In May 1986, a parallel census of long-stay elderly patients in hospitals in Durham Health Authority was conducted to provide information about patients in the comparison group hospitals (Acquilla et al., 1987a), and additional collections of information on new patients have been made periodically since then to provide further comparative information. In 1987, a parallel census was conducted in private and voluntary residential care and nursing homes in Darlington on the same date as the hospital day census, and a census of residents in residential homes managed by Durham Social Services Department, forming the latest in a series of biennial censuses, was also held at the same time. Descriptions of the results of the censuses held in local authority residential homes in Durham up to and including the 1985 census are given in Coles (1985a,b). Details of the contents of the 1986 and 1987 day census questionnaires used for hospital patients are shown in the Appendix to this chapter.

The characteristics of the physical and social environment of the hospital wards from which Darlington Project clients and comparison group patients were drawn were recorded using the Ward Environment Questionnaire, which was adapted from the environment questionnaire developed for the monitoring and evaluation of the Care in the Community Initiative as a whole (Renshaw et al., 1988). Prior to the appointment of the research officer funded by the Joseph Rowntree Memorial Trust, the environment questionnaire developed for the Care in the Community study was completed for hospital wards in Darlington, and the information common to both questionnaires was used to complete the Ward Environment Questionnaire. Details of the contents of the Ward Environment Questionnaire are shown in the Appendix.

Most patients selected for the Darlington Project were discharged from six wards: two acute and two long-stay in the main district general hospital, and two long-stay wards in the adjacent hospital. These wards contained a total of 168 beds. The average size of these wards was 28 beds, and the average number of patients at the time of completing the Ward Environment Questionnaire was 25. Forty-eight patients (29 per cent) were in sleeping areas with four beds or fewer and the rest in larger groups. The comparison group patients were identified from nine wards in two hospitals. These wards contained 184 beds giving an average ward size of 20 beds, while the average number of patients was 19. Ten patients (5 per cent) were in sleeping areas of four or fewer beds and the rest were in larger groups. On most indicators of privacy and personal space, such as the number of toilets and presence of lockers, the wards appeared to be adequate for the number of patients. However, the availability of material for recreational activities varied. In Darlington there appeared to be none on the acute wards or on two of the long-stay wards. More recreational facilities were available in the comparison group wards. All patients could have drinks whenever they wished, but snacks were available in only some of the wards, and were available in more of the comparison group wards. Schools and voluntary groups visited most of the wards on a regular basis. There were no ward meetings for patients except in one comparison group ward. In Darlington, morning visiting was restricted in three of the six wards, including the two acute wards, but the overall pattern was flexible. In the comparison group wards, friends and relatives were able to visit at any time.

Interviews with elderly people

As noted above, the elderly people in Darlington and in the comparison group were assessed in hospital and followed up after six months. For the elderly people in Darlington, the follow-up took place six months after discharge from hospital. In addition, the elderly people in Darlington were also interviewed about six weeks after discharge to obtain further information about their social networks, once these had been re-established in the community and developed within the context of the Darlington Project, since the information about their social networks prior to their admission to hospital was collected retrospectively at the time of the initial assessment in hospital, this information was likely to be very unreliable. The number of elderly people included in the study is shown in Table 3.4. All elderly people who entered the project during the three-year period of funding under the Care in the Community Initiative were included in the evaluation, and thus follow-up interviews continued until September 1988. Recruitment of elderly people to the comparison group ceased in February 1988. Initially it was intended that a third group of elderly people, who had been identified as potential project clients but who did not join the project, would be included in the comparison. However, it was not possible to devote the necessary resources to identifying and following up all such individuals, and several

Table 3.4

Number of questionnaires completed for elderly people and their principal carers

Interviewee	Interview number[a]	Darlington Project	Comparison group	Darlington Day Hospital
Elderly person	1	101[b]	113	30
	2	82	–	–
	3	67	100	–
Principal carer	1	75	27	30
	2	46	–	–

a Follow-up interviews with elderly people were held 6 weeks after discharge (number 2) and 6 months after discharge/6 months after interview number 1 (number 3). Follow-up interviews with principal carers were held 6 months after discharge (number 2).
b Individuals discharged to the project. A further 17 elderly people who were interviewed did not join the project.

died before they could be discharged. In addition to the 101 project clients, seventeen elderly people were interviewed following identification as potential project clients, but did not join the project. Of these, eight died in hospital before they could be discharged. The 30 elderly people from the day hospital in Darlington and their principal carers were included to form an additional comparison group of carers, as described below. The destinational outcomes for the elderly people in Darlington and in the comparison group are shown in Chapter 7. The number of follow-up interviews of elderly people, shown as interview number 3 in the table, correspond to the number of Darlington clients who were still at home after six months and, apart from one omission, to the number of elderly people in the comparison group who were alive after six months. Only three elderly people in Darlington who had received the services of the project, and who were still alive after six months, no longer lived at home. Information for the monitoring and evaluation of the Care in the Community Initiative was collected for thirteen individuals, eleven of whom were discharged to the project in the autumn of 1985, prior to the appointment of the research officer in Darlington, and information common to both studies was transferred to the questionnaires used for the Darlington evaluation. In addition, using project records, the research officer collected information retrospectively for a further ten individuals who had been discharged to the project prior to her appointment and who had not been included in the Care in the Community research. Thus, the information collected for the individuals discharged to the project before the appointment of the research officer was incomplete.

The information collected about the elderly people in Darlington and in the comparison group included dependency levels using the Behaviour Rating

Scale from the Clifton Assessment Procedures for the Elderly (Pattie and Gilleard, 1979); assessments of key activities of daily living (Challis and Davies, 1986); a set of questions to identify organic disorders (Bond et al., 1980); a measure of depression using the twelve-item General Health Questionnaire (Goldberg, 1972); measures of morale using the Philadelphia Geriatric Center Morale Scale (Lawton, 1975); indicators of social network using the Interview Schedule for Social Interaction (Henderson et al., 1981); indicators of quality of care (Challis and Davies, 1986); and ratings of social resources, economic resources, mental health, physical health and performance of activities of daily living from the Older Americans Resources and Services Multidimensional Functional Assessment Questionnaire (Duke University Center for the Study of Aging and Human Development, 1978). In addition, information on social activities, drawn from the work of Wing (1989), and general questions on the interviewee's expectations and reactions to the services received were included. Full details of the contents of the questionnaires are shown in the Appendix.

In addition to the routine medical assessment described in Chapter 2, it had been planned that full research medical assessments would take place, as part of the study, at the time of the initial interviews in hospital and the follow-up after six months for the elderly people in Darlington and those in the comparison group. However, it did not prove possible to implement this due to a lack of availability of medical staff.

Interviews with carers

Since the Darlington Project was principally concerned with improving the experience and environment of elderly people requiring long-term care, the experience of the carers of Darlington clients was compared with two other groups of carers: a subgroup of individuals selected from among the carers of the elderly people remaining in long-stay hospital care and who formed the client comparison group; and a group of the carers of elderly people in Darlington selected from those attending day hospital and receiving the usual range of health and social services while living in the community. Underlying this three-way comparison was the expectation that discharging elderly patients from hospital to care in the community should preferably lead to less, and certainly no more, stress on carers than that experienced by caring for a frail elderly person at home receiving the usual range of services, or of being a carer of an elderly person remaining in long-stay hospital care. There is some evidence that not all burdens and stresses are removed from carers once the elderly person is in institutional care, since feelings of guilt and loss occur (Brane, 1986; Challis and Davies, 1986; Müller, 1987), particularly since families frequently retain close links following institutionalisation. This also suggests that the notion of abandonment is largely a myth (Dobrof and Litwak, 1977; York and Calsyn, 1977; Smith and Bengtson, 1979). The Clifton

Assessment Procedures for the Elderly Behaviour Rating Scale, which was included in the interview schedules for elderly people in the project and the comparison group, was used to provide comparative information on the level of functioning of the elderly people in Darlington who attended the day hospital.

In the following chapters, the group of carers whose relative was a client of the Darlington Project are termed 'project carers'; the group of carers in Darlington whose elderly relative attended the day hospital are termed 'day hospital carers'; and the group of carers of elderly people in long-term hospital care are termed 'hospital carers'. The group of project carers included all carers of Darlington Project clients who could be identified. The day hospital carers were identified with the help of the sister at the day hospital and the district nursing sisters working in the community. On identification, a letter was sent asking if the carer was willing to be interviewed. The compliance rate was very high, with only two refusals. The hospital carers were selected with the assistance of hospital ward sisters and the patients themselves. Those relatives who retained a regular, reliable pattern of visiting and involvement with the elderly person were contacted by letter and asked if they would be willing to be interviewed. Only one person refused to participate, although in five cases contact could not be made, or a change in circumstances led to the cancellation of the interview. The project carers were interviewed on two occasions, about two weeks after the elderly person was discharged from hospital to the project, and again at six months. A before-and-after measurement of the effects of the service on the project carers was not possible, since it was impossible to see carers before they were apprised of the discharge of the elderly person from hospital. Thus, there was insufficient time for the research officer to interview project carers before the elderly person was discharged from hospital. Furthermore, the knowledge that the elderly person was being considered for the project could have influenced the responses by project carers in any such interviews. The hospital and day hospital carers were interviewed on one occasion since it was not practicable to collect change measures for these carers. Therefore, a comparison was made between the experience of carers of elderly people receiving the services of the project, as recorded in the first interview, carers of elderly people receiving the usual home care services, and carers of elderly people receiving long-stay hospital care. The number of interviews obtained from each group of cases is shown in Table 3.4.

In the terminology of Campbell and Stanley (1966), the research design used for the comparison between the groups of carers was a *static-group comparison*. As noted above, pre-treatment measurements are needed to establish the similarity of groups in a non-randomised study, and thus the conclusions drawn from the study of carers must necessarily be more tentative than the conclusions drawn from the study of elderly people. In addition, differences between the groups in a static-group comparison may be due to differential selection effects and differential mortality or drop-out (Campbell and Stanley, 1966). All groups of carers were composed of individuals who maintained close links with the elderly person, but the project carers group was most likely to include some carers with less close links, as well as those strongly in favour of the elderly person joining the project, thus minimising the likelihood of introducing a positive bias in favour of the project into the study of carers. This, together with the restriction of the availability of the Darlington Project to hospital patients and the positive response to participation in the project among those eligible, and the level of response to the invitation to join the comparison groups, would suggest that differential selection effects were not a major problem. Differential mortality was minimised, as far as possible, by the timing of the interviews, and by the inclusion in the first interviews of carers of eight Darlington clients who had died soon after discharge to the project, although only parts of the questionnaire could be completed in these interviews. As for the comparisons between the groups of elderly people, covariance adjustments were used to adjust for differences in the characteristics of the elderly relatives of the carers in the results presented in later chapters.

The interviews with the informal carers of the elderly people covered the care tasks undertaken by the carer, aspects of the behaviour and symptoms exhibited by the elderly person, the effects of caring on the carer and their family, and support received from relatives, friends, and health and social services, and the financial costs of care. The interview schedules were based on the Social Behaviour Assessment Schedule (Platt et al., 1983), amended to be suitable for the carers of elderly people in the Darlington Project and the two comparison groups. The Social Behaviour Assessment Schedule (SBAS) was designed to estimate the 'objective burden' of adverse effects on others and the distress, or 'subjective burden', caused by disturbances in the patient's behaviour, by the patient's limited social performance or by the objective burdens. The rating of distress includes the category of 'resignation', to cover cases where the informant describes long-term resignation to disturbed behaviour which has been in evidence for a considerable period (Platt et al., 1980). The questions on behaviour were amended to be suitable for geriatric patients, rather than the acute psychiatric patients for whom the SBAS was originally designed (Platt et al., 1980). The interview schedules also included the Malaise Inventory of Rutter et al. (1970), and questions on the positive benefits of caring, drawing on the work of Qureshi et al. (1983, 1989). Full details of the contents of the questionnaires are shown in the Appendix.

Cost and service information

Weekly cost information was recorded in the case records completed by the staff of the project. This information, supplemented by material recorded elsewhere in the project records, was used to provide cost information on flows of resources to each client for a period of six months following discharge from hospital, to permit the analysis of costs and benefits borne by different parties as a result of the scheme, including the social services department, the National Health Service and society as a whole. Comparison group patients' use of services was tracked over the same period. Information about care process issues came from a variety of different sources. Information on care management activities was derived from interviews with the care managers themselves, and also from structured case notes and regular reviews based on earlier studies (Challis and Chesterman, 1985). The work of the home care assistants was examined by means of analyses of care tasks undertaken, and interviews at intervals with a cohort of home care assistants during their initial training and during their work with clients. In addition, a survey of the activities undertaken by home care assistants was conducted during one week in September 1987. Interprofessional issues were examined through interviews with a range of different service providers.

Summary

The information presented in this chapter includes a brief history of Darlington, a description of health, social services and housing provision in Darlington, and a description of the research design and method. The subsequent chapters examine the process of providing care, covering care management, the activities of the home care assistants and the coordination of care across agency boundaries, and issues of costs and effectiveness, covering outcomes for clients, the experience of carers and the costs of care, using the methodology described in this chapter.

Appendix: Research schedules

This Appendix summarises the information collected in the schedules used in the evaluation of the Darlington Project. The fieldwork records completed by the staff of the project, which included assessment documents, cost records, case review forms, reassessment documents, home care assistant activity forms and reviews by other professional staff (Challis et al., 1987) are not included. However, details of the community care records used in the Kent Community Care Scheme are shown in Challis and Davies (1986).

The following schedules are described in this Appendix:

- Day census questionnaires
- Ward environment questionnaire
- Interview with elderly person in hospital
- Interview with elderly person after discharge
- Follow-up interview with elderly person
- Interview with principal carer
- Interview with principal carer of patient in hospital

In addition, the Clifton Assessment Procedures for the Elderly Behaviour Rating Scale (Pattie and Gilleard, 1979), which was included in the interview with the elderly person in hospital and in the follow-up interview, was used to collect information about the elderly people in Darlington who attended the day hospital and whose carers formed the 'day hospital carers' group.

Additional instructions for the interviewer were prepared for the elderly person and carer interviews. Copies of the schedules are contained in Challis et al. (1988b).

Day census questionnaires

The questionnaires used in the day censuses conducted in hospitals in Darlington in 1983, 1984 and 1985 were designed by Darlington Health Authority staff, and copies of the questionnaires are included in the report by Acquilla (1986). The questionnaire used for the 1985 census incorporated some questions used in the questionnaires developed for the overall monitoring and evaluation of the Care in the Community Initiative, and some questions on topics covered in the questionnaires prepared for the evaluation of the Darlington Project. For the 1986 census, and the parallel census in hospitals in Durham Health Authority, the questionnaire was shortened slightly, and for the 1987 census the wording of some of the questions was modified in the light of the results of the 1986 census or for greater compatibility with information collected in the interviews with Darlington Project clients and elderly people in the comparison group. However, the same summary dependency measures could be produced for both the 1986 and the 1987 censuses.

The questionnaire used for the 1987 census was also shortened slightly. Copies of the questionnaires used in the 1986 and 1987 day censuses in Darlington, and in the 1986 day census in Durham Health Authority, are contained in the reports of the three censuses (Acquilla et al., 1987a,b,c). The topics covered by the 1986 and 1987 censuses were: hospital and hospital ward; date questionnaire completed; patient number; date of admission; age; sex; marital status; next-of-kin; social and domestic circumstances; availability of property (1986 only); consultant; referral; specialty of admission; medical reason for admission; type of admission; main reason for admission; number of previous admissions; main reason for remaining in hospital; visitors; incontinence — day; incontinence — night; vision; hearing; mobility; conversation/mixing with patients (1986 only); confusion; sleep pattern at night; wandering; clarity of speech (1986 only); washing; bathing; dressing; eating habits (1986 only); depressed mood; comprehension (1986 only); transfer; giddiness; risk of falling; breathlessness; using toilet; feeding self.

Ward Environment Questionnaire

The Ward Environment Questionnaire was designed to obtain a profile of the physical and social environment of the hospital wards from which the Darlington Project clients and the comparison group patients were selected. The questionnaire was based on a similar questionnaire designed for use in the overall monitoring and evaluation of the Care in the Community Initiative (Renshaw et al., 1988). The information collected in the questionnaire is shown below.

Section	Information
1	Basic details: hospital and hospital ward; date form completed.
2	Size of ward and staffing: number of beds; number of patients; number of staff by grade and number appointed in previous year.
3	Sleeping areas: size of rooms; bedside lockers; mirrors.
4	Bathrooms and toilets: size of bathrooms; mirrors; number of toilets; availability of toilet paper; privacy; adaptations for disability.
5	Dayrooms and facilities: day facilities and location; availability of books and games; number of televisions; availability of radios; equipment for activities and therapy; garden or outdoor area; adaptations for disability; eating arrangements.
6	Food: written menu; choice of food; availability of snacks and drinks; kitchen facilities for patients; location of kitchen.

7   Daily life: access to sleeping area; patients' clothing; patients' pos-
         sessions; pets; individual or group bathing and dressing; organised
         activities; choice of time of rising and retiring to bed; restrictions
         on television viewing at night; meals shared with staff; staff in-
         volvement in activities; skills taught by staff; ward meetings; choice
         of clothing worn; choice of new clothing; locking of outside doors;
         visiting times.

8   Social contacts: frequency of visits by voluntary groups; telephone;
         contacts with other wards.

9   Turnover of patients: number of discharges in previous 12 months
         and destinations; number of admissions in previous 12 months.

Interviews with elderly person

The schedules for the interview with the elderly person in hospital and the
follow-up interview included the same questions, with the exception of information which was only relevant to one of the settings, for example feelings
and expectations about the future in the hospital interview, and the experience
of the project and care services in the follow-up interview. The schedule for
the elderly person after discharge was shorter than the other two interview
schedules and was designed principally to cover the elderly person's social
network. The information collected in the hospital and follow-up interviews
is shown below. In addition to the sources of scales, the sources of individual
questions or groups of questions are shown, where relevant. The schedule
for the elderly person after discharge was based on sections 1, 6, 7 and 8 of
the schedules for the hospital and follow-up interviews.

Section   Information

1   Basic details: sex; date of birth; age; hospital and hospital ward;
         date of admission to/discharge from hospital; household details;
         housing problems; date of interview.

2   Organic symptomatology and mood state: questions to identify
         organic disorders (Bond et al., 1980); 12-item General Health Ques-
         tionnaire (Goldberg, 1972); self-rated health (Challis and Davies,
         1986).

3   Physical health, disabilities and activities of daily living: symptom-
         atic health, including mobility (Acquilla et al., 1987b), eyesight and
         hearing (Pattie and Gilleard, 1979) and physical health (Challis
         and Davies, 1986); Clifton Assessment Procedures for the Elderly
         Behaviour Rating Scale (CAPE BRS) (Pattie and Gilleard, 1979);

miscellaneous behaviour questions (Knapp et al., 1992); activities of daily living (Challis and Davies, 1986).

4   Social activities and leisure: frequency of leisure activities (Wing, 1989); boredom (Challis and Davies, 1986).

5   Subjective wellbeing and independence: 17-item Philadelphia Geriatric Center (PGC) Morale Scale (Lawton, 1975); felt degree of control over own life (Challis and Davies, 1986).

6   Social networks: Interview Schedule for Social Interaction (ISSI) (Henderson et al., 1981); frequency of visitors; loneliness (Challis and Davies, 1986).

7   Feelings and expectations about the future (hospital interview)/ experience of the project/care services (follow-up interview).

8   Interviewer summary: reasons for incompleteness of or errors in responses; speech problems (Knapp et al., 1992); ratings of shortfall in care (Challis and Davies, 1986); mental state assessment (Challis and Davies, 1986); Older Americans Resources and Services (OARS) Multidimensional Functional Assessment Questionnaire rating scales (Duke University Center for the Study of Aging and Human Development, 1978); summary of interviewer's impressions of elderly person's needs and circumstances.

In section 3, the question on incontinence in the CAPE Behaviour Rating Scale was subdivided into separate questions on incontinence of urine and incontinence of faeces, for compatibility with the questions used in the Kent Community Care Scheme (Challis and Davies, 1986). In sections 3 and 8, the questions taken from Knapp et al. (1992) were drawn from the Interview for Skills and Behaviour for elderly people used in the evaluation of the other projects funded under the Care in the Community Initiative. The list of activities of daily living drawn from Challis and Davies (1986) was modified slightly, and additional questions about the reliability, effectiveness and sufficiency of help (Challis, 1981) were included. The leisure activities included in section 4 were drawn from the work of Wing in her study of the closure of Darenth Park Mental Handicap Hospital in Kent, which was subsequently described in Wing (1989). The 17-item PGC Morale Scale included in section 5 is an anglicised version prepared by Challis and Knapp (1980), and is shown in Goldberg and Connelly (1982). The version of the ISSI included in section 6 was designed by Henderson and his colleagues for use with elderly people (Henderson et al., 1986), and is slightly shorter than the full version reported in Henderson et al. (1981).

Interviews with principal carer

The schedules for the interview with the principal carer and the interview with the principal carer of patients in hospital included the same questions, with the exception of information which was only relevant to one of the settings, and amended where necessary to relate to a specific setting. The schedule for the interview with the principal carer was used for both interviews with carers whose relative was a client of the Darlington Project ('project carers') and for the interview with carers of elderly people in Darlington who attended the day hospital ('day hospital carers'). The schedule for the interview with the principal carer of patients in hospital was used for the interview with carers of patients in the comparison group in Durham Health Authority ('hospital carers'). The information collected in the interviews is shown below. The schedules were based largely on the Social Behaviour Assessment Schedule (Platt et al., 1983), as described below.

Section   Information

1   Basic details and introduction: sex; age; marital status; relationship to elderly person; household composition; length of tenure; general feelings about hospital/project care; date of interview.

2   Care tasks: dressing; grooming; transfer (community interviews); personal care or heavy lifting; pop-in visits; supervision (community interviews); prepare meals (community interviews)/take food and drink (hospital interview); light housework (community interviews); laundry; tasks outside home/hospital; companionship.

3   Elderly person's behaviour: misery; withdrawal; slowness; complaints about bodily aches and pains; worry; indecisiveness; suicidal behaviour; underactivity; overdependence; requiring physical or nursing care; risk of falling/mobility; incontinence — urine; incontinence — faeces; forgetfulness; wandering — during day; nocturnal disturbance; uncooperative behaviour/rudeness; restlessness/overactivity; odd ideas; embarrassing behaviour; irritability; other aspects of behaviour (heavy drinking, aggressiveness, destructiveness, self-neglect, deafness, speech difficulties, unpredictability, other).

4   Effects upon others: physical ill health; child's emotional ill health; child's disturbed behaviour; child's relationship with elderly person; child's time away from home; child's contact with friends; child's loss of schooling; child's school performance; carer's physical health; carer's emotional ill health; Malaise Inventory (Rutter et al., 1970); carer's social life; carer's leisure time; carer's disposable

income; carer's work performance; time off work/study; disruption of carer's life; household relationships; disruption of others' lives; most difficult problem in caring/hospital care; positive benefits of caring/hospital care (Qureshi et al., 1983, 1989); most rewarding aspect of caring/hospital care.

5   Support received: support from relatives; support from friends/ neighbours; support from health and social services; thoughts of giving up caring and resolution (community interviews); best location for elderly person; financial costs of care.

6   Interviewer assessment: attitude to interview; strain on carer; tension in home; warmth towards elderly person; hostility towards elderly person; difficulties for carer; relief experienced (hospital interview); descriptive summary.

Most of section 3, most of section 4 (excluding the Malaise Inventory), and the questions in section 5 on the support received from relatives, friends and neighbours, and from health and social services, were based on sections B, D and F of the Social Behaviour Assessment Schedule. The SBAS was designed to estimate the 'objective burden' of adverse effects on others and the distress, or 'subjective burden', caused by disturbances in the patient's behaviour, by the patient's limited social performance or by the objective burdens. Earlier work by Grad and Sainsbury obtained ratings of burden by examining the effect of the patient on various aspects of family life (Grad and Sainsbury, 1968; Sainsbury and Grad de Alarcon, 1971), but did not record disturbing behaviour unless it worried the family, and did not measure subjective reactions to burdens (Platt et al., 1980; Platt, 1985). Objective and subjective aspects of burden were distinguished by Hoenig and Hamilton (1969), but both objective and subjective burdens were presented in terms of overall ratings rather than for different aspects of behaviour, and the objective and subjective aspects of burden were blurred in the case of patient behaviour (Platt et al., 1980; Platt, 1985). The aspects of behaviour and effects on family life covered by the SBAS were developed from the work of Grad and Sainsbury, Hoenig and Hamilton, and others (Platt et al., 1980), but the SBAS specifically indicates whether an adverse effect, or objective burden, is present and whether the informant perceives it to be related to the patient, and provides ratings of distress, or subjective burden. Distress is rated on a four-point scale, using the categories 'none', 'moderate', 'severe' and 'resignation', the category 'resignation' being included to cover cases where the informant described long-term resignation to disturbed behaviour which had been in evidence for a considerable period (Platt et al., 1980). The four-category rating of distress was also used for the questions on care tasks included in section 2. The behaviour items included in the SBAS were chosen to be relevant to acute psychiatric patients and their relatives (Platt et al., 1980) and, therefore, additional behaviour items relevant to elderly geriatric patients were included in section 3 and irrelevant items deleted. The ratings of the time of onset of adverse events, included in the SBAS, were not included in the schedules, as sanctioned by Platt et al. (1983). The questions on the positive benefits of caring included in section 4 were drawn from the work of Qureshi and colleagues in the study of helpers working in the Kent Community Care Scheme (Qureshi et al., 1983, 1989).

4 Care Management in Practice

In Chapter 2 the main structural features of care management in the Darling-ton Project were discussed. This chapter focuses on how the care management role was implemented in practice and how this contributed to the relative effectiveness and efficiency of the service.

Definitions of care management abound. They usually involve the delineations of functions; specification of goals; differentiation of key features; specification of the characteristics of recipients of the service; multi-level response to need; and the performance of a series of core tasks (Challis, 1994a,b) (see Box 2.1). The latter set of activities, often termed the client pathway (Steinberg and Carter, 1983), are variously described, but there is a considerable consensus about their content. The core tasks are case-finding, or raising referrals, and screening; comprehensive assessment of need; care planning, and arranging and coordinating services; monitoring, reviewing and adapting services as required; and case closure, or the ending of care at home (Challis and Davies, 1986; Challis et al., 1990; Davies, 1992).

In this chapter, the core tasks are used as a framework to consider the activities undertaken by the care managers in the project.

Case-finding and screening

Case-finding is designed to ensure that a high proportion of those eligible for the service receive it, and screening is undertaken to ensure that a high proportion of those who receive the service are those for whom it is designed. Case-finding and screening are contributory mechanisms to achieve horizontal and vertical target efficiency (Challis and Davies, 1986; Davies and Challis, 1986). They refer respectively to questions of uptake and eligibility which Austin (1981) described as efficient and effective targeting. In setting up a care management service both of these are important concerns for the care managers and their managers. Achieving the right balance between horizontal target efficiency, through such case-finding mechanisms as broadening referral sources, and vertical target efficiency, by attempting to minimise the acceptance of individuals who do not meet the stated criteria ('false positives') is a difficult task requiring careful monitoring. As in any screening programme in health care, there is a trade-off between sensitivity (the probability of identifying people requiring the service, or 'true positives') and specificity (the probability of identifying people who do not require it, or 'true negatives') (Bowns et al., 1991).

In the early stages of the project, the care managers focused their activity upon defining the target population, defining explicit criteria and raising referrals. Precisely defining the characteristics of the target population — patients needing long-stay hospital care — did not prove easy, as has often been the case in identifying individuals needing long-term care (Kemper, 1988; Weissert, 1988; Applebaum and Austin, 1990). Indeed, the definition of a long-stay elderly patient is itself problematic. Golding et al. (1987) have noted that some apparent long-stay patients retained their accommodation two and three years after admission. One study found that, of patients who had been in hospital for more than six months, nearly one-quarter were discharged within a year, 10 per cent to their own homes (Hodkinson and Hodkinson, 1981). Ramsay et al. (1987) suggest that the definition of long-stay be based on social and medical state rather than time spent in hospital, or perhaps ward of origin. Over time an operational definition emerged, with a long-stay patient defined as one who remained in hospital beyond the time when treatment was deemed to be fruitful, yet was too dependent to be discharged to either Part III residential care or home help domiciliary support.

Case-finding had particular importance for the first two care managers employed by the project as they had responsibility for establishing the credibility of the service. In the early days they played a part in reviewing the physical, mental and social circumstances of occupants of the long-term care wards, in order to find suitable candidates for the scheme. They then found they had the challenging task of providing information and reassurance to relatives and clients about a service which was totally new and untested. This initially involved spending time building relationships with staff on each ward, so they were ready to discuss potential clients.

Once this process had raised awareness of the possibilities offered by the new service, it was necessary to establish a referral procedure with the consultant geriatrician and the multidisciplinary team. At first no standard referral procedure existed and referrals came from a number of different sources within the hospital. This created problems of lack of consistent assessment and decision criteria across referrals. To resolve this, it was decided that all referrals should come through the geriatric multidisciplinary team and be subject to a uniform assessment by the different disciplines therein. Thus, referrals from consultants in other specialties to the geriatric multidisciplinary team for assessment and rehabilitation included cases for the project. Being members of the geriatric multidisciplinary team, the care managers were regular participants at the team's weekly case conferences, and were able to contribute to discussions about referrals and their appropriateness for the service. The geriatric multidisciplinary team included consultants, ward sisters, physiotherapists, occupational therapists and medical social workers. During the project life, senior district nurses and the care managers were also included in the weekly case conference discussions.

Through their awareness of the condition and circumstances of all geriatric inpatients, the care managers could keep abreast of likely referrals and remind the multidisciplinary team of this service as one of a range of options available for long-term care. Often the care managers would have heard a patient discussed at case conference for two or three weeks before they were referred to the project. Other sources of referral were the project's own occupational therapist and physiotherapist, particularly from within their peer groups. All patients whose medical treatment was reaching its conclusion were discussed in the light of their likely discharge or continuing care plans. For cases whose mobility, self-care and continence needs were too great to consider routine discharge, with or without referral to normal community services, alternatives were explored. The available alternatives included residential care, nursing home care and long-term hospital care. Membership of the geriatric team meant that the project came to be considered as one of the available alternatives for people who wished to return home but who would otherwise have been considered for long-term hospital or nursing home care.

On the whole these arrangements worked well as a means of both case-finding and screening, since inappropriate cases were often screened at the initial discussion prior to team assessment. One group of potential clients not accepted were those who were confused and previously living on their own. In part, this reflected the original funding stipulation for clients to be mentally alert but physically frail. However, as long as a confused person was relatively immobile and not wandering they were considered for the project. Although some clients with mental health problems were accepted onto the project, two patients were referred by consultants but were not accepted due to their aggressive and potentially violent behaviour.

In practice, the need for night cover proved to be an important factor in selection for the project. This was a particular source of concern, and defining what necessitated night cover was not easy. If there were concerns about security or toileting, these could often be resolved without actually providing regular supervision at night. However, those who were seen as requiring night cover and were considered not to be suitable for the project had medical problems which impinged upon their management during the night, but which were not necessarily technically complex. These included patients with chest problems who needed to be propped up regularly, and who would have been at risk of slipping if they were not supervised at intervals during the night, and those who needed to be turned regularly. Generally the referral procedure was effective in screening cases, and patients with insufficient levels of dependency were only referred when there was considerable pressure to close a ward. These patients were not accepted for the project.

Nevertheless, at times there were different views about the appropriateness of referrals expressed by the patients themselves, their relatives and hospital staff. The care manager had to resolve these in the most satisfactory fashion. For example, sometimes hospital staff were unsure of a patient's ability to cope at home:

> An elderly man with a terminal illness who was felt to be unsuited to home care by his consultant nonetheless requested care at home. The care manager was able to act as his advocate for his right to home care, and arranged care for him in his own flat until his death.

> The husband of one patient was eager to have her home, although he could not actively contribute to her care. The hospital ward assessment indicated this woman was too heavy and difficult to manage at home, but the care manager arranged a ward assessment with the home care assistant who demonstrated sufficient coping skills to ensure that discharge and care at home were possible.

On other occasions, families were unwilling to accept the risk of supporting a person at home or found difficulty in relinquishing and sharing their role:

> An elderly woman with a terminal illness wanted to be cared for and to die at home. Her family could not accept the responsibilities this involved and after careful consideration it was decided that discharge was not possible.

> A man whose previous stroke had left him with substantial speech problems and other disabilities was identified as likely to benefit from a regular therapy programme which could be pursued at home by home care assistants, instructed by speech and physiotherapists. His wife rejected all offers of help, but through patient understanding and supportive visits the care manager was ultimately able to arrange a service acceptable and beneficial to both client and spouse.

Although these arrangements contributed to more effective screening, a number of obstacles to effective case-finding and horizontal target efficiency remained. First, there was the requirement imposed by the funding that the project should be an alternative to long-term hospital care. This necessarily prevented consideration of referrals from the community, regardless of need. It also led to a perverse situation that some moderately dependent elderly patients, who wished to return home from hospital, did not meet the criteria, but were not able to be supported adequately by the 'standard' community services. These people were forced to opt for a residential care placement in a local authority or private home, because of the lack of alternatives. Second, although establishing the geriatric multidisciplinary team as the sole source of referral solved the problems about screening and assessment of referrals, it may have acted as a barrier to some referrals from non-geriatric wards within the hospital, probably due to lack of knowledge about the project. Third, there was the sheer practical difficulty of re-introducing the possibility of discharge for some long-term patients whose horizons and expectations were restricted to the hospital setting, who had relinquished their homes, and whose family carers were no longer willing to assume care tasks and responsibilities. Fourth, there was a change in the availability of housing between the planning and implementation stages of the project. A change of political control of the district council led to the withdrawal of an earlier offer of public sector housing. At the same time, funding from the Housing Corporation to a local housing association, which had offered to provide accommodation for patients, was deferred. Consequently, finance for caring and support services was available but not the anticipated housing facilities. This illustrates one of the practical problems of a predominantly revenue-based service with only a small amount of capital funding available to effect the discharge of long-stay patients. The most effective way to establish such a service for elderly people who are in long-stay care might be to identify those who retain accommodation, since these are the people who can be most readily discharged, further reducing dependence on the cooperation of other agencies (Richardson and Higgins, 1990, 1992). However, this again militates against horizontal target efficiency, since it entails client selection by supply criteria.

Clients referred and accepted

A total of 101 elderly clients were discharged to the project: 36 men and 65 women. The care managers' initial concern was for patients in long-stay wards, but, in the absence of housing for clients who had given up their homes, they were forced to focus on patients who still had the possibility of accommodation, either alone or returning to live with willing relatives.

In the event, only ten patients (two men and eight women) were discharged after spending six months or more in a long-term care ward, which emphasises the difficulty encountered in finding accommodation and re-activating enthusiasm for discharge in clients and carers who have accepted the finality of a long-term hospital placement. Five of these had suffered disabling strokes, and five suffered from disabilities linked to arthritis, heart failure, diabetes, sight loss and circulatory problems. One man returned to live alone having retained the tenancy of his council flat; two women returned to live with their single sons, who contributed to a limited extent to their mothers' care; two women were allocated new tenancies to enable a planned discharge to the project; three were discharged to family placements where families received payment through Department of Social Security regulations; and two women, accompanied by another woman who had been receiving the project services for a while, were discharged to a group-living arrangement in a housing association property adapted to offer a shared tenancy for three frail elderly people.

The difficulties involved in arranging discharge for established long-term patients gradually led to a change of focus, with potential clients being identified at the conclusion of their treatment or rehabilitation, when they would have either joined a waiting list for a long-term care bed, or been advised to consider a nursing home placement. The project thus became one of the options considered for long-term care, offering an alternative to entry to long-stay beds as much as a means of discharge from them. In many ways this shift of emphasis was fortuitous since it made the project more relevant to the development of care management approaches associated with the implementation of the 1990 National Health Service and Community Care Act. By necessity, therefore, the project developed more as an alternative to hospital care for patients living at home than had been initially envisaged.

The shift in focus meant that the majority of clients were discharged from the two acute geriatric wards in the Darlington Memorial Hospital. These, although physically identical to the long-term care wards in the hospital, inevitably had the environment of a busy acute and rehabilitation ward with emphasis on admission, treatment, discharge and rapid patient turnover. In this situation, patients whose disabilities and level of dependence militate against prompt discharge can soon feel discouraged and dispirited as they see other patients come in, receive treatment, recover and leave. The environment is geared to transience, with discharge home as the target. It is not surprising, therefore, to find that a very high proportion of project clients appeared depressed before their discharge from hospital, particularly if they had been there for several months.

As Table 4.1 shows, 67 clients were discharged from the acute geriatric wards. The most significant group (over one-third) being those who had suffered disabling strokes leaving them immobile and unable to care for themselves. Other disabilities and illnesses included Parkinsonism, arthritis, respiratory and chest diseases, heart failure, circulatory problems, amputations and cancer. Most of the remaining clients were either discharged from acute wards elsewhere in the district general hospital (six clients), or from the long-term care wards after a period of less than six months in that ward (sixteen clients). Finally, two women were referred by the primary health care team as needing intensive domiciliary support to prevent admission to long-term hospital care and, following a domiciliary visit, were recommended for project care. One who was terminally ill with breast cancer was determined to die in her own home, but her care needs could no longer be met by the standard services provided by home help and district nursing. The second suffered from muscular dystrophy, and her gradual deterioration had led to immobility and incontinence which could not be adequately managed without a much more intensive level of personal care and support.

Table 4.1
Source of referrals accepted

Source	Number
Long-stay geriatric ward, over six months	10
Long-stay geriatric ward, under six months	16
Acute geriatric wards	67
Other acute wards	6
Community referrals	2
Total number	101

Assessment

Assessment by the care managers was designed to examine the feasibility of discharge home, the differing requirements and attitudes of elderly people and their carers, the suitability of the domestic environment and the range of resources necessary to compensate for the person's disability.

It was normal for the geriatrician, as well as nursing staff, to discuss a patient's future plans with the patient and any relatives before a referral was made. They would indicate the possibility of an intensive domiciliary support service, but detailed discussion was left to the care manager. Initially the allocation of cases to care managers was on a rota basis although, with the appointment of a third care manager after about a year, each took responsibility for a different geographical area.

The assessment process

Since the elderly person was already an inpatient, physiotherapists, occupational therapists, nursing and medical staff would have carried out their assessment of the patient's needs from their own professional standpoint. Frequently the medical social worker had also made an assessment of social and familial circumstances. Usually a consensus view emerged that a patient had a level of need to warrant referral to the project. Initial discussion between the care manager and the patient and their carers usually took place on the ward, arranged at a time when all parties could join in the discussion and ask questions freely about the service, although the procedure followed by each care manager would sometimes vary according to the individual circumstances. The care manager would make a further visit to the patient in hospital and to a carer at home to discuss, explain, seek and give information, and become familiar with all the relevant circumstances. In about half the cases

a home visit was undertaken with the elderly person so that the physiotherapist, occupational therapist and care manager could assess the suitability
of the person's home environment for their discharge. The project physiotherapist and occupational therapist proved to be important links with their
counterparts in the hospital at this point.

There were several reasons for including a home visit in the assessment
process. First, there would be uncertainty about the client's level of functioning
at home which needed to be tested in situ, and the result of this influenced
decisions about the feasibility of discharge. Second, it was necessary to ascertain the types of aids and adaptations required at home. Third, the team
wished to discuss, reassure or challenge the views of caring relatives or other
family members who might have held unrealistically optimistic or pessimistic
views about the feasibility of the proposed discharge. Relatives frequently
needed help in accepting the need to modify or adapt the environment to
suit the disabled client's limitations, such as to remove rugs, to bring a bed
downstairs, to have a commode on the ground floor, or even to have a hoist
or ramp fitted.

As well as coordinating further assessments — particularly those of the
ward staff, occupational therapist and physiotherapist — the care managers
also completed their own documentation on the needs and disabilities of
elderly people and the problems of the families. This summarised health
needs, the capacity to perform a range of personal and instrumental activities
of daily living, mental health problems, the clients' housing and financial
circumstances, carer availability and support. Some of this information was
re-assessed at regular case reviews to enable care managers to note major
changes in status.

The needs of carers

Following these discussions, the elderly person was frequently impatient of
delay and eager for discharge, but the relatives, in contrast, frequently needed
time and sensitive reassurance about the practicalities of effecting discharge.
Many had a history of struggling to care with barely sufficient or insufficient
service back-up in the past, and had considerable anxiety over whether this
new service could truly meet their needs in a reliable manner. Conversely,
a number of caring relatives — in particular, women caring for their frail
husbands — felt anxiety and distrust over relinquishing care to someone else.
This could be linked to the belief that a 'stranger' would not give such good
care, or to understandable concern at the intimate nature of much of the
personal care required, or to feelings of guilt or failure at their own inability
to cope any longer. For discharge to be successful, many of these issues
needed to be addressed at this stage. Hence the apparently clear boundary
between assessment and intervention was in practice necessarily a blurred
one (Challis, 1994b).

Involvement of different occupational groups

In establishing credibility and acceptability within the hospital setting, it was seen as important that the care manager should respect the domains and professional expertise of the different services. It was the practice for each member of the team to make a written assessment report available to the care manager. However, in the case of ward sisters, this involved completing a standard project assessment form, covering care needs and functional capacity in the ward.

An observation by the head of one of the hospital therapy departments illustrated the success of the care managers' efforts in acknowledging the professional expertise of others and being accepted as members of the team:

> Individual professional expertise is respected, and because that respect is there, there is also a lot of trust ... so there isn't a problem, and as yet, to my knowledge, there has been no problem [in accepting them and their role].

However, issues of territory and control emerged over the home visits. District nurses, who understandably felt that the provision of services to frail disabled people in the community had been their particular domain, felt usurped when occupational therapists, physiotherapists and care managers made home assessment visits without including the local district nurse as a member of this visiting assessment group. By contrast, early in the life of the project, it became clear to the care managers and the geriatric multidisciplinary team that, if a patient was a potential referral for project service, it was appropriate for the care manager to undertake a home visit, normally in the medical social worker's place. Perhaps surprisingly, this did not lead to resentment by the medical social worker, who went to considerable lengths to assist and support the care managers in establishing their role. There were fewer therapists and social workers than nursing staff, and one factor which may have distinguished the different professional groups in their delineation of territory was their relative scarcity. This is examined further in Chapter 6. Managing these territorial concerns between professional groups was important for the project to progress. Whereas discussions between individuals regarding clients were the concern of the care managers, negotiating the interprofessional agreements was an important role of the project manager. This, again, illustrates the importance of the issue of the management of care management.

From assessment to care planning

The process of undertaking these initial assessments, usually building upon work already undertaken by members of the geriatric multidisciplinary team, took place between the first case conference at which a potential client was identified and a second conference two weeks later when the overall picture was considered. The information acquired from these varied assessments contributed to a comprehensive view of the referred client's functioning and needs within the hospital environment. It gave a picture of the range of help, care, supervision, stimulation and therapy required. The care manager's second task was to discuss needs, wishes, preferences, and the type and availability of alternative support with the prospective client, family and others who formed part of their network. The combination of these two sets of information fed into the process of drawing up a care plan. There was usually a two to three week period between first referral to the project and discharge from hospital. In a few cases, however, where circumstances were appropriate, clients were discharged within a few days.

Care planning, arranging and coordinating services

Care planning was designed to achieve an optimum balance between the mix, style and type of services provided, and the assessed needs and preferences of the clients and their carers. Inevitably, care planning with such a frail client group and the type of intensive service provided could not be a once and for all activity, and the care plan required constant revision in the light of changing circumstances. This was particularly so in the first weeks after discharge.

The nature of care management involves creating effective linkages between individuals in need and agencies who provide services, across sectors of care (Moxley, 1989). For the project care managers, the main foci of activity were clients and their carers, home care assistants, and a range of other services. In the case of clients and carers, this included finding ways of making services acceptable, balancing the needs of and risks to the different parties, and having regard to what was feasible within their budget, while ensuring that the clients' needs for personal care, therapy exercises, meals, shopping, domestic care, social contacts and social and emotional support were being met. For family carers this involved enabling them to maintain their care role within their capacities.

The major sources of care for clients were almost exclusively home care assistants and carers. It had been one of the aims of the scheme to ensure the performance of a range of tasks by one person, so as to reduce the number of personnel and the possibilities for confusion, gaps and overlaps. It remained a continuing priority to use home care assistants in most circumstances. However, in a small number of cases where a neighbour or friend was involved in supportive visiting and caregiving, the devolved budget enabled the care manager to formalise this informal care role and make a payment for regular performance of agreed tasks. Care managers were also responsible for initiating, coordinating and terminating other services in a flexible way to respond to changing circumstances.

Building upon the assessed needs of client and carer

Making the service acceptable. For many caring relatives the hospitalisation of the elderly person was a time of worry and uncertainty, and they needed the opportunity to discuss these anxieties and any future plans relating to discharge. Some carers — usually wives or daughters — had already spent a number of years in the caring role with insufficient support and relief, and were naturally sceptical about the level of support being offered by the new scheme. They transferred their previous experience of standard services to the new service. As one care manager said:

> Yes, but we are the first people who have ever been able to promise. No one else has ever had the resources.

This indicates the importance of control over resources to effective care management.

Sometimes carers needed to establish realistic boundaries to their commitment. For example, one woman felt unable to resume any personal caring for her mother, having had to carry a heavy burden in the past. Faced with the competing demands of her young family, she was willing to provide meals and do laundry if personal care needs were met by the project. For this woman, an agreement about personal care provided such a boundary.

In several cases, wives who had borne the physical and emotional loads of caring were suffering from stress-related health problems. These women wished to have their frail and disabled husbands at home but needed counselling and support to help them relinquish some of the care burden to the home care assistant. The reasons for this reluctance were varied. In some cases the wife felt her own role to be threatened if she was unable to provide the necessary care herself. In one case this led to a prolonged introductory period during which the caring spouse of a disabled stroke victim came to terms with her inability to meet all the needs of her husband, and began to trust the home care assistant sufficiently to permit her to undertake some of the care tasks. In another case, the need to introduce care at a pace acceptable to both client and relatives was crucial:

> The wife of a severely impaired stroke victim was initially hostile to accepting help. With encouragement she agreed to the introduction of twice-weekly therapy and activity sessions for her husband. Two home care assistants worked together to carry out a therapy regime devised by the physiotherapist and speech therapist. This level of involvement proved acceptable to the carer as her role was not usurped, and yet she herself clearly also derived some benefit from the social support of the home care assistants.

Balancing client and carer needs. The importance of realistic discussions with relatives or other carers could not be overestimated since the role and function of the service was to complement and maintain this support:

> An 83 year old single woman living alone, sometimes confused, had a neighbour who played an increasingly important role in her support. This neighbour's willingness to continue with her support depended on the sense of purpose and usefulness this caring role gave her. If this feeling of being needed and valued by her elderly neighbour had been undermined or supplanted by insensitive care planning, this vital relationship might well have been destroyed.

The strengths, tolerances and capacities of each family, relative, neighbour or supporter had to be realistically matched with the client's need and the gaps filled as necessary. In two cases where elderly widows lived alone, their daughters wished to retain some involvement, with other care tasks being performed by home care assistants. One elected to put her mother to bed each evening, the other did so on certain agreed evenings. In each case, the carer was able to sustain this commitment for over two years because it was manageable within her life.

The needs and distress of caring relatives were closely monitored by care managers, who could respond by offering relief of care burdens through increased home care assistant hours, or respite care for the client to give the carer a break. In one case, a daughter who had agreed to take meals to her mother every day found this too onerous and increasingly turned to the home care assistant to relieve her. This led to renegotiation of the care plan and the level of carer involvement. In another case, it was arranged for the home care assistant to stay with the client for one or two hours on two or more days a week, to enable her husband to visit his local club for a drink and relaxation.

Regular respite care was set up for several clients. Not surprisingly, in some instances it was not easy to get a client to accept the need for respite care. One elderly man suffering from Parkinson's Disease was cared for by his wife. Although he was well cared for, their relationship was antagonistic at times, and even with the help of home care assistants her need for respite care was great. The care manager had to help him to realise that if he wanted to remain at home then he would need to compromise, in this case by accepting respite care, as the alternative prospect might be long-term institutional care.

In instances where the client wanted to stay at home, but the family was either not prepared to support them or did not want them living there, then the care managers tried to find alternative accommodation. Often this was not possible and it was necessary to give the client and family sufficient information on which to base their decisions, and to help resolve conflict between clients and carers. Sometimes the conflict of views could not be resolved. One elderly man chose to return to long-stay care when his family gave him an ultimatum: either he went into a nursing home where they would visit him regularly, or he could remain at home with the help of the project, but they would have no contact with him whatsoever. In the end he chose to go into a nursing home.

Sometimes there were problems with inappropriate carer input. In two cases, a caring spouse with confusional problems frequently forgot to provide food or fed the client inappropriately, and this required careful monitoring.

Two other factors needed to be taken into consideration in the care planning process. First, there was the need to balance promotion of client independence with providing an adequate level of care. Home care assistants frequently commented that it took much longer to encourage the client to do what they were able in the way of self-care than to do it for them. Second, enhancing a client's social network was sometimes necessary. This required knowledge of the client's needs and desire for a social network, and access to a variety of local facilities such as lunch clubs, day care, self-help groups, pubs and clubs, and transport, as well as volunteer visiting or night-sitting services.

Managing acceptable levels of risk. The care managers had to take responsibility for establishing an acceptable degree of risk for each client or carer, particularly for those with confusion. This involved negotiation with relatives, general practitioners and consultants, as well as other service providers such as district nurses, since perspectives were often conflicting. This occurred with regard to night care, since nurses in particular were concerned at the lack of 24-hour supervision. Balancing the different perceptions of risk of several service providers, the elderly person and their carers could sometimes prove to be a difficult and stressful task. One care manager described having to clarify the precise nature of the fears of different parties and then reach an agreement of risk least unacceptable to all, given the elderly person's strong desire to be discharged home.

Risk of falling was an important concern. It was necessary for the care manager to ensure that the service was reliable and that people called when they said they would at specific times during the day, in order to avert the risk of falling and concomitant problems of being left lying on the floor for some considerable time. One elderly woman was anxious about the possibility of falling at night, even though this had never happened. In this instance, the problem was solved by keeping the room heated at night and placing a pile of blankets and a pillow under her bed, so that if she were to fall she could cover herself and keep warm until somebody called in the morning.

Acting as an advocate. Advocacy was an important role of the care managers in articulating clients' rights for care at home and to help them receive appropriate services. In one case, a woman of 87 with a terminal illness had been discharged to the project. She was re-admitted to hospital for a blood transfusion as treatment for leukaemia and was given chemotherapy as part of a trial. The client appeared not to understand nor consent to this treatment, which was making her sick. The care manager discussed this with her next of kin, who had been unaware of the treatment. They ensured that the treatment was stopped and the client was discharged home. For the last few weeks of her life she was nursed at home, which was where she wanted to be.

Balancing needs, demands and scarcity. Cost-consciousness played a part in decision-making. Each care manager was also a budget-holder and as such had an awareness of the relative costs of different components of the service. They had to cost the service they provided to clients, working, as noted earlier, to an average budget of two-thirds of the cost of a long-stay hospital bed. Although budget-holding was designed to enable care managers to use a wide mix of care services, in practice relatively little alternative provision was developed because resources were committed to the employment of home care assistants. During the three years of the project, the number of clients referred and supported never reached the anticipated limit, and thus the care managers were operating with spare capacity of home care assistants. This fact, and the need to keep home care assistants fully employed, led to a reluctance to explore alternatives to any great extent. This indicates that the innovatory element of devolved budgets is likely to work principally at the margin and when the service is running at full capacity.

Nevertheless, neighbours or paid helpers were recruited to perform designated tasks in several cases, as a more appropriate and more cost-effective option than allocating extra home care assistant hours. These tasks included taking clients for social outings or visiting them to make tea and provide companionship. In three cases, paid helpers were chosen to provide the extra stimulation of a visitor, even though this may not have been the least costly option. However, the potential use of paid helpers was never fully explored. Interestingly, where paid helpers were used, it was important to ensure their 'fit' with the respective home care assistants involved. On occasions, home care assistants were apprehensive of the role of such helpers in relation to their own. These concerns included substituting social aspects of the work which the home care assistants valued. Care managers had to consider how the groups of carers involved with a client would interact with one another.

The budget was also used to influence existing services so as to make them more appropriate to the needs of project clients. It was considered desirable to provide respite care for some clients in local authority residential homes, and ways of augmenting the care staff quota to take account of the greater dependency of project clients were discussed. One suggestion that home care assistants might provide this augmented service for their own clients was deemed unacceptable, so in a few cases additional funds were made available instead for the officer-in-charge to buy in extra care hours from her own regular staff.

Discharge. Clients were normally discharged home either by ambulance or in the care manager's car. Using the ambulance service meant that the time of discharge could not be predicted, and as the home care assistant expected to be waiting at the client's home this often led to a substantial waste of time, as well as anxiety for the client and their relatives. Care managers found the time devoted to escorting patients home was often worthwhile in ensuring a smoother and less traumatic experience for all participants.

Home care assistants

Introducing home care assistant and client. Once the patient, relative and care manager had decided that the patient would be discharged with project support, then a discharge date could be agreed and the home care assistant introduced. The care managers were concerned to match the characteristics, capabilities and skills of the home care assistants to their clients. This included ensuring an appropriate match between the personality and physical characteristics of the home care assistants and the needs of the situation, particularly in cases of terminal care or a large or heavy client. As a consequence of the careful matching, many clients and carers came to build strong relationships with particular home care assistants, who were often described as being 'like a daughter to me'.

The introduction of the home care assistant to the client took place in the hospital ward. The care manager would take the allocated home care assistant to meet the patient and they would spend an hour or two together, perhaps repeating the visit the following day. The purpose of these ward visits was twofold. First, the home care assistant and client had time and opportunity to begin to get to know each other, and second, the home care assistant could be instructed by nursing and therapy staff on the patient's particular care needs. The project physiotherapist and occupational therapist were often involved at this point, and thereby contributed to easing the transfer from hospital to home care. In order to make best use of this instruction time, the home care assistant normally visited the ward first thing in the morning so that they could observe and participate in the routine of washing, dressing, transferring and assisting the patient with toilet needs and in any regular therapy exercise programme. For most patients this intense individualised care and attention from the home care assistant was much appreciated, particularly when contrasted with the usual busy routines on a geriatric ward with shortages of nursing and therapy staff.

Achieving the appropriate level and timing of care was a gradual process. Although generalised plans could be made in response to known care needs prior to discharge, it took time for each individual to re-establish confidence in their home setting and for carers to determine their realistic sustainable contribution. As a result, this early period was a time of trial and testing to ensure adequacy of care input, without overproviding and thus undermining the client's or carer's independence. Sometimes home care assistants could be required to lift and transfer a heavy, dependent client on their own, or could need help to accomplish this safely, which might require frequent monitoring by the physiotherapist. The care manager had to ensure that any level of risk was acceptable and tolerable to client and home care assistant alike.

In the early months of the project, care managers used the concept of the key care assistant in order to manage care assistant work routines most efficiently. Each client and carer would get to know a particular home care assistant who had key responsibility. With the introduction of teams, discussed in Chapter 5, the client also got to know a locally-based group of home care assistants who provided support and shared work rotas for a local group of clients. When their key home care assistant was on holiday or sick leave, the client would receive care from one of a local group of about six home care assistants, who in time became familiar to the client. In some areas, late evening visits were also organised on a rota so that the client would have any one or two members of the local team to help put them to bed in the evening.

Whereas some clients and carers found it difficult to accept changes in personnel, particularly if the home care assistant was relatively new or unfamiliar, other clients came to appreciate the variety and stimulation of seeing different home care assistants who brought in different news, views and conversation. As a general principle, it remained important that the home care assistants were organised so that they knew well the group of clients they visited, became familiar with their care requirements and thus ensured continuity of care.

Home care assistant activities. A wide variety of care tasks were organised. After discharge, most clients received primarily a personal care service which might include assistance with washing, dressing, toileting, bathing, transferring, and care of feet, hair, nails, teeth or dentures and pressure sores. They might also need assistance with walking, managing medication, catheter care, colostomy care, incontinence or following a therapy programme. Those who had no carer available and willing to meet their domestic and social support needs could receive assistance with housework, shopping, meal preparation and laundry as well as with managing finances, collecting pensions, correspondence and bill-paying.

From a social point of view, care managers encouraged home care assistants to engage their clients in conversation and provide social and emotional support. Home care assistants would also attempt to provide some social stimulation or activity, including organising visits to a lunch club, outings in a wheelchair, jigsaw puzzles, talking books, shopping trips, and Christmas and Easter parties. As well as supporting the client, the home care assistant was accessible to the carer to provide relief from regular care tasks when necessary, and to stay with the client to permit the carer to go out from time to time. Relief for carers was given a priority by the service, and for some clients and carers this was a regular agreed part of the weekly programme.

Tailoring resources to needs: the allocation of home care assistant time. Care managers allocated the time of home care assistants in a flexible way, so that there was substantial variation according to clients' different personal circumstances. This is clear from examination of the pattern of the allocation of home care assistant time. It is helpful to consider those individuals receiving relatively high levels of care, whether overall or at certain times compared with those receiving low levels of care. For this comparison a high level of care has been defined as more than 40 hours a week and a low level of care as less than 15 hours a week.

A high level of hours of home care assistant time appeared to reflect a high level of dependency, such as terminally ill clients, or those living alone with limited social support (Wenger, 1992), or complicated family relationships. This is illustrated in the case of a highly dependent woman with problematic family relationships:

> Mrs A. was physically one of the most dependent clients of the project. She was doubly incontinent, unable to wash, dress or feed herself and immobile without assistance. She lived with her daughter and her family, who undertook no personal care. Their role was confined to cooking a main meal daily and doing laundry. She had limited social contact. The home care assistant provided the full range of personal care, including feeding at all meal times and also gave social support and took her on regular outings in her wheelchair. The care manager needed to intervene in crises frequently because of family relationship problems, alcohol abuse and a tendency for the family to involve the home care assistant in these difficulties. This necessitated withdrawing home care assistants, renegotiating the care package and introducing new home care assistants approximately every six months.

Apathy and low motivation on the part of the client were also associated with a high number of home care assistant hours. In one case this led initially to an increase in the number of home care assistant hours and finally to the breakdown of care when the need for a high care input became excessive:

> Mrs B. was a large woman who was suffering from loss of sight and mobility and, more significantly, who lacked motivation, was constantly tired and lethargic, and expressed little interest in life. She believed there must be some physical cause for her constant tiredness and her loss of appetite, although none was found. After discharge her continuing passivity and lethargy led to the need for a high input of care, including two home care assistants. A decision was taken, after discussion with the client and her family, to end care at home. The client returned to hospital and died approximately six weeks later.

It is interesting to note that this was a client about whom ward nursing staff had expressed reservations, being aware of her lethargy and low motivation.

For those people who were discharged to a group living home, there were special circumstances which resulted in high levels of home care assistant provision, particularly for night cover. This was most necessary in the case of one of the three clients:

> Mrs C. was alert, but highly dependent. She was physically large, was severely disabled by chronic arthritis and was wheelchair-bound, although she able to move herself around to a limited extent in the wheelchair. After nearly three years in long-stay hospital care she was transferred to the group living scheme. It was decided to provide night care at the group home, and as she was ostensibly the most heavily disabled of the three clients, extra care time was almost certainly attributable to her, rather than shared out evenly among the three. This was evident during the early weeks after her discharge, since she was the client who most frequently made calls on the night care assistant because of sleep problems.

Most of those clients receiving a high level of support needed some night care, or needed two home care assistants for a variety of reasons. Some clients received a high number of hours during week days (over 25 hours per week). These cases seem to illustrate a trend within the project to take on the support of both clients and their immediate carers, often encompassing some care and support for a frail spouse or other member of the family. Such an approach reflects the care managers' commitment to support carers in their own right (Twigg, 1993). For example:

> Mrs D. returned to live with her 89 year old husband after suffering a severe stroke. She required full assistance with personal care as, without supervision and prompting, she suffered from lethargy, passivity and self-neglect. Her husband, though physically able-bodied, was confused and prone to alcohol abuse. He required frequent supervision for his own and his wife's safety as he tended to eat her food, give her alcohol rather than food, and was unable to manage shopping, cooking, financial matters or fires safely.

High levels of evening or night time care (over six hours per week) were required by some clients. Such clients tended to be deteriorating physically or dying, or were experiencing a degree of social isolation, or chose to be put to bed later in the evening.

In contrast, lower levels of care characterised those clients living with an 'active' carer (Wenger, 1992), a good social and practical support network already in existence, or a slightly lower level of dependency. Substantial amounts of support by carers and other relatives and friends often enabled the home care assistant to fill in any care gaps, although providing relatively few hours of care:

Mrs E., seen as a somewhat difficult and demanding woman, lived with her single daughter. She was generally physically frail, suffered from incontinence and immobility, as well as shingles and a blood disorder. Her daughter had retired from work on health grounds, but undertook all domestic and household care. Relatives and friends provided regular social support, and the home care assistant role was limited to providing personal care for the client.

For some clients, a substantial improvement in their level of dependency following their adaptation to living at home again, led to their discharge from the project to a less intensive form of care. This was particularly the case where home care assistants were mainly performing domestic and social support tasks. Low levels of evening or night care by the home care assistants also reflected the choice of the elderly person to go to bed early, and those cases who were bedridden.

Coordinating other services

Over six months the average number of services used, including hospital and residential care, was between six and seven, with a range of between four and eleven. Table 4.2 shows the average amounts of services used over a six-month period. Of course, these figures do not represent a typical care

Table 4.2
Use of services over six months

Service	Mean total 6 months
Home care assistant (hours)	495.00
Care manager (visits)	17.27
Community nurse (hours)	10.28
Physiotherapist (hours)	2.88
Occupational therapist (hours)	1.06
Speech therapist (visits)	0.30
Chiropodist (visits)	0.27
Long-stay hospital (days)	6.23
Acute hospital (days)	2.76
Private nursing home (days)	0.24
Home help (hours)	4.52
Meals-on-wheels (meals)	2.37
Day care (days)	0.82
Local authority residential care (days)	0.08
Informal helpers (£)	13.30

package, since not all services were used by all clients. For example, a few clients were discharged to the home help service and no longer received support from the home care assistants. Not surprisingly, the largest amount of service was provided by home care assistants with the next largest inputs being those of community nurses and the care managers.

For some clients, discharge involved the care manager in coordinating the services of many agencies, often beyond the realm of immediate health and social services provision. Where interagency resource development was required, the role of the project manager was also important. To enable two elderly women who had spent more than three years in long-term hospital wards to be discharged required coordination of housing provision, benefit applications, purchase of essential living requirements, and careful preparation and planning with relatives, wardens of sheltered housing, therapists, district nurses, the continence adviser and home care assistants in order to achieve a planned, smooth discharge and to minimise trauma for the client.

In the case of one frail, confused woman whose privately rented house was in a bad state of repair, the care manager had to negotiate with a solicitor as well as the landlord in order to get repairs underway. Arrangements had to be made for her care during the building work and, as her morale and physical condition began to decline rapidly when placed in a hospital respite care bed, a temporary placement was arranged with neighbours who could provide support and reassurance during the upheaval.

After discharge it was normal for various services to visit the client at home: for the district nurse to instruct the home care assistant in the client's personal care needs; for the occupational therapist to ensure that aids were supplied and used appropriately; for the physiotherapist to instruct and monitor the home care assistant in activities such as lifting, transferring, assisting with walking and to demonstrate any therapy exercises; and for the general practitioner to assess and prescribe any medication. Other personnel, such as speech therapist, dietician, chiropodist and specialist continence adviser, could also be called in if necessary. In the early period following discharge, clients and their relatives received visits from a substantial number of people, and there is no doubt that for some clients and carers this could be stressful. The care managers saw it as their role to coordinate this process to minimise difficulties, although the problem of numbers of visitors was never fully resolved since all parties had a legitimate and recognised role.

Since it was one of the aims of the project to achieve a reduction in care personnel through the more coordinated use of one hands-on care worker, this plethora of visits soon after a client's hospital discharge might appear contradictory. However, this pattern of visits compared favourably with the usual procedures after discharge from a prolonged hospital stay to services provided in neighbouring localities. In these settings, home help organisers, district nurses and the occupational therapist undertook home visits after discharge but before allocating home helps, nursing care or aids and adaptations. Since such visits were not coordinated because staff were accountable to separate agencies or separate hierarchies within the same agency, the sense of confusion and helplessness experienced by the client and carer were potentially much greater, particularly as they often experienced difficulty in recalling or distinguishing the names, identities and purposes of all these personnel, and had no single point of contact.

In contrast, project clients received daily care from a familiar home care assistant, who had direct access to the various health and social service providers, if and when the need arose, as well as direct access to the care manager who carried ultimate responsibility for the coordination and management of the total care input. So, although numerous personnel might visit the client's home, access was channelled through the home care assistant, which was designed to provide a greater degree of continuity of care for the client.

Coordination was also required to maintain the package of care as problems arose. At times, additional services were required to support other members of a family whose needs impinged upon the effective care of the elderly person. On occasions this involved setting up a case conference or mobilising other services. One example was of a woman whose mentally ill son was making unrealistic demands on the home care assistants and spending the family income so as to leave no provision for feeding his mother. At a case conference organised by the care manager, it was decided that a community psychiatric nurse should support the son, and the client's financial position was resolved through involving a solicitor and a trustee. This showed clearly the need for care managers to set boundaries to their own involvement where family problems were extensive and not readily attributable to the needs of the elderly person. The elderly person and their carers were the primary focus of the care manager's attention. Broader problems outside their remit necessitated the involvement of other services. This boundary setting has been observed in a number of other care management developments (Challis and Davies, 1986; Challis et al., 1990; Pilling, 1992).

Another case was of a woman who lived with her daughter and family. The family were embroiled in difficulties over health, finances and marital conflict that threatened the client's future care. After organising a family discussion, the care manager called in the general practitioner and an independent social worker to assist the family.

Sometimes home care assistants faced conflicting demands from different professional staff. When the need arose, home care assistants initiated contacts with other service providers, thus avoiding delays and misunderstandings. But inevitably there were times when home care assistants needed support in coping with the demands of the role, or in resolving problems of conflicting advice or information from different service personnel or from relatives. On one occasion, a home care assistant was treating a client's sore heel as instructed by the district nurse, when the physiotherapist countermanded these instructions without prior consultation with the district nurse. The care manager intervened and insisted that disputes should be brought to her to avoid contradictory pressures upon the home care assistant.

Documentation and records

As part of the overall system of records, care plans were laid out on a grid consisting of times of the day and days of the week. This simple device, shared with other care management schemes (Challis and Davies, 1986; Challis et al., 1990), with a copy left in the client's home, served to communicate the package of care to other professionals, families and the client. In addition, the home care assistants kept diary sheets in the client's house which detailed their activities, times of visits, observations about the client's needs or changes in wellbeing, and details of other service inputs. Health service staff involved with clients also undertook their own reviews.

Monitoring and review

Continuity of involvement

Continuity of care is one of the desired features of care management. Once they had established a care plan, care managers regularly monitored its adequacy and effectiveness and made alterations as necessary. Care managers reported that, on average, they visited clients fortnightly to monitor the situation. In the first month after discharge, however, the average was more than six visits, reflecting their attempt to adjust carefully the services to the needs of clients re-establishing themselves at home. The times of these home visits were varied to occur when the home care assistant was there, as well as at other times when the client could be seen alone or with a relative.

Analysis of case notes and reviews indicates that care managers were in contact with a number of different services. Use of all health and social services increased through time, except for the home help service, which was substituted by home care assistants when clients were discharged from hospital. The most frequently noted services were home care assistants; aids for mobility, toileting and bathing; and the provision of a telephone. Also important were district nursing, incontinence aids, chiropody, physiotherapy and occupational therapy. Unsurprisingly, care managers were most frequently in contact with district nurses, general practitioners and geriatricians, and other important contacts were the Department of Social Security and the home help service.

Continuity of involvement meant that service alterations could be initiated speedily in response to changing circumstances. In times of family crisis, the level or content of care might need rapid adaptation. An example of this was a client whose wife had a sudden heart attack necessitating hospital admission, so increased home care assistant input and overnight care were urgently needed to enable him to remain at home. On discharge, her additional needs for care and recovery also needed to be met by the project staff.

In several cases when clients were approaching death in their own homes, the level of home care assistant input was subject to daily review. For example, a man aged 86, living with his elderly wife, was bedridden during his last days and required two home care assistants to provide him with total care. In this and similar cases, the care manager chose to give the home care assistants considerable autonomy to make decisions on the frequency and duration of visits, and on the appropriate timing of care during the night.

Table 4.3
Problems tackled by care managers[a]

Problems associated with	%
Mobility — indoors	73
Bathing	69
Transferring — bed, chair, commode	67
Washing	64
Toileting	64
Dressing	63
General liability to fall	61
Achievement of relief for carer	59
Managing medication	51
Mobility — outdoors	49
Light housework	45
Making snacks/drinks	40
Laundry	37
Making meals	35
Anxiety and/or depression	32
Heavy housework	32
Shopping	31
Attending to fires/heating	22
Inappropriate input of carer (in quantity or quality)	21
Acute illness	19
Difficult behaviour	19
Feeding	19
Visual difficulties	14
Feelings of loneliness	13
Self-neglect	13
Managing affairs	12
Relationship difficulties	11
Mental confusion	10

a Based on problems identified in 10 per cent or more of cases. Based on several case reviews per client (147 reviews).

Case reviews

A formal review procedure was undertaken six weeks after discharge from
hospital and six-monthly thereafter. The care managers and other staff involved in the care of the client participated in this process. The review
documents completed by the care managers provided an assessment of the
needs which had been tackled and those requiring action; and activities
undertaken and planned in relation to clients, carers, home care assistants
and other services. This document was derived from work in earlier care
management schemes (Challis and Davies, 1986; Challis et al., 1990). Discussion of the outcome of reviews subsequently took place between the
relevant care manager and project manager, and responsibility fell to the care
manager to put any decisions into practice.

Table 4.3 shows the problems tackled by care managers over 147 case
reviews, which included a maximum of three reviews per client. The major
areas included mobility, transfer and other problems associated with activities
of daily living. Also of major importance was the provision of relief for carers
and assistance with instrumental activities of daily living, such as housework,
laundry and meals. The major obstacles to the successful implementation of
the care plan appeared to be client attitudes and difficulties in the informal
network, often due to relationship problems or unwillingness to relinquish
care. The provision of relief for carers and assistance with mobility outside
the home, often provided through home care assistants were the problems
tackled most frequently.

Table 4.4 shows the care managers' activities which were focused directly
on the client. The most frequent were assessment and re-assessment, pro-

Table 4.4
Care manager activities: client-related[a]

Activity	%
Assess/re-assess	91
Support/monitoring	91
Care planning	89
Information/advice	79
Emotional needs	54
Negotiations with agencies	41
Advocacy	35
Directing/negotiating client behaviour	33
Escorting	13
Work with client in groups/outings	11

a Based on activities identified in 10 per cent or more of cases. Based on several case
  reviews per client (147 reviews).

viding support, monitoring wellbeing and planning care. This indicates how these processes recur in undertaking the core tasks of care management. The provision of information and advice was frequently noted, and responding to emotional needs was evident in more than half of the reviews. Advocacy was noted in just over a third of reviews. This shows how the care management role not only involved brokerage activities such as arranging services, but also required the exercise of interpersonal skills.

Care managers also worked closely with the client's informal network. Table 4.5 shows that frequently performed activities included the exchange of information with carers, obtaining carers' views of client needs, ascertaining carers' needs and providing support to carers themselves. Table 4.6 shows care managers' activities with service providers. The main activities, as might

Table 4.5
Care manager activities: informal network[a]

Activity	%
Information exchange	85
Evaluation of carer need	67
Evaluation of client need	66
Emotional support	54
Monitoring/negotiating carers' specific role/tasks	47
Advocacy over client interests	37
Promoting teamwork/meetings	29
Modification of carers' attitudes/behaviour	26

a Based on activities identified in 10 per cent or more of cases. Based on several case reviews per client (147 reviews).

Table 4.6
Care manager activities: service providers[a]

Activity	%
Information exchange	77
Negotiation over change in service	41
Advocacy over clients' interests	33
Promoting teamwork/meetings	33
Administrative work	29
Request for major intervention/resources	24
Education/understanding	18

a Based on problems identified in 10 per cent or more of cases. Based on several case reviews per client (147 reviews).

be expected, were exchanging information, negotiating changes in the service provided, advocating for clients' interests, and improving communication and coordination through meetings.

It was part of the care manager's role to notify the other service providers involved of a forthcoming review and to try to ensure that they contributed to the process. In addition, reviews were undertaken by other staff involved with the elderly person. This included circulating review forms for completion by each service provider involved. These review forms provided an indication of the providers' input to clients, carers and home care assistants. Review schedules were completed mainly by district nurses, physiotherapists, occupational therapists and occasionally by continence advisers and speech therapists. Most identified their role as contributing to assessment. However, physiotherapists were more likely than others to have provided clients with information and advice and carried out direct treatment. They were also more involved in supervising home care assistants and in teaching specific techniques to home care assistants and carers. This probably reflected the appointment of a physiotherapist specifically for the project team.

The formal review documentation from other professionals proved to have limited usefulness for the care managers, who frequently found that other providers were slow to complete and return their forms, and that the information supplied was relatively limited. Nonetheless, formal review discussions were seen as serving a purpose in clarifying thoughts on client progress or setting new targets, although, as the main thrust of the work was aimed at maintaining a long-term care population, the target-setting element was necessarily limited. In practice it was the regular contact with clients, carers and home care assistants that enabled the most effective monitoring of each situation and ensured the possibility of a prompt response to changes.

Counselling

The care manager role incorporated a responsibility for overall client welfare which was seen as including the social and psychological welfare of both client and carer. Table 4.4 indicates how care managers were involved in meeting clients' emotional needs and negotiating behaviour, and Table 4.5 shows the importance care managers attributed to providing emotional support to carers and evaluating their needs. Counselling, listening, reassuring, confronting and problem-solving took up a substantial amount of the care managers' time. Particular foci included helping people accept recent disability, problems in relationships, support for carers and dealing with the imminence of death.

Over one-third of project clients had suffered disabling strokes. Although many of these clients had been disabled for some years, there was a significant group whose disability was relatively recent, and who needed help and support in accepting the changed nature of their lives. For carers, in particular, this frequently involved accepting the changed nature of relationships, especially where speech, communication and personality were affected by the stroke or other illness.

In a number of families, long-standing relationship difficulties re-emerged when a client was discharged home, and it fell within the care manager's remit to mediate, challenge, confront and support different members of the family group to prevent further deterioration or crisis in relationships. In one case, it had been suspected that a client had been physically abused by her husband prior to her hospitalisation. The care manager took the responsibility for supporting both the client and husband, and for monitoring the situation after discharge. In another case a female client had a strained relationship with her son, linked to his constant demands for her money and her fear of refusing him. This became a challenging problem which was not amenable to any quick solution, as each time the client initiated a complaint against her son, she later withdrew it.

In several cases the client's own personality and behaviour led to repeated conflicts or clashes with relatives or others. Sometimes this arose because of the demanding, attention-seeking behaviour exhibited by the client, or rejection of the help offered by services. On occasions, time spent by the care manager counselling and confronting the client with the consequences of their behaviour achieved some resolution and enabled the situation to be maintained. But in the remaining cases the client ultimately chose to receive other services. In two cases, clients chose not to continue the project service, while continuing to make heavy demands on their reluctant daughters, and a further two clients returned to hospital.

Evaluation of carer needs inevitably required a good relationship with the carer, and understanding of, their situation and feelings. On occasions, care managers spent a high proportion of their time working to build and retain constructive relationships and to support a carer. This could sustain their willingness to accept the project service and avoid the build-up of stress which might lead to crisis re-admission to hospital. In some cases the care manager established a regular pattern of respite relief care for the client in order to ensure that the carer received much-needed breaks from a demanding care role. The frequency and continuing appropriateness of this service required regular monitoring, and sometimes the client needed support in accepting respite care in the interests of their relative's physical and emotional wellbeing. Nonetheless, it could happen that the caring relative felt unable to accept respite relief because of the client's pattern of unhappiness and physical deterioration during periods of hospitalisation. In these cases care managers needed to monitor the carer's need for relief particularly carefully and to organise day care, more home care assistant time, or to recruit someone to sleep in for night-time relief if these seemed appropriate.

Where evident, the ambivalence of carers over continuing in the caring role needed to be acknowledged and accepted. Sometimes this acceptance enabled the carer to continue with support. In one case a temporary nursing home placement was arranged for a male client, but the carer changed her mind and decided to have her husband home again after all. Given the frequent guilt reported by carers over the need to admit a relative to institutional care (Brane, 1986; Challis and Davies, 1986; Müller, 1987), care managers tried to acknowledge carer's feelings without exercising judgements. Of course, there were clearly complex dilemmas when a carer's wishes ran counter to those of the client, such as over respite care or transfer to a nursing home.

For clients who were terminally ill or dying, care managers took on an important and difficult role in helping clients and carers accept and cope with the nature of the illness, its implications, preparations for death and its aftermath. They normally visited for a period after the client's death to provide some continuing support to relatives, attended funerals and gave guidance with many of the practicalities which follow a death. With such a frail group of individuals, it is not surprising that this type of support and counselling formed a significant part of the care managers' workload.

Monitoring and supporting home care assistants

Table 4.7, drawn from the case reviews, shows care manager activities in relation to home care assistants. The most frequently noted activities were

Table 4.7
Care manager activities: home care assistant-related[a]

Activity	%
Regular supervision/monitoring of home care assistant performance	96
Emotional support/outlet	93
Information exchange	93
Calling meetings/promoting teamwork	88
Temporary/minor changes/relief cover	79
Education — in skills/tasks/understanding	75
Integrating home care assistant role with formal network	71
Supporting/reinforcing home care assistant role with client	70
Matching/introduction to client	66
Formal training/courses	59
Additional administrative work	46
General recruitment/training	30
Helping with day groups	27
Major change/intervention in home care assistant role/tasks	21

a Based on activities identified in 10 per cent or more of cases. Based on several case reviews per client (147 reviews).

providing supervision, giving support, exchanging information and promoting teamwork. Considerable effort was also put into training and enabling home care assistants to understand client needs better.

Care managers monitored the work of home care assistants through frequent visits, particularly in the early stages of providing a care package. Sometimes home visits involved seeing both the client alone and seeing the client and home care assistant jointly. The aim of these visits was to supervise the work of the home care assistants, to build relationships with them and to ensure the quality of the care and support given. The respective health staff also monitored the work undertaken by home care assistants on their behalf. Meetings with home care assistants were held either in the office, at their own homes or in group settings, and there was also considerable telephone contact. In addition, the home care assistant diary sheets were read carefully by care managers to monitor care.

Supervision was held both on an individual and on a group basis. Individual supervision of new home care assistants tended to be on a monthly basis and for more experienced staff on a two-monthly basis. The care managers needed to judge the varying support needs of different home care assistants. Quite frequently, supervision took the form of support and counselling. This sometimes involved helping home care assistants to cope with the death of someone to whom they had given considerable support and with whom they may have developed a close relationship.

Group support sessions aimed to examine difficulties experienced by home care assistants and to work out coping strategies. They also attempted to consider their development and to identify rewarding aspects of the job as well as problems. These meetings often enabled home care assistants to realise that the same problems were met elsewhere and that approaches to managing them could be learned from one another. Group support was made easier by a shift from a keyworker system to a team approach. This is described in Chapter 5.

Case closure, discharge and death

Some care management schemes have been designed to facilitate hospital discharge for a general elderly population and may therefore be short-term in duration and expect a high turnover rate (Applebaum and Austin, 1990). However, this project was designed to provide long-term care at home for frail elderly people. It was not expected, therefore, that many people would be discharged to less intensive modes of care. For most individuals, the project was expected to provide care at home as long as was desired and deemed possible or until death.

In practice there were four factors which influenced the decision to end project care: discharge to a less intensive mode of care; discharge to a more intensive mode of care; problems for the carer due to their own disability or increasing relationship problems with the client; and death of the client or carer.

Discharge to less intensive care

From time to time the review process was used to reach a decision that a client no longer required the project service because of improvements in health and coping abilities. During their first year after entry to the scheme, seven clients were discharged to the home help service. In these cases responsibility for coordinating an effective discharge remained with the care manager. This could involve particularly sensitive handling to allay the inevitable anxieties expressed by clients about the capacity of other support services — such as home help, meals-on-wheels and district nurses — to meet their needs. Such transfers required a planning meeting between the client and other service providers, where specific undertakings could be made about the level of service to be provided after discharge from the project. For example:

> For six months, a 78 year old woman living alone had received a high level of care and support from a home care assistant, who became a much loved and trusted friend. At the six-month review it became clear she had recovered some independent coping skills, and could now toilet, wash and dress herself and no longer needed such an intensive level of support. A planned discharge to home help support was arranged, and the home care assistant helped prepare her for this and support her during the transition.

Discharge to more intensive care

Some of the most difficult decisions were made when community support appeared no longer viable. The need to maintain the service at its most cost-effective, and to ensure its availability to those most able to benefit from it were factors which influenced decisions about discharge to another service. Even when discharge decisions involved clients in painful adjustments to new services, these decisions were seen as justifiable:

> A heavy 86 year old woman was discharged from hospital, but by the time of the six-week review it became clear that she was insufficiently motivated to assist with transfers, washing and dressing, and so it was becoming risky for the home care assistant to attempt these activities on her own. The cost implications of providing two home care assistants to perform all personal caring tasks did not seem justified when set against the low motivation of the client and the limited benefits she received from the service. A decision to end the service was made after discussion

with client and relatives, and she returned to hospital where she died a few weeks later.

Carer disability and relationship problems

Sometimes a declining family situation led to the need to end the project service. The husband of one client became increasingly confused and unable to maintain a safe environment for his disabled wife. After instances when she had unexplained injuries, and when her husband was unable to manage the fire safely, they agreed to a placement in a private nursing home, and the care manager supported and assisted them in the transfer.

In some cases, conflicts of interest developed between the client and carer over continuation or termination of project care. In two cases, caring wives had ambivalent responses to the care role and its burdens. The care manager had a part to play in counselling the carer and enabling the expression of negative feelings about the client, but she also had a potentially conflicting role as advocate and provider of service to the client who wanted to live at home. In one instance, with regular respite care relief, the wife felt able to continue to care until her husband's death. But in the other, the wife arranged a placement for him in a private nursing home. Her ambivalence was finally resolved by this trial placement. Her husband's evident unhappiness led to her arranging for his return home where he was cared for, with project support, until his death.

Death of client or carer

Over the three-year pilot phase, 43 clients died while receiving support from the project, of whom 27 died in their own homes. Organising effective care during the last days of a client's life, and supporting relatives over this difficult time, were part of the care manager's remit. The home care assistant, providing care and emotional support to the client and family, needed to be freed of other demands on her time and to be well supported. It was part of the care management function to ensure that adequate back-up was also forthcoming from other services, such as general practitioner and district nursing.

After the client's death, if the carer's needs and circumstances required it, support was continued by the project until referral to other support services could be implemented. An example of this was the death of one client whose wife was supported by home care assistants until a sufficient package of support from home help, meals-on-wheels and the warden could be effected.

In three cases the client survived their spouse and the project service was adapted to meet the needs of the client living alone rather than as one of a couple. In these situations the home care assistant was encouraged to help the client express feelings of grief and come to terms with their bereavement.

Managing care management

In the literature much discussion has focused on the performance of the core tasks of care management and upon styles and types of fieldwork practice. However, the nature of care management as a system-wide activity involving change in provider patterns and requiring a suitable managerial context is also important (Applebaum and Austin, 1990; Steinberg and Carter, 1983). This linkage between care management practice and care management systems is commonly found in American work (Miller, 1983; O'Connor, 1988). Moore (1990) argues that the degree of horizontal integration in care achieved by care management practice, through coordination of diverse services, requires a degree of vertical integration at system level, through managerial arrangements, in order to be effective. The point is also made in the Government guidance on assessment and care management with the production of separate practice and management documentation (SSI/SWSG, 1991a,b). The model of care management which located care managers, employed by social services, within a geriatric multidisciplinary team was discussed in Chapter 2. The care managers were responsible to a project leader, who was, in turn, responsible to a joint coordinating group of health and social services managers. In order to achieve Moore's (1990) concept of vertical integration, the role of the project manager was crucial. The immediate management of care management requires a focus, on the one hand, on the quality, adequacy and effectiveness of practice and the policy implications of changes in practice and, on the other hand, on the interagency, agency and structural constraints within which practice occurs (Challis, 1994a,b). There are four levels relevant to the management of such a project: client-level care management, involving casework and service coordination to individual clients; scheme coordination, ensuring that operational systems function smoothly and undertaking day-to-day liaison outside the immediate department; day-to-day line management, involving supervision and financial monitoring; and system management, including interagency liaison (Challis and von Abendorff, 1992). The integration of these four levels of management activity is necessary for an effective care management system.

The position of the care managers in the care system was at the pivotal point of several potential conflicts. This was not a design problem of the project, but rather a logical outcome of the role of care management designed to resolve conflicts between needs and resources, scarcity and demand, effectively. A number of different conflicts were experienced by the care managers in their day-to-day work. These included differences of view between client and their carers; conflicts about the roles and responsibilities of different service providers; conflicts between clients' wishes and desires for home-based care and other providers' concern for their safety and security; balancing the service mix between home care assistant provision and other modes of care; and balancing the needs of different home care assistants who were all supporting very dependent elderly people. Not surprisingly, at times this could be very stressful for the care managers and this required support from management. Informal peer group support was important, of course, and simply sharing an office meant that some issues could be discussed between the care managers, which was found to be of considerable benefit. Individual one-to-one supervision was also provided by the project manager. However, it appeared that providing time in which peer group support could be formalised was also of value in handling and balancing issues that, of their nature, permitted no easy solution. This occurred for only a short period during the project, but it would seem from the experience of this and other care management systems that such an arrangement is useful both as a means of lateral supervision and also as a means to encourage the spread of new ideas and approaches.

In short, it is necessary to focus both upon the quality, performance and environment of day-to-day practice and on the strategic implications and service development effects of the style of practice employed. In many ways, in a small team environment, the managers' appreciation of both elements is enhanced by carrying a small caseload and functioning both as practitioner and manager (Challis et al., 1990). In this way they can develop an understanding of the impact of the organisational environment upon day-to-day practice, and of the implications for budgets, purchasing and service development of changing practice. However, in this project the team leader did not carry a caseload, except at times of sickness and holiday when he would act on behalf of an absent care manager. The role of the manager was mainly concerned with development, supervision of the care managers, interagency management and consideration of the project's contribution to the strategic development of health and social services in the locality. In a more general implementation of this approach, it is doubtful whether the overhead costs of such a post could be justified to cover such a small team, and a manager might be required to manage several such care management units.

Similar questions about the role of project manager posts were raised in the development of care management in Australia through the Community Options programme (DHHCS, 1992). Such a position is a critical link between client-level activities of care management and system-level issues of interagency coordination and service development. The focus of the coordinator or project manager roles in Australia was seen as predominantly planning and establishing the local projects, and little attention was given to that role when services were fully operational (Kendig et al., 1992). Certainly, different activities and skills are required in the different phases of projects, reflecting a shift from innovation to maintenance responsibilities. These important aspects of the management of care management are discussed further in Chapter 11.

The care management role and the wider service system

Hospital services

By the time the care managers had been in post for a year, the initial anxieties and role adjustments had been overcome. At this stage, both consultants said they had confidence in the project team and their ability to provide a good service to their clients. One of the consultants also commented favourably on how a planned and coordinated discharge was more easily effected through the care managers, as they took responsibility for all necessary arrangements, including notifying community services and general practitioners, as well as setting up the necessary domiciliary support. This removed a considerable burden from ward sisters. Hospital nurses and the medical social worker were satisfied to be able to offer the prospect of intense community support to patients who needed such support and who were eager to return to their own homes. Initially, several ward sisters had recorded their doubts about whether some frail or difficult patients really could be adequately cared for outside a hospital ward. They were now pleasantly surprised and reassured at the level of success of the project, and expressed confidence in the care managers' ability to coordinate the discharge effectively and set up adequate care at home. These ward sisters stressed the importance of ensuring that home care assistants were thoroughly prepared for their role, by spending time on the ward getting to know the patient and their needs, thus ensuring effective continuity of care.

Therapy services

The manager of one of the therapy groups commented on the good relationships and communication that had been established between the project team and other services. She believed this had been accomplished through the skill and effort of the project team, who had made it their business to gain trust through demonstrating their respect for the roles of other professionals, and had ensured that other service providers came to understand the care management role they performed.

Services in the community

The expectation that social services department staff, such as social workers, would see the care managers as taking their role did not materialise, as might have been expected. Indeed, if anything the reverse was true, with the hospital social worker in the geriatric service positively supporting the care managers. However, like many outposted staff, the care managers felt rather isolated from the social services department. One care manager described it as a feeling of being 'out in the cold', the social work teams generally having little interest in their work, reflecting a low status attached to work with the elderly. The main exceptions to this were support from senior management of the local social services department, although the amount of management time that could be devoted to supporting the project inevitably was limited, and support from the existing hospital social worker in the geriatric service.

In the early phase, the view of the home help service was that the project was of little relevance to them as it was an entirely separate service. This can be seen to relate to the experience of home care in other local authorities where separate and parallel developments have taken place within social services departments (Simons and Warburton, 1980). One probable benefit of separate development is a clearly-targeted service which will remain so, but at the cost of relatively little impact upon the development of the mainstream service. Conversely, the cost of location in the mainstream could be seen as leading to less clear targeting and a greater risk of slippage in criteria (which greatly exercised the minds of the district health authority personnel in the consideration of further funding), although the benefit would be the dissemination of more intensive and flexible approaches across the mainstream. Certainly, the home help service in the locality became more aware of the possibilities for expansion of the home help role through training, as a consequence of exposure to the project, since it provided a practical demonstration of certain aspects of broader national policies and developments in home care (SSI, 1987). The need emerged to negotiate a smooth and effective transfer to the home help service for clients whose condition had improved and no longer needed the intense support of the project. At this point it became clear that an earlier failure to establish good links between these two services needed to be remedied through personal contact and individual case discussions. Agreement was reached that the home help organiser would receive copies of written assessments of need by members of the project team, including the occupational therapist and physiotherapist where appropriate, and would incorporate these in their own assessment procedures.

District nurses appeared to experience most conflict in their acceptance of the care management role, obviously seeing the development of this as intruding upon their role in assessing and planning nursing care at home. It may be that, because all three care managers had backgrounds in nursing, and two also had backgrounds in social work, that the issue was manageable. In addition, district nurses were also experiencing an invasion of their territory by the development of domiciliary occupational therapy and physiotherapy. Conflicts often arose over issues of the balance of risk between hospital and home-based care. One care manager described it thus:

> They [district nurses] talked about 24-hour care [in hospital] but when we actually looked at what the patients were receiving, you could usually break it down to a few hours a day. So in hospital, there might be someone around all day, but it didn't mean that the client was getting individual

Box 4.1
Care manager: roles and tasks

AIMS	ACTIVITIES	PROGRAMME
Home care assistant-related aims		
Managing the budget for a team of HCAs.	Team meetings.	Monthly team meeting.
Effective deployment of a team of HCAs.	Individual supervision. Arranging staff training.	Monthly staff supervision.
Identifying training needs.	Budgetary control.	
Promoting growth through problem-solving.	Giving knowledge and information.	
Linking HCA to all necessary resources.	Team building.	
Ensuring HCA is aware of the whole network.		
Ensuring that the demands on the HCA are realistic and not overburdening.		
Client-related aims		
Assessment of needs.	Coordinating inputs from several professionals.	Fortnightly home visits.
Ensuring the client is aware of the whole of the network and what the different parts do.	Home visits to talk to client/family.	
Checking how the client feels about the adequacy of the network and whether the network is meeting the client's needs.	Support, counselling, advice, advocacy. Monitoring wellbeing directly and individually through discussions with HCAs and other professionals.	
Ensuring uptake of welfare benefits.		
Ensuring continued client wellbeing.		
Network-related aims		
Effective coordination of all necessary resources for the client, avoiding conflict between formal and informal.	Discussions with professionals. Recruiting paid and unpaid helpers.	Individual client care planning meetings.
Ensuring each part of the network knows the role and function of the other parts.	Linking different professionals. Support, counselling, advice. Ensuring planning approach.	Face-to-face meetings with professionals and caregivers.
Ensuring the adequacy of the network.	Upward flow of information via project manager.	Project team meetings.
Generating, where necessary, new parts for the network.		Multidisciplinary team meetings.
Strengthening existing parts of the network.		Coordinating group meetings.
Minimising strain on informal carers.		Service planning meetings.
Contributing to service development.		

care, [our clients] ... probably get more individual care at home.

Indeed, despite the extent of expressed concern about 24-hour care, it is noteworthy that at no time during the three-year pilot phase did any of the 101 clients experience a crisis at night, since these were anticipated by providing additional services.

For therapy services, the project appeared to be valued because it had performed a bridge-building role. It had contributed to the establishment of a pattern of their work in the community as members of the project team. The gain for therapy staff was the extension of their role into community services, coupled with their having no particular professional expectations of undertaking an overall care management responsibility, unlike many nursing staff.

The main anxiety expressed by general practitioners had been about the extent to which the project as a whole would generate extra demands, such as increased call-out at night. In the event this did not prove to be a problem, although one planned response had been to provide regular consultant medical review in the community. This, as we have noted in Chapter 2, did not prove possible to implement, although referral for geriatric reassessment could occur, particularly at review times, due to the participation of consultants in reviews.

Conclusions

In this chapter we have seen how the project team created a role, that of care manager, which, despite initial scepticism and a degree of resistance among some local providers, came to be valued and seen as appropriate and necessary by the majority of actors in the service system. A summary of aspects of that role is shown in Box 4.1. In terms of practice it appeared that location in the multidisciplinary team made case-finding, screening and the achievement of a complete multidisciplinary assessment considerably easier. However, despite attempts to establish suitable arrangements for regular geriatric medical reviews of patients, this was never successful. In part this reflected the prevailing boundaries of geriatric medicine and primary care, the problematic nature of clinical responsibility in home from hospital schemes, and indeed some of the disincentives faced by hospital-based doctors in developing community-based services. The pattern of activities undertaken by care managers was a broad one, encompassing all the core tasks of care management (Steinberg and Carter, 1983; SSI/SWSG, 1991a,b), and required them to provide counselling and social support as well as the brokerage functions of service arrangement and monitoring. This was surprising to some of the local service providers, who appeared to have seen the role as one of service arrangement and brokerage, with services such as counselling to be 'bought in' as and when appropriate. Of course, such a narrow conception of care management is inevitably attractive to some groups, reflecting a degree of inherent organisational inertia, since it requires little or no adjustment in their roles in response to the development of care management. However, as care managers attempted to fulfil their role, those with such a view would be likely to experience most difficulty with the more extended range of functions required.

Therefore, some staff found considerable difficulty in differentiating between the narrow service management functions of recruiting, allocating, monitoring and supporting home care assistants, as distinct from the broader care management function. This problem is not dissimilar to the difficulties with which many local authorities have been grappling in trying to establish purchaser/provider relationships in social services departments, and certainly proved to be a cause for concern in the later development of the service in Darlington, as will be discussed in Chapter 10. As discussed in Chapter 11, the effective management of this separation of roles is crucial, and requires clarity of analysis regarding who does what, why and for whom. All such organisational arrangements have both costs and benefits and it is important to be clear about the relative balance of these for the particular service in question.

5   The Home Care Assistants

Integrating the nursing auxiliary/home help role is not a new development in home care (Ferlie, 1982; Salvage, 1985). Such developments have been advocated for some while (Hopkins, 1982), reflecting concerns about cost, rigid demarcation of roles and appropriate care. However, the Darlington Project attempted to move further, by enabling care workers to be instructed and used by a variety of different professionals, in an attempt to integrate much of the work of several different 'hands-on' providers into the activities of a single worker. The functions of a home help, auxiliary nurse and an aide to several occupational groups were combined in one person. The home care assistant was available to, and could contact, consult and be instructed by, several different health and social services personnel, according to the differing needs of the individual elderly people. The aim was both to extend the range of services and to reduce the number of individuals involved in providing care, since activities such as basic physiotherapy, personal care and meal provision, usually carried out by staff from several different agencies, could be provided at home by fewer and less specialised personnel.

Thus the role of the home care assistant was a new one, attempting to span both agency and professional boundaries through the means of a single 'hands-on' care worker. Unlike most care workers, home care assistants spanned health and social care agencies in the tasks which they undertook. The coordination of services at the level of the care manager, described in the previous chapter, was complemented by the coordination of a series of previously discrete care tasks through one person. The development of such a role was subsequently recommended in the Griffiths Report (Griffiths, 1988), but there have been relatively few attempts to develop it in practice, reflecting, in part, the difficulty of bridging the health/social care divide.

The previous chapter noted how the recruitment, training and effective development of these multipurpose care workers were the responsibility of the project management team, comprising one project manager and initially two, later three, care managers. This chapter describes the characteristics and backgrounds of the care assistants, their preparation and training for the role, and their pattern of working. We also consider the way in which this workforce was deployed, instructed, supervised and managed in order to work as cost-effectively as possible, and how this developed over the time of the project. Five main sources of information have been used for this chapter. These are shown in Box 5.1.

Background and previous experience

During the project, 83 home care assistants were employed on varied contracts. Most worked 29 hours per week; some in the outlying villages worked 15-18 hours per week; and some on casual weekly contracts provided short-term or sickness cover. All staff employed as home care assistants were female. Nearly all applicants for the jobs were women, and the few male applicants were found to be unsuitable. The home care assistants ranged in age from 18 to 59. As shown in Table 5.1, the largest group (40 per cent) was aged between 30 and 39, and the 20 to 29 and 40 to 49 age groups each formed about 25 per cent of the total.

Table 5.1
Age of home care assistants

Age	Number
Under 20	2
20-29	21
30-39	33
40-49	20
50 and over	7
Total number	83

Table 5.2 shows the previous experience of the home care assistants. The largest group (24) had either part-time or full-time experience in residential care homes in both the private and the public sectors. Seventeen had previously worked as home helps, and a further thirteen as domestics in hospital or in residential or similar settings. Five came to the project as trained nurses, and a further five had been employed as auxiliary nurses or therapy helpers. Thus 64 (77 per cent) had some previous paid experience in domestic or caring work. Of the remainder, thirteen had previously done clerical or shop work, and six had other paid or voluntary work experience: two had done

Box 5.1
Main sources of information

Client diary sheets. These were kept in clients' homes. They recorded the daily activities and working routines of home care assistants, and provided a running record of other visitors to, and care provided for, the project clients.

Home care assistant activity survey. This was carried out over one week in September 1987. Each care assistant completed a detailed diary sheet during this week on which they recorded the tasks performed each day and estimated the time spent on different tasks. This survey provides a snapshot of the breadth of the home care assistant role.

Interviews with the monitor group. Of the 83 home care assistants employed over three years, one group of nine home care assistants recruited together in April 1986 was selected to be monitored in depth. Several interviews were carried out with this group: before and after their training, six to eight weeks after starting work, one year and two years later. Information obtained in these tape-recorded, semi-structured interviews provides a view of how the role developed and changed over time, and how it was perceived by this group of care assistants.

Interviews with sixteen home care assistants. In late 1986, approximately a year after the first clients were discharged from hospital, a further set of semi-structured tape-recorded interviews was carried out with sixteen home care assistants. The purpose of these interviews was to look in detail at areas of difficulty, conflict or stress in the role of the home care assistant. The group was selected by means of a postal questionnaire sent to all home care assistants. The completed questionnaires enabled the selection of sixteen who had at some time experienced difficulties in performing their role. This interview provided comparable information to that obtained from the monitor group. Twelve of this group of sixteen had been members of the first cohort of 24 care assistants to be employed at the beginning of the project, and the remaining four had been part of the second group employed at the beginning of 1986, so all had been working for at least nine months at the time of interview.

Observational data. The research worker, being based in the project office, was able to record patterns of working and meetings between care managers and home care assistants.

factory work, one had been a laboratory technician, and three had done voluntary work with Red Cross, Community Task Force and Vietnamese refugees, respectively.

Table 5.2
Previous experience of home care assistants

Previous experience	Number
Residential care assistant	24
Home help	17
Domestic	13
Clerical or shop worker	13
Trained nurse	5
Auxiliary nurse/therapy helper	5
Voluntary work (Red Cross, etc.)	3
Factory work	2
Laboratory technician	1
Total number	83

Recruitment

The initial methods of recruitment for home care assistants involved general advertisements and personal or written contact with relevant potential employees. Advertisements were placed in the local daily newspaper; details were sent to current home helps and residential care staff in local authority homes; and notices were placed on hospital notice boards where they might be seen by nursing assistants. The response from these was sufficient to recruit the first group of home care assistants, and to maintain a constant trickle of enquiries to the project office. After each enquiry an application form was sent out and, if completed and returned, was held until a home care assistant was needed in that area, in which case the applicant would be contacted and interviewed by one of the care managers.

From time to time there was a specific need for a home care assistant in a particular area, often in the more outlying villages. In these cases an advert was placed in the local shop or post office. These home care assistants were then employed on temporary contracts and, in the event of death or entry to hospital of their client, the contract was continued if further work was required in the locality.

On occasions, for example when there was a sudden increase in referrals, or when the group living scheme for three clients was being established, advertisements were placed in the Department of Employment Job Centre, and several applicants came from this source. As may be expected, in these cases there was less likelihood of the applicant having previous relevant caring experience.

Motivation for joining the project

Brief interviews were carried out with the monitor group prior to their training to establish their motivation for joining the project. Their responses can be broadly grouped into five themes:

- A job with better pay, hours or greater permanence than the current one (eight out of nine). This was particularly relevant to those who had previously worked on casual contracts in residential units.
- Pleasure in working with elderly people, in feeling needed and doing something worthwhile (six out of nine). 'Older people are rewarding ... you feel needed.'
- A wish to provide more comprehensive individualised care than had been possible in the residential settings where many had worked previously (five out of nine). One home care assistant commented that she hoped to be able to 'give that little bit extra ... to get involved'.
- The prospect of greater variety, flexibility, challenge and responsibility than their current situation allowed (five out of nine). For example, one home care assistant said she wanted 'to have a say in a person's care, not just take orders'.
- Enthusiasm for the aims of the scheme, such as enabling frail elderly people to be cared for in their own homes (four out of nine). One of the home care assistants typified this attitude in saying that, 'Old people need to be in their own homes ... in institutions they lose their self-respect.'

It is interesting to note that these responses resemble the kinds of motivation found in helpers of the Kent Community Care Scheme (Qureshi et al., 1983, 1989), indicating the similarity of factors which are likely to influence people to work with dependent elderly people. Particularly evident were factors associated with the helping process, the sense of feeling useful, and enhancing skills. Interestingly, the specific features of the project, such as care at home, were important for this group because of their previous work experience.

Training the home care assistants

As home care assistants were to undertake a new and challenging multi-purpose role in the community, it was considered essential by the project team that they should receive a basic training at the outset to prepare them for this work. Since they had to work with and on behalf of a range of different health care staff, as well as undertake domestic tasks, it was regarded as important to ensure that they had a clear understanding of the range of problems of elderly people, the roles of different staff, as well as of the objectives and values — such as greater client self-determination — under-lying the project. The initial training reflected similar concerns to those of the project in Oxfordshire described in Chapter 2 (Oxfordshire Social Services Department and Oxford Health Authority, 1982).

The first-stage training was seen as giving a foundation in attitudes, essential skills and relationships. The underlying aims were threefold:

- to convey the aims and objectives of the project — its purposes and desired attitudes to clients;
- to teach a range of basic skills that home care assistants may require in the course of their work; and
- to familiarise the home care assistants with members of the project team, the other professionals involved and their various roles.

All newly-recruited groups of home care assistants were required to attend this first-stage training, which took place in the nurse teaching unit at the hospital. Individual training sessions were presented by the same professionals, who would subsequently instruct home care assistants in their work with individual elderly clients. This meant that home care assistants left the training period knowing who these staff were, where they could be contacted, and what their roles were. In their turn, the various professionals had encouraged home care assistants to make use of their expertise when required. Over the period of training, new home care assistants had also had a good opportunity to get to know the project team and current home care assistants at their team meetings on the course.

The programme used to fulfil these aims was broadly the same for each new group, though it varied from three weeks to two weeks in length, and later was compressed into one week. The programme used for the monitor group of home care assistants is shown in Box 5.2.

Interviews with the monitor group of home care assistants indicated that the initial training sessions were appreciated. The practical sessions, such as learning about lifting from the physiotherapists, were seen as particularly relevant. Although most home care assistants appreciated the practical focus to training, had acquired confidence and were eager to begin work, a few anxieties remained. Some expressed anxiety at dealing with terminal illness, and one was concerned about the inevitable vagueness of the boundaries of the caring role.

The initial training was the foundation for the individual client-specific instruction which followed, which was designed to equip the care assistants with the skills to perform specific tasks and activities required for the care of particular clients on discharge from hospital.

There was a commitment by care managers to identify and meet further training needs, and care assistants had the opportunity to attend refresher skills training days as well as a more formal training programme during the project. Some twelve months after employment of the first group of home care assistants, a second-stage training programme was developed in response

Box 5.2
Typical programme of initial training: April 1986

Day 1 a.m.   Introduction to the project, its aims, its history and its personnel. An outline of the evaluation of the scheme (project manager and care managers).

p.m.   Attitudes, and relationships with other professionals; the sensitive nature of relationships when care assistants are on a client's home territory; client's right to self-determination; and acceptance of a degree of risk-taking (project manager and care managers).

Day 2 a.m.   The use of reminiscence and the needs of carers. This used two short videos on the problems experienced by family carers as a basis for discussion (project manager).

p.m.   Death, dying and bereavement: video and discussion enabling some of the assistants to voice their own feelings and anxieties (care managers).

Day 3 a.m.   'Know your body': essential parts of the body, situation and function. Illustrated through the use of skeleton, skull and plastic models of the organs of the body (nurse tutor).

p.m.   Team meetings — getting to know other home care assistants within the team groups.

Day 4 a.m.   Common illnesses of the elderly: their symptoms and effects (nurse tutor).

p.m.   Occupational therapy in the OT Department: using wheelchairs and other aids to daily living, as well as an opportunity to find out about the range of aids that are available (OT).

Day 5 a.m.   Diet, nutrition and the elderly: suggestions on stimulating appetite, as well as controlling the diet when necessary (dietician).

p.m.   Introduction to chiropody: basic foot care for the elderly. Information on hygiene, nail-cutting and simple first aid measures for feet (chiropodist).

Day 6 a.m.   Nursing tasks in the community (community nursing): the role of the district nurse, and the prevention of hypothermia (district nurse).

p.m.   Ensuring safety in the home, and basic first aid: video presentations and practical activities (district nurse).

Day 7 All day Home visits with district nurses.

Day 8 a.m.   Care of the incontinent patient and the promotion of continence: use of continence aids (continence adviser).

p.m.   Team meetings.

Day 9 All day Physiotherapy: information on the nature of the spine, and the necessity for the use of proper lifting techniques; demonstration of appropriate lifting skills and repeated practice under supervision (physiotherapists).

Day 10 All day Video and discussion. Evaluation of the course.

to requests from home care assistants. This took the form of a half-day release course, one afternoon a week over ten weeks, totalling twenty hours.

The aims of the second stage training were:

- to increase understanding of the ageing process and the needs of elderly people;
- to develop insight into their own role as care assistants, and into the relationships between themselves and with clients and their social network;
- to develop skills in organisation and management of time and work; and
- to develop understanding of the structure and nature of families, relationships between generations, and the behaviour of individuals within different family situations, especially with regard to elderly people within a family.

The method of teaching was based on workshop techniques, group exercises and discussion. Contributions were made mainly by the course tutor at the further education college, with three or four health and social service personnel invited to make a specific input. This course was run for two groups of sixteen care assistants. Each was a mixed group working with different care managers, as well as being at different stages in their caring experience. The course content is shown in Box 5.3.

The response to these aspects of secondary training was generally positive. On the whole, however, it seemed that care assistants would have preferred less about theories of ageing and further contributions from professional staff. They particularly appreciated discussions on improving communication and

---

Box 5.3
Secondary training for home care assistants

Week 1   Introduction, aims and scope of course.

Week 2   The role of the home care assistants.

Week 3   The effect on the family of caring for elderly people at home.

Week 4   A problem-solving approach to care at home.

Week 5   Physical and psychological aspects of caring.

Week 6   Stress and the carer.

Week 7   Social aspects of ageing.

Week 8   Communication.

Week 9   Death and bereavement.

Week 10   Course evaluation, feedback, discussion.

understanding family relationships, and being able to consider their experiences with other care assistants. They also valued training as part of their overall support and as giving them due recognition sometimes lacking in home care services (Bond, 1979, 1980).

During the early stages of the project, home care assistants were recruited in groups and it was possible to organise specific training sessions for them. Once the service was running at its planned level, however, recruitment was necessarily sporadic, occurring as and when vacancies arose, and this required a different approach to training for new staff. An induction programme was devised which involved staff spending time with key health care workers. This was followed with a one-week block of training which was provided when a sufficient number of new home care assistants were available to participate. The induction programme is shown in Box 5.4.

Box 5.4
Induction programme for home care assistants

Individual instruction by community physiotherapist, in particular in lifting techniques.

Individual time with project occupational therapist.

Two days with district nurses to cover:
- attending to personal hygiene requirements, e.g. bed-bathing;
- certain aspects of prevention and treatment of pressure sores;
- observation of dressing wounds and receiving instruction on dressings; and
- taking part in an active rehabilitation programme.

An example of further training was an individual programme planning workshop attended by a group of twelve home care assistants early in 1988. This was organised by a health authority training specialist working in the learning disability field, and was adapted specifically for the home care assistants. The workshop was organised since it had become apparent that the home care assistants, with their direct knowledge of the clients and their circumstances, should be involved in contributing to the care plans for their clients. The emphasis of the workshop was on the home care assistants involving their clients in setting goals, and focused on identifying strengths rather than problems. For example, one home care assistant discussed the difficulties she encountered in trying to promote independence in an unmotivated client. The workshop enabled her to identify a positive approach in recognising her client's strengths and abilities, and led to a rekindling of the enthusiasm to involve the client in discussions about realistic small goals they could work to achieve together.

Given the frequent criticism of the lack of training for direct care staff (Hillingdon Social Services Department, 1974; Merton Social Services Department, 1976; Howell et al., 1979; Goldberg and Connelly, 1982), the investment in training by the project was noteworthy. It is staff such as the home care assistants for whom the development of National Vocational Qualifications (Cmnd 9823, 1986) will be particularly relevant, given the difficulty of organising training for sporadic intakes of staff.

Working with clients

Introduction to the client

The care managers employed similar techniques to match care assistants to clients as were used in the Kent Community Care Scheme (Challis and Davies, 1986). These included matching personality, attitudes and coping strengths, as well as more pragmatic considerations of geographical proximity. Where the client was heavy as well as severely disabled, an additional factor was the physical capacity of the care assistant. These factors were examined further in Chapter 4.

The home care assistant was introduced to the client in hospital. The usual practice was for the home care assistant to visit the ward on two occasions. The purpose of these visits was, first, to begin to form a relationship with the client and, second, to be instructed by nursing and therapy staff who were familiar with the individual's needs and treatment requirements. It was then normal practice for the care assistant to visit the client's home with the care manager in order to meet any relative or informal carer, and get to know the care environment. The care assistant would then be at the client's home on their discharge from hospital.

Planning and effecting discharge depended on a good level of cooperation and coordination between hospital ward, the nursing staff, the other health care staff and the project team. Inevitably there were times when this system broke down, with unfortunate results. In one instance, during the regular care manager's absence on sick leave, a new care assistant was recruited to support a new client who was to be discharged from hospital after a stroke and a period of rehabilitation. Another care assistant, who was to provide relief care to this client, spoke of the difficulties they encountered getting adequate information and preparation for their role:

> It's like the secret service, that hospital. We had a new client to get out and two mornings the care assistant went in to get to know her. Both mornings when she got there the lady was dressed, and she never saw anybody. I went in and this lady was saying she can get on her feet and do this and that ... a (junior) this doctor said, 'No, she cannot walk, she

cannot weight bear' ... we never saw the physiotherapist, occupational therapist or anybody. So she (new care assistant) sat there three mornings and nobody said anything about the client.

Clearly, the role of the care managers in coordinating and planning the discharge process was crucial. Owens (1987) has referred to the importance of ensuring a coordinated and planned discharge to the community for severely disabled people. In Darlington, when the system worked smoothly, introduction and preparation enabled the home care assistant to be a part of this coordinated process, ready to meet the client on discharge and maintain continuity of care.

The early days after discharge were inevitably a time of anxiety for clients, carers and care assistants. To some extent, these difficulties were compounded as a variety of service personnel would need to make visits in these early days to ensure that any equipment had been delivered and was being properly used, and that the care assistant was correctly instructed and monitored in the performance of any specific nursing or therapy procedures which had been delegated to her.

The care assistant had an important role at this time in providing reassurance, reliability and a familiar face, as well as being alert to any problems which arose.

Tasks undertaken

It was a central concern of the project that traditional role definitions and role boundaries should be broken down, and that the care assistants should carry out the full range of caring tasks needed by their clients. By this means, it was hoped to avoid the confusion and duplication which so frequently arises when a variety of service providers visit the same client, each pursuing their own service aims (Salvage, 1985).

The home care assistants performed the following tasks:

- simple nursing tasks under the instruction and supervision of the district nurse;
- therapy tasks as instructed and supervised by the physiotherapist, occupational therapist or speech therapist;
- foot care tasks as delegated by a chiropodist;
- domestic and personal care tasks; and
- social and emotional support for client, also assisting key members of the client's network where appropriate.

No hard and fast rules were laid down as to what would or would not be a suitable task for delegation to the care assistants; rather, it was a matter for the instructing agents to satisfy themselves that the particular care assistant

Figure 5.1
Home care assistants: personal care

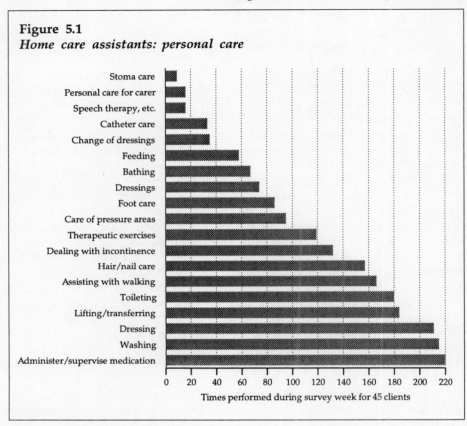

Times performed during survey week for 45 clients

had the competence to perform the task. As would be expected, the range of tasks delegated was extended as the relevant professionals gained confidence in the ability of care assistants to follow instructions correctly and seek advice or information if they encountered any difficulties.

In September 1987, when the project had been running for about two years, a one-week survey of activities carried out by home care assistants was undertaken. At that time, 53 part-time assistants participated in the survey, providing care for 45 clients. In all this represented 238 working days. The information collected on personal care and on domestic and social activities in the survey are shown in Figures 5.1 and 5.2. The data provide a count of the frequency with which tasks were undertaken over the survey week, without giving any weighting for the time taken. Although administration of medication was the most frequently performed task (220 times during the survey week), it would not have been as time-consuming as less frequently performed tasks such as bathing (67 times). It is noteworthy that the most frequently performed personal care tasks were toileting, transfer, management of medication, dressing and washing, as shown in Figure 5.1. Figure

Figure 5.2
Home care assistants: domestic and social activities

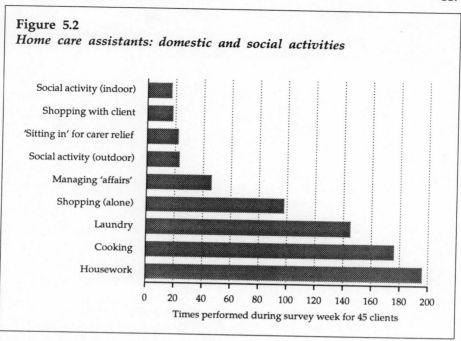

Times performed during survey week for 45 clients

5.2 shows that housework, cooking and laundry were the most frequently performed domestic care tasks, indicating a substantial overlap with the home help service. There was also a social aspect to the care giving, such as providing companionship. These social activities, also shown in Figure 5.2, took place predominantly during the performance of more instrumental activities, but also specifically included 'sitting-in' to give a carer relief (22 times during the survey week) and taking the elderly person out (23 times during the survey week).

A picture of the activities undertaken is also available from the care assistant activity reviews, which were completed for each client during case reviews. These recorded home care assistant activities with individual clients and their frequency. The information is based on 147 activity reviews, up to three for each client.

Table 5.3 shows the frequency with which the different personal care tasks were performed, and the proportion which were undertaken every day. Home care assistants were involved in assisting nearly all their clients in and out of bed, bathing and dressing them, usually on every day of the week. For a high proportion of the activity reviews, and therefore of the clients, they were involved in toileting, helping with transfer and medication, usually every day. Tasks such as foot care and taking clients out of their homes, although undertaken to a considerable extent, occurred less frequently. Night care was recorded in only a small proportion of the activity reviews, usually

Table 5.3
Home care assistants' activities — personal care

	% of activity reviews where undertaken	% of which daily/nightly
Dressing client	99	86
Bathing/washing all over	95	92
Helping in/out of bed	90	96
Toileting	81	89
Transferring from chair	79	91
Assisting with medication	71	93
Taking client out of home	64	8
Foot care	59	8
Night care	8	64

Table 5.4
Home care assistants' activities — domestic care

	% of activity reviews where undertaken	% of which daily
Housework	81	70
Making hot drinks	74	81
Laundry	66	49
Preparing meals	65	82
Shopping	61	28
Managing fire	35	69

when terminal care was needed, but when provided it was often every night.

Table 5.4 shows the frequency with which domestic care tasks were recorded in the activity reviews and the proportion which were undertaken daily. The wide range of domestic care activities undertaken is clear and the major activities of housework, meal and drink preparation were usually done every day. In nearly two-thirds of the activity reviews, home care assistants were doing shopping for clients, often every day. However, this would be accounted for by the regular purchase of small items such as milk and newspapers.

Table 5.5 indicates the range of social activities undertaken by home care assistants. In this table some activities have been subsumed under others. Sitting in to provide carer relief is included as part of the process of providing carers with a more predictable routine. Most of the activities were directly supportive of the client or carer. The proportion of activity reviews where outings are mentioned is lower than in Table 5.3. This reflects the difference between more instrumental outings, such as accompanying a client to an appointment, and those specifically for social and recreational activities.

Table 5.6 shows the proportion of activity reviews in which home care assistants had been acting on behalf of different health care staff, and Table 5.7 shows the main contacts initiated by home care assistants. Clearly, care assistants were working most frequently with the physiotherapist and the district nurses, reflecting the extent of clients' mobility and activity problems as well as their need for nursing care. The substantial involvement in foot care — usually a less frequent activity — is demonstrated by the 30 per cent of activity reviews where home care assistants were acting on behalf of the chiropodist. Work on behalf of the occupational therapist was less frequent, probably reflecting the major occupational therapist input at the initial re-settlement of the client into their home. In a small proportion of activity reviews, home care assistants were acting on behalf of speech therapists, particularly in the rehabilitation of stroke patients. The contacts initiated by home care assistants shown in Table 5.7 were chiefly with the district nurse and the general practitioner, with the two staff dedicated to the project —

Table 5.5

Home care assistants' activities — social activity

	% of activity reviews where undertaken
Companionship — client	92
Dealing with client worries	79
Emotional support — client	70
Helping to provide regular carer relief	70
Dealing with carer anxieties	61
Emotional support — carer	51
Social outings for client	47
Companionship — carer	43

Table 5.6

Home care assistants' activities — therapeutic interventions

Acting as agent on behalf of	% of activity reviews where undertaken
Physiotherapist	77
District nurse	59
Chiropodist	30
Occupational therapist	23
Speech therapist	13

Table 5.7
Contacts initiated by the home care assistant

Contacts initiated	% of activity reviews where undertaken
District nurse	70
General practitioner	69
Physiotherapist	43
Occupational therapist	30
Chiropodist	22

the physiotherapist and occupational therapist — the next most frequently contacted.

The evidence above shows that the care assistants undertook a wide range of tasks. This is also revealed by the examples of, first, the care given to an elderly person living alone and, second, to one living with a spouse. These examples are shown in Boxes 5.5 and 5.6, respectively. Each home care assistant was able to exercise a degree of discretion over the allocation of hours, but had responsibility to see that the totality of daily and weekly care needs were met for the client.

Whether the performance of tasks is examined in a specific week or across the whole group of project clients, it is clear that home care assistants had undertaken a wide range of tasks normally associated with several different helpers. How does the activity pattern of home care assistants compare with that of other groups?

Home care assistants and other care providers: a comparison

In order to locate the activities of care assistants in a broader context, it is helpful to compare the activities of home care assistants with the work of the two groups with whom there was the greatest overlap of roles: community nursing and home helps. Table 5.8 compares the tasks carried out by home care assistants with surveys of nurses and auxiliary nurses in the community (Dunnell and Dobbs, 1980) and of home helps in an experimental project which provided substantially higher levels than usual of home help support (Latto, 1982). The first two columns refer to the activities of district nurses and auxiliaries, the third refers to the home help study, and the fourth to project care assistants. There is considerable variation between the different groups, but home care assistants undertook a wider range of activities and tasks than either home helps or nurses. It is worth noting that home care assistants spent the same proportion of their time on personal care as the district nurses (about 41 per cent), although this involved fewer technical

Box 5.5
Tasks undertaken for a client living alone

Mrs F. was a 78 year old widow with right-sided hemiplegia following a stroke two years before. She suffered from some night and day urinary incontinence, and could walk a short distance with a tripod and the assistance of one person. Her stroke had left her with dysphasia, leading to a substantial communication difficulty. She had been in continuing hospital care since her stroke as she had no local relatives able to care for her. In 1986, having previously given up her home, she was allocated a bungalow by Railway Housing Association so that she could be discharged from hospital to live alone with project care.

Mrs F. had a key home care assistant with primary responsibility for her care, and this home care assistant was paired to another care assistant who normally provided cover on days off. Mrs F. was also familiar with a small group of about six to eight home care assistants, members of the local team and participants in the night visiting rota.

Care needs met by home care assistants
Morning. Assistance with getting up, washing and dressing, bathing, regular toileting, care of hair and nails, pressure area care; pursuing a daily exercise programme to promote mobility and communication, as instructed by the physiotherapist and speech therapist; domestic and household tasks including laundry, housework, shopping and meal preparation; assisting with budgeting, bill-paying, collecting pension, claiming social security benefits and letter-writing; and companionship, enabling outings in a wheelchair or car to shops and a social centre.

Afternoon/evening. Assisting with meal preparation, undressing, washing, toileting and going to bed.

Approximate times. Morning: from 8 a.m. as required, one and a half to four hours. Midday: meal, toileting, half to one hour. Mid-afternoon: tea, toileting, half hour. Evening: from 8 p.m., put-to-bed visit carried out by alternating members of the local team of home care assistants on a rota, approximately half an hour.

tasks, as might be expected. However, the home care assistants spent less time travelling than district nurses or auxiliaries. They spent markedly less time on domestic tasks than the home helps (25 per cent compared with 78 per cent). Given that this comparison is with a substantially extended home help service, the difference would be greater compared with other home help services even given the move towards the greater provision of personal care which has occurred in recent years (SSI, 1987). In the home help study, only 29 per cent of total time was spent on personal care and more socially supportive tasks. To a substantial extent, the activities of home care assistants

Box 5.6
Care for a client living with a spouse

Mr G., an 87 year old married man, was admitted to hospital from residential care as a result of loss of mobility, frequent incontinence, general frailty and dependence. He suffered from frequently recurring chest and urinary tract infections and his general health and functioning varied according to his state of health. He was discharged from hospital to return to live with his 90 year old wife in a ground-floor warden-controlled flat. When his health was poor, Mr G. needed two people to transfer and assist him in walking from the bed to the chair or toilet. His wife, owing to her own frailty, was unable to assist in day care for her husband, although she was independent in self-care. She could not leave the flat unaided and was unable to cook a meal safely or perform any but the simplest of household tasks.

Care needs met by home care assistants
Morning. Assistance with getting up, washing, dressing and care of pressure areas; catheter care and assistance in the administration of medication and an inhaler as instructed by the district nurse and general practitioner. Mr G. refused to have a bath, instead he was bed-bathed as taught by the district nurse. Assistance with walking from bed to living-room chair was often required which needed the help of another home care assistant working locally. The home care assistant also assisted Mrs G. with bathing. Domestic tasks including housework, laundry, shopping and meal preparation. (Mr and Mrs G. had a daughter living locally who collected the pension and paid the bills.) Companionship and conversation with both client and spouse, and encouragement to participate in occasional social activities either singly or jointly.
Afternoon/evening. Assistance with meal preparation, undressing, washing, catheter care, toileting, transferring and walking from living room chair to bed, administering medication, putting to bed.
Approximate times. Morning: 9 a.m, one and a half to four hours as required, including dinner preparation and meal time. Mid-afternoon: tea, catheter care, half to one hour. Evening: approximately 7 p.m. according to client preference, put-to-bed visit carried out by alternating home care assistant on the night rota, half an hour.

were overcoming the barriers of role demarcation and reducing task duplication, filling a distinctive role which was broader than was undertaken by similar staff elsewhere.

Table 5.8

Tasks of home care assistants, district nurses and home helps

Tasks	District nurses[a]	Auxiliaries[a]	Home help study	Project care assistants
Domestic work total (%)	1	2	78	25
Preparing food/drinks	+	+	+	+
Housework	+	+	+	+
Laundry	+	+	+	+
Shopping	+	+	+	+
Collecting pensions/prescriptions	+	+	+	+
Managing affairs				+
Shopping with client				+
Personal care total (%)	38	55	−[b]	41
Injections, stitches, tests, etc.	+	+		
Dessings/pressure sore care	+	+		+
Enemas, etc.	+	+		
Catheter care/bladder washout	+	+		+
Stoma care	+	+		+
Therapeutic/rehabilitation exercises	+	+		+
Bathing	+	+	+	+
Incontinence care	+	+		+
Prevention of pressure sores	+	+		+
Toileting	+	+		+
Washing	+	+		+
Dressing	+	+	+	+
Care of hair/nails	+	+	+	+
Care of feet	+	+		+
Feeding	+	+		+
Giving medicine	+	+		+
Lifting/transferring	+	+	+	+
Personal care for carer				+
Social activity total (%)	8	4	−	
Activities/outings			+	+
Chatting/listening	+	+	+	+
Dealing with client/carer problems	+			+
Counselling	+			
Reassurance	+	+		+
Education	+			
Sitting in to give carer a break				+
Administrative total (%)	26	16	na	6
Record-keeping, diaries, etc.	+	+		+
Telephone calls	+	+		+
Meetings	+	+		+
Contacting others for client/carer	+	+		+
Requesting/supplying equipment	+	+		+
Training/teaching	+	+		+
Travel total (%)	24	21	na	11
Other total (%)	2	2	3	na

+ indicates task is undertaken. 'na' = information not available.

a   Nursing data exclude time spent with younger patients.

b   Social and personal care tasks amalgamated = 19%.

Home care assistants' relationships with clients

As the project developed, the three care managers each took responsibility for a team of home care assistants within a particular locality. Organising home care assistants into geographically-based teams encouraged flexibility, a prompt response to need, mutual support and reduced travel time. On occasions, home care assistants could also become part of a client's immediate social network. This blurring of roles was seen as advantageous by care managers, because it reduced the distinction between formal and informal care (Abrams, 1977). Clients saw such an arrangement as giving them greater security, knowing that it might be possible to call on a familiar local home care assistant in an emergency. It also made it possible to respond to the needs of caring relatives who might need urgent relief if they found themselves unable to cope in the event of illness or urgent family demands. Once home care assistants were established in working with a client, they were encouraged to see their role as wider than solely meeting practical care needs. They were encouraged to identify and initiate social and recreational activities that might enhance clients' lives. Inevitably these possibilities for social activities were constrained by competing demands on their time and the sheer amount of practical care required, but they and the clients had a degree of freedom to make decisions about priorities within the daily and weekly care programme. For example, home care assistants on occasion chose to save time by taking a client's laundry to do at home or prepared meals in advance to give time for outings. Home care assistants' families sometimes also became involved with clients. This illustrates how the blurring of formal and informal caring roles may enhance the quality of care provided. This has also been observed in the home help service (Goldberg and Connelly, 1982), and in the Kent and Gateshead studies (Challis and Davies, 1986; Challis et al., 1990). The intensity of relationships which may develop through care arrangements may be more akin to those shared between carers and their dependants, and are characterised by greater flexibility and responsiveness to changing circumstances. As such, they are what Litwak (1978) has described as 'boundary roles' between informal and formal caregiving.

A number of examples may be found of this more flexible approach, with the boundaries becoming more fluid between care sectors:

> Mrs H. was a 95 year old chairbound lady who suffered from dementia and the effects of a stroke, and lived with her daughter. Her daughter saw it as most important that she and her mother should have frequent outings together around the village. This could, however, only be accomplished with the help of the home care assistant to help to manoeuvre the wheelchair in and out of the flat. A flexible arrangement was made which ensured that the caring daughter could call for this help when needed and when the weather permitted, rather than being tied to a fixed timetable.

Elderly people also gained reassurance from this approach, as in the case of Mr J., an 89 year old man who lived alone and frequently became rather anxious and confused over the time of day and whether or not he had had his dinner. He gained considerable comfort and reassurance from having the telephone numbers of his two neighbouring home care assistants printed on large cards next to his telephone, on his chair-side table, and he would quite frequently call them simply to be reassured that he had not been forgotten, and to find out what time of day it was.

However, such arrangements may impose costs as well as benefits upon care providers. As others have reported, paid staff may experience similar difficulties to those experienced by relatives, and they may also develop close personal relationships with those for whom they care (Goldberg and Connelly, 1982; Owens, 1987). Latto (1982) reported that the extension of the home help role in Coventry Home Help Project led to greater stress for home helps, but this was outweighed by the greater job satisfaction from being more involved with and more important to their clients. The evidence from interviews with home care assistants indicates that they did, at times, establish close personal relationships, which could be demanding and stressful, but this was counter-balanced by the rewards of feeling valued, and observing the progress and contentment of their elderly clients. One home care assistant commented:

I thought it was a brilliant idea. Just to get people out of hospital wards ... into their own home. I haven't met one client who has not said that they are pleased. Every one of them is pleased to be home. And, as I say, just to see the look on their faces, honestly it makes you think you are doing a worthwhile job.

Another said, 'To be needed is important, isn't it? It's nice to be needed, I like to be needed.'

Of course, in such instances as these, demands on the home care assistant can become great, and it was incumbent on the care managers to monitor such informal arrangements to ensure that the demands did not become excessive or unreasonable.

Management and support of home care assistants

Given these intense levels of personal involvement and commitment to their clients, it quickly became clear that good support for the home care assistants was essential. Each care manager worked with an average of fifteen to eighteen clients, and managed a team of approximately eighteen part-time home care assistants caring for those clients. Individual support, team building and the ongoing training described earlier were strategies used to support the home care assistants and enhance their effectiveness.

Individual support

In viewing the way in which individual support for home care assistants developed, a pattern emerges of increasing autonomy through time. In the early days of the project, with relatively few care assistants, the care managers were able to maintain close contact with each individual to provide support. As the numbers of care assistants and clients increased, it was necessary to formalise these arrangements and a system of monthly meetings was developed, ensuring that each home care assistant met individually with her care manager. These meetings were used for problem-solving, identifying strengths and weaknesses in coping skills, or discussing and supporting care assistants with personal problems if these impinged on their work. Later, as the care managers worked to develop the team support strategies, the importance of these individual support sessions declined and the frequency was reduced to once every two or three months. At that time care managers would convene or attend the small team meetings of care assistants and continue to facilitate these groups and promote team building so that they could become more self-managing and self-sustaining. This is described later in this chapter.

The changes that occurred in their relationships with care managers are evident in interviews over a two-year period with the monitor group of home care assistants, of whom six remained in post throughout.

At the six to eight week stage of the project when they were new to the job, five of these six were in regular contact with care managers, felt able to approach them about any problems, and felt adequately supported. 'Each client I've been to ... she pops up ... or phones to keep in touch.' These five shared the view that the care manager was there to solve problems of rotas, client and family situations and to offer personal support. However, the sixth recorded a feeling that some 'difference' had arisen between herself and her manager. She said, 'I've never brought any problems to her ... to me if you have to keep going to your boss with things it means you can't cope. I just talk to the other girls in my team, we can sort it out between ourselves.'

After a year, four out of the six had experienced a change of care manager caused by staff turnover or their relocation into another team. In spite of this, most still felt positive about the value of support received. One care assistant commented, 'There's never been a time when I have gone to her and she has not been able to help out, even if just with advice.' Another said, 'I can talk and bring the feelings out with [care manager].' One care assistant expressed regret at losing the care manager who had previously given her a lot of personal support with her own family's health problems, and said she was keeping an open mind about her new manager. However, interestingly, one drew attention to the emerging importance of the 'team' as a source of mutual support, leading to less reliance on the care manager.

After two years, a clear shift had occurred in the nature of relationships with care managers. Home care assistants were more confident to resolve their own difficulties or get support from the local team. One said, 'I don't feel I need [care manager] any more. If I had any problems I would talk to [another care assistant] before anyone else.' Another said, 'When you start this job you need more support ... now if I had a problem I would ring [care manager] anyway ... but I feel able to cope now ... don't have any major problems.' A third said, 'We tend to know more about what is going on than the manager ... because of going in there every day.' Most seemed quite satisfied with the current support system and were confident that there was a care manager in the background to be kept informed of any changes or difficulties. One care assistant had to cope with a client whose spouse exhibited increasing problems with cognitive impairment. She commented of the care manager, 'When I did ring and say he [caring spouse] had flipped his lid ... she was there straight away ... I couldn't ask any more from her.'

It is a credit to the care managers that they enabled and encouraged the growing autonomy and confidence of home care assistants to the point where they themselves were seen as less necessary by staff who had developed their own problem-solving capabilities in all but the most critical situations. The value of this support is demonstrated in a comment made by one home care assistant:

> I've gained a lot of experience and confidence from this job, and I think that's basically from working with people who have confidence in you and build your confidence as my care manager did with me. She did an awful lot for me when I first started, supporting and making me aware that I could do things, and giving me the confidence to go ahead and do it.

The key carer approach

At the outset, all home care assistants worked as key carers for one client, a system which, through time, was seen to have some clear advantages as well as serious drawbacks. The key carer role was seen as offering the opportunity to bridge formal and informal care (Litwak, 1978) through permitting the development of special relationships.

Close relationships certainly developed between client and home care assistant which could be rewarding to both:

> I really enjoy being with the same client, you get into a routine so they get to know you and you get to know them. I think it really works that way ... you work a routine around that client.

In many instances, the home care assistant was able to act as a valued support to the carer as well as to the client, showing considerable understanding for the carer's situation. This could be psychological:

> She [carer] likes to talk and I say to her it does help to have a cry now and again. I've seen the tears come, but she's never really broken down, she says it's great just to talk.

Sometimes the care could be practical:

> I do most that there is to do. Whenever I can I do what I can to help her [the carer].

There could also be costs from crossing boundaries. If these workers took on many of the attributes of the informal care sector through developing close personal relationships with the person cared for and through more flexibility of times, roles and tasks undertaken, they risked experiencing burdens similar to those of caring relatives. These included anxieties over risk and responsibility:

> I've worried about them like I have worried about nobody. I could see the house going up in flames or — you know, the whole situation. I was never happy about it, never at ease.

Demands made by the client on the home care assistant could also increase over time and the sense of excessive personal significance and dependency was sometimes stressful:

> If you're in there all the time with just the one client they get possessive, and sometimes it makes it very difficult for the other carers to go in.

Relationships within families of frail clients often posed particular demands and stresses on the home care assistants. Problems or conflicts within this area could be attributed to many causes, ranging from the caring spouse who felt jealousy or resentment at the care assistant's ability to perform a role he or she was unable to, to the relative who appeared to be repeatedly using the relationship with the client to secure money. The care assistant, in the front-line everyday caring role, could bear the brunt of these conflicts. Complex family, personality and relationship problems could affect client care:

> We've been told not to get too emotionally involved, but it's unavoidable if you're with somebody regularly and they have family problems and you know it's the family ... if the family has been in and he's subdued when we walk in we know what's happened.

Such situations were inclined to cause feelings of anger and resentment for care assistants who felt their client's rights or interests were suffering through the relative's actions. Indeed, sometimes relatives' own needs led to their making excessive demands on home care assistants:

> They were such an unpredictable couple [relatives] ... it didn't matter how much you gave, we were giving everything, we stopped taking days off, they wanted more.

On the other hand, care assistants felt sensitive to their own impact upon carers:

> You would feel very annoyed if you have been with this man all these years, and then somebody comes in and does for him things you can't do any more. It must make her feel inadequate, mustn't it? I think, with a husband and wife situation, you have got to tread very carefully.

Thus there was the constant dilemma for the care assistants in maintaining a balance between the welfare of the client and the rest of their family. Being intimately involved in clients' lives while trying to remain detached from family problems was inevitably demanding. It was the remit of the care managers to develop strategies to help home care assistants cope with the demands of their role. Overall, it seemed that the training and support provided offered home care assistants a sense of value and helped them cope with the demands of the job. Providing opportunities to discuss problems and gain mutual support, avoiding isolation and close monitoring by care managers are strategies which have been successfully employed elsewhere (Owens, 1987).

Team building

As well as regular individual support sessions there was an emphasis on team building to enhance mutual support among groups of home care assistants, and to establish limits to the demands upon them. Teams were geographically based, and over time were subdivided into smaller localised units within which all home care assistants would have some familiarity with all the local clients. Mutual support, assistance and shared working rotas then became a realistic possibility. The advantages cited for this approach were: first, that teams of three or four workers could all become familiar with a small group of clients thus ensuring continuity when illness or holidays occurred; second, that care assistants could take it in turns to do evening and put-to-bed visits so that each was not required to work every night; third, in the event of an emergency change of circumstances, for clients, their families or the care assistants, there were others to fill the gap.

As the teams developed, each began to adopt different approaches to organisation, reflecting both the different characteristics of the area they covered and the different styles of care managers. The first, team A, combined a 'key carer' approach with a night rota; the second, team B, developed a shift-based approach; and the third, team C, continued with the original 'key carer' approach. Each of these is examined separately below.

Team A. This team had the considerable advantage of being geographically quite compact, and the way forward was seen as the maintenance of the attached keyworker with primary responsibility for one client, but each keyworker paired with another to act as a regular relief. This ensured clarity of key responsibility, but enabled some sharing of difficulties and support. One of the most demanding features of the job was the long day as, even if the care assistant was not at work, she did not feel that she was truly off duty until after the last visit of the evening. To improve this, a night rota was established, with two care assistants on duty for the full evening to put five or six clients to bed. These two assistants might work from 6.30 until 10 p.m. but this would only be necessary two or three times a week. As care assistants got to know each other better by working together, the effectiveness of the team improved. As clients got to know and trust a wider group of care assistants, the difficulties created by sickness and holidays diminished as there was a wider pool of home care assistants familiar with each client, and therefore more acceptable to the client.

This team retained this model of working throughout the project life, and experienced little staff turnover. The system of paired workers, along with the shared night rota, resolved the problems of social isolation and stress induced by the intensity of the client/worker relationship.

Home care assistants recognised the benefits as providing more time off, getting to know their colleagues and sharing stresses:

> We would prefer to keep the keyworker for the continuity of (therapy) exercises and keeping that relationship there, but to break it slightly in the evening and instead of going out every night to our own client, two of us would go out and put all the clients to bed ... the maximum is six.

Inevitably, clients' views were mixed:

> Mrs K. loves seeing different people and having a natter the same as Mr L. ... But Mrs M. no ... she doesn't take too kindly to different ones going in.

> Well, at first everybody thought of it in a different way. Some thought it was confusing, which it must have been a little bit ... but now they know us all, it's not difficult. If, say, somebody is ill and you have to go into that client, it's not difficult for you or them because they know you. In the beginning it was hard for them and easier for us ... it was difficult for them to get to know everybody, but now they do they are all quite happy with it.

Team B. In Team B an experiment was made with a shift-working model which broke a group of nine care assistants into three groups of three. One group worked the early morning and evening shift; one the middle shift which included morning care, preparing dinners and teas; while the third group of three covered days off. This required home care assistants to move from one home to another, more in the manner of home helps, with three people covering seven or eight clients during their shift. Of the five care assistants interviewed from this team of nine, two favoured the team working positively, two were uncertain and one remained convinced that an individual approach could meet client needs more satisfactorily. This shared model of working appeared to combat problems of worker isolation and the sometimes intense worker/client relationships, but left several care assistants in some doubt as to whether clients were getting a sufficiently consistent client-orientated service. After some months of working with this model, it was clearly more expensive than the previous arrangements because much of care assistant time was spent on travel, and therefore more hours were needed to achieve the same level of client care. Under a new care manager the care assistants moved back to a more individual care model, but worked in pairs or in threes to provide support and cover for each other.

A group of home care assistants from this team identified both gains and problems arising from the shift approach. Problems included less detailed knowledge of clients, leading to possible excess caring and overdependence, and communication difficulties:

> I enjoyed the one-to-one but sometimes I wished I had two clients for a change. I enjoy going round, but sometimes I feel I'm not in each home for long enough.

> I've strong feelings about washing and dressing because Mrs N.'s quite capable of dressing herself, yet we do it ... I feel we are taking that little bit of independence away from them, but maybe that's because we haven't got the time now to stay with somebody and let them take half an hour to put their clothes on.

At times it could lead to confusion over responsibility, particularly in ensuring that tasks were done for confused elderly people. Initially there were misunderstandings which were resolved over time:

> In the beginning when I came from being a keyworker onto the team, there were a lot of difficulties because I felt that certain things weren't getting done ... but now we've got it reasonably sorted out. If we do anything, we mark it on the sheet [client diary sheet] ... so you can see what's been done.

Advantages of this sharing of care were also evident, since care assistants experienced relief from the reduced burden of responsibility:

> I'd rather work this way doing several clients than one to one because if you get stuck with someone you don't like you can't give them your best.

Also, different staff or less frequent contact could lead to better observation of changes in a client's condition or circumstances:

> If anything they're noticed more. I've been away from Mr O. four days and I noticed straight away he had a chest infection. I think you tend to

notice things more when you don't go in every day.

However, the clients were less enthusiastic about this approach, although some dissatisfaction was associated with change rather than the arrangements. Some clients enjoyed varied visitors, while others clearly did not:

> One client clearly found it very hard to come to terms with different girls going in ... Now I think she likes all the different people going in because it is more stimulating. Now she'll talk to anyone that goes, which has opened her life.

> People [clients] have said to me ... there's sometimes too many, they don't know who's coming. ... I feel sometimes we're letting them down a bit.

Team C. This team covered a geographically more dispersed area and continued to operate a key carer model for longer. Care assistants' views were mixed. Three of the six care assistants who were interviewed expressed problems about the key carer role, such as the lack of variety, the number of visits and client demands.

However, a little over a year later, this team was broken down into three smaller geographically based groups of four or five, who had a shared night rota and acted as support and cover to each other for sickness, holidays and days off. The clients knew and were known to all the care assistants working in each neighbourhood. This team had established a sound self-supporting system within which there were certain nominated care assistants who held details of the rota and could be contacted by others if they needed support or relief in a crisis, without having to contact the care manager. The rota holder knew who was on duty and could ensure that cover was provided.

Home care assistants indicated greater satisfaction with this particular team approach. Benefits included less frequent night work and meeting more clients:

> I have a client of my own, but I have been to a few different clients. I did not like the old system because you were out morning, lunchtime, tea-times and nights. You were just exhausted and always looking at the clock. It's not so bad now.

Rural areas

The project also provided a service to a number of clients in several small rural villages outside the town, and to a few clients in a nearby new town, bordering the Darlington District Council area. In these areas, which had their own local community characteristics, substantial efforts were made by the care managers to recruit local care workers who could be paired to provide a supportive partnership. Typically, these rural workers were employed for fifteen hours a week each. Not only was using local workers cost-effective, but since they were members of the local community they could respond quickly and flexibly to any changes in the client situation. In addition, they were more effective in mobilising any local services because of their being 'known' and accepted within their immediate community. The obvious disadvantage was that home care assistants recruited for local need could lose their employment on a client's death or when care was no longer required in the locality.

Acting as auxiliaries to health care professionals

Underlying the use of the single 'hands-on' community care worker was the reduction of duplication and the increase of delegation (Hopkins, 1982). An interesting parallel to the increase of delegation and the relationship with health care professionals can be taken from a third world concept of the village worker (Werner, 1978; World Health Organization, 1982). Unlike health professionals, it is argued that village workers are not outsiders but originate from the community in which they work, derive their knowledge from experience and brief training rather than specialist education, are accessible, and have similar backgrounds to patients. Such a description could also be applied to care assistants. The range of health care professionals for whom the home care assistants acted as auxiliaries included district nurses, occupational therapists, physiotherapists, chiropodists, speech therapists, the dietician, the continence adviser and the stoma care nurse. As noted earlier, the health care professionals were responsible for deciding the range of tasks to be undertaken, which broadened as the experience of the care assistants increased.

In this section an examination is made of how the assistants worked with different staff: district nurses, occupational therapists, physiotherapists, the chiropodist, speech therapists, general practitioners and hospital staff.

Auxiliaries to community nurses

Salvage (1985) and Owens (1987) have both referred to conflicts engendered in nursing by demarcation and boundary disputes. In the light of recommendations incorporated in Project 2000 (UKCC, 1986) and by Griffiths (1988), the issue of unqualified — albeit trained — community care workers acting as aides to nurses has particular significance. In Darlington, initial misunderstandings and conflicts did occur, but the fact that district nurses gained familiarity with individual home care assistants through participating in their training helped to resolve many of these. They were reassured by the commonsense and practical abilities of home care assistants. Comments made by district nursing sisters in the research interviews illustrate this:

> Because they are in the home they know what medication the patient is on, and they can notice the changes in people when they take different tablets.

According to one district nursing sister, the relief could be considerable when caring for terminally ill clients:

> There were quite a few terminal care cases and you could be there up to two hours. If you've got fifteen or sixteen patients a day, you find you're working your lunch hour and getting off at six instead of five. That was really quite killing. It was such a relief to me when I got a home care assistant in there.

The comments of home care assistants bear out the importance of developing trust, familiarity and good relationships in the success of their role. As one home care assistant recalled:

> On my first week on the scheme, I heard one [district nurse] talking of how it would never work and it was going to be a total disaster. Now she's all for it. That was maybe because she didn't know enough about it. I mean, nobody did when it first started. I think everybody was apprehensive.

On the question of dressings for sores, another care assistant explained:

> You follow the nurses' lead; if they say it's alright, you to do it. I wouldn't just do it. The district nurse came for a while and then she showed me how to do it [the dressing] and I carried on doing it until we got it better.

One of the monitor group, who had worked on the project for two years and spent eighteen months caring for the same client, demonstrated how far trust and cooperation had been established between herself and the primary health care team:

> Usually if I run out of anything, I just go to the surgery. They are so helpful over there, I don't have to call the nurse at all, I just go across there, tell them what I want and get a prescription. They all know me over there; there is sort of a rapport between us.

Specialist nurses

As a high proportion of the project clients had continence problems, the continence adviser was clearly an important source of advice and regularly contributed to the care assistant training programme. During the first months of the project operation, she was willing to be contacted direct by assistants seeking advice. However, demands on her time later forced a rethink of this policy, and she became an adviser to the district nurses, more clinic-based, and less available to do home visits and act as an adviser to individual care assistants. In spite of this, several care assistants found her advice invaluable. One said:

> She's been out quite a few times while I've been there ... very helpful, any problem and I would be quite happy to go down to the clinic any day and ask her ... some people are approachable and she's one of them.

A second told how her client's incontinence was becoming quite a problem:

> I told the care manager and she brought the continence adviser in, and it was treated with medication. The tablets she had been taking were creating a problem with holding water, and weakening the muscles controlling the bladder.

Auxiliaries to therapists

Physiotherapist and occupational therapist. During the project phase, funding was included in the budget for the employment of a half-time physiotherapist and a half-time occupational therapist who contributed to the formal training for care assistants and who worked in both the hospital and the community, instructing and supervising the care assistants and, in the words of the physiotherapist, 'acting as general problem-solvers'. Although changes of staff and maternity leave meant that the personnel did not remain the same throughout the three years, the fact that these therapists were employed by the project ensured a clarity of role so that the care assistants knew whom to contact for advice, where to find them, and over time mutual trust and confidence were established. Advice over quite mundane but crucial matters — such as getting an elderly person downstairs — was provided, as well as more general information. One care assistant commented, 'She taught me a lot [the physiotherapist], things she probably didn't have to do, but because I was there she showed me, she was willing to explain things to me so I learned a lot.'

Speech therapist. The number of clients who received speech therapy was fairly limited, and this was usually of short duration as the speech therapy service applied a rationing policy in order to try and meet the many competing demands upon it. As a consequence, it was often difficult for the care assistant to be present when the therapist visited, if this was not at a set time. However, it was important for them to be there if their work was to contribute to the programme. One regularly accompanied her client to hospital appointments to continue the therapy at home. Another care assistant said:

> With one client I used to sit in, because the speech therapist used to come on a morning and I was already there. She used to leave a leaflet, but it

was better on a one-to-one when you could be there, because you knew then what was needed.

Auxiliaries to the chiropodist

Although all care assistants received basic instruction in foot care at their initial training, it took time for them to gain confidence in doing more than maintaining general foot hygiene. Reasons for the chiropodist's continued high level of involvement can be traced in part to the fact that at least two clients had particularly difficult foot problems and another was diabetic, but some problems were created by the perceptions of clients who saw themselves as in need of, or entitled to, the service of the chiropodist and continued to request domiciliary visits.

This situation changed in the second year of the scheme, when the senior chiropodist took the initiative in providing refresher training for each of the three teams of care assistants, and ordered clippers and files for their use so that they could take over all routine care of nails as well as feet. Indeed, when the final round of interviews was carried out with the monitor group, only one client was still receiving domiciliary visits by the chiropodist. Many care assistants commented on the good support they received from the chiropodist, and the good relationships the chiropodist maintained with their clients. For example, one care assistant, who was going to care for a terminally ill man, described what happened when she went to meet him in hospital:

> His big toe nail had gone right over, and it was all dirty and matted and horrible, and the physiotherapist said to the nurse, 'Can you clean it up, he is going home tomorrow' ... but it was still the same, still not done ... so the care manager and I got the chiropodist out and it was done the next day. In the hospital three months, and he had been home one day and it was done.

Auxiliaries to general practitioners

For general practitioners, this project raised the possibility of more frail, dependent elderly people being added to their patient lists and increased workloads as a result. With the limited amount of time that general practitioners have available even on home visits, it is not surprising that it took time for many of them to understand the care assistant role. Interviews demonstrated some of the misunderstandings that arose, as well as the good relationships that developed. Inevitably the responses were varied. One care assistant who had been in contact with several general practitioners said:

> The majority have been quite interested in the scheme, but have not really

known what it's all about. Some of them have asked a lot of questions, others aren't really interested, we are just there and that's it.

One care assistant described how initial assumptions can cloud appropriate responses:

> Mrs P. had a fall and we called her GP in because she was in a lot of pain. She was in so much pain when he moved her, and he called us out the back and said he thought we wanted to get her put in hospital. We said we don't, and he said, 'Well, we get so many calls like this and the family are wanting to put them into hospital.' But you see he didn't wait for us to say, he just assumed, but that's only one GP.

On the other hand, one care assistant in this group had experienced good support in the terminal stages of her client's life:

> There was a set routine actually, he used to come once a fortnight always when she first came home, and then as time went on he came once a week, and then ... it came so he came every day ... he was marvellous ... very funny as well ... he was lovely!

General practitioners responded positively to good patient care. A care assistant showed the doctor in to her male client who lived alone:

> He couldn't believe the improvement in the house or the appearance of [the client], he said, 'I'm very impressed and shall make a note of it.' I thought that was nice.

After two years in the job, one of the monitor group said, 'When you take a client to the doctor and go in with them you are treated alright, as if you were a daughter maybe.'

Auxiliaries to hospital staff

A variety of hospital staff were involved with care assistants. These included ward personnel, outpatient staff and specialist services such as those provided by the stoma care nurse and the pain control clinic. It was to be expected that the nature of these relationships would be as various as the personnel involved. Care assistants often received excellent support and information, but at other times were left badly in the dark. When problems did arise, the care manager was usually able to intervene to sort out problems and smooth the way for the care assistant. Difficulties most frequently occurred when clients of the project were admitted to hospital for acute treatment, or to provide relief to the caring relative. Home care assistants were often encouraged to visit the ward, to provide some continuity for the client, or to maintain the regular exercise programme. In one of the long-term care wards which had beds for respite care, home care assistants were encouraged to continue to play a part in the personal caring for the client while in hospital.

Of the other hospital staff, the psychologist and dietician were involved. A clinical psychologist was involved in a pain control and behaviour modification programme with one client, and instructed the care assistants working with this client how to maintain this programme over a short period. The dietician had an important part to play in training for care assistants, as well as advising and instructing individual home care assistants on their own clients' dietary needs. Several clients required special diets because of illness or obesity.

Job satisfaction and rewards

Qureshi et al. (1983, 1989) made a detailed study of factors which motivated and rewarded the paid and unpaid care helpers in the Kent Community Care Scheme. Motivations for joining the project were discussed earlier in the chapter. In Darlington, the home care assistants were employed as part-time salaried social services staff instead of casual paid helpers, but there are parallels in the rewards and job satisfactions reported to the research interviewers in both services. Qureshi et al. (1989) defined a number of key benefits or rewards which included: use of spare time; diversion from other life problems; meeting people; human capital building (or skill and experience development); sense of usefulness; independence; satisfaction from a sense of personal contribution; satisfaction from improved client state; financial reward; client's gratitude; and stimulation. Interviews with 23 care assistants provided a picture of these rewards, and the topics are comparable with those found in the Kent scheme. Their responses are summarised in Table 5.9. All 23 felt rewarded by the sense of personal contribution to improved client state; 22 of the 23 had experienced a sense of usefulness or feeling valued and needed by client or carer; and 20 had experienced satisfaction at improvement in client welfare. Most home care assistants had previously been in part-time paid employment so satisfaction related to using spare time did not feature significantly. Satisfactory pay and holiday conditions were commented on as important by fifteen care assistants, and the same number had found rewards in the friendships and social contacts made. Care assistants' own words perhaps best illustrate these rewards. All care assistants cited the satisfaction of contributing to client wellbeing:

> You feel you've helped them, but on the other hand they have helped you. I get a lot of comfort from knowing what I've done.

The sense of valued contribution or usefulness was also important:

> I remember the last time I went in to [Mr Q. who was dying] ... as I came out of there, I felt as though I had made that man comfortable in his last days.

Table 5.9
Home care assistants' rewards and job satisfaction

Reward	Number	%
Satisfaction from personal contribution	23	100
Usefulness	22	96
Satisfaction from improved client state	20	87
Affiliation	15	65
Payment	15	65
Human capital building	11	48
Stimulation	9	39
Independence	8	35
Gratitude	3	13
Time to spare	3	13
Diversion	0	0

For others, it was simply the improved wellbeing of the client:

Rewards are just seeing people who have been in hospital, and are coming out to their own home. Seeing their happiness, because I don't think I've come across any of them that aren't happy in their own home. Seeing them get over the problems of being at home and seeing them learn to cope with it. There's a lot of job satisfaction in it, but I don't think you could go into it as a job as such ... it becomes part of your life.

Giving people choice and independence. When they go into a 'home' [i.e. residential care] this is taken away from them ... You just see them come in and go downhill straight away. They think, 'I'm in a home' ... they give up and lose the will to live. It's the way they get treated. Half the time they are treated like kids and it annoys me to death.

I like caring and cooking for people and looking after them — especially old people.

For a number of care assistants, payment was important:

It's unusual to have a job you like doing and the pay is satisfactory. Many a time you've wanted a job you like, but unfortunately the pay has never been adequate, but I do think we get well paid.

To be honest the money is attractive. It's quite a high paid job for somebody who hasn't got any qualifications.

However, the extra demands of home-based care were evident:

> I feel it should be a lot more pay than what you would get in a residential home.

For some it was the kind of job which offered social relationships:

> I have made new friends. I didn't know any of the girls when I started and I have made new friends.

There was also a small group of home care assistants who particularly valued the challenges and the potential for increasing their knowledge and experience, a reward described as investment in human capital (Becker, 1964; Mueller, 1975; Qureshi et al., 1989):

> I think, personally, I have benefited from this scheme maybe more than the clients. I've gained a lot of experience and confidence from this job. I think it is one of the best moves I've made.

In addition to the rewards in Table 5.9, a source of particular job satisfaction to some home care assistants was provided by their role in providing care and support for terminally ill clients who wished to live their last days and die in their own homes. They compared this with people's experience of institutional care:

> I've worked in private nursing homes and to see what they pay and what care they get ... I think they deserve more, and what we are doing on this [project] people are getting more, getting individual attention ... to die at home ... and that to me means more than anything.

Staff turnover

As indicated earlier in this chapter, 57 of the 83 home care assistants employed during the pilot project were still employed at the end of the pilot phase, and 26 had left. The latter are shown in Table 5.10. Eight of the 26 were on contracts to care for a certain client in one of the outlying areas, and on the death of the client or withdrawal of the service from that area the contract automatically terminated. Four left to take up other employment, of a more permanent, full-time or career-advancing nature. Of the remaining fourteen, there were six whose reasons for leaving raised concern. Four resigned with feelings of dissatisfaction. In three instances these feelings seemed to relate to being 'messed about' through frequent reorganisations in client allocation or in the rota or team working system. Two resigned because they were becoming overinvolved and stressed by the job and felt unable to switch off.

Of the 83 home care assistants employed during the three-year project, all those remaining at the end of the pilot phase signed contracts of continuing employment with the health authority. At this stage, the majority were given

Table 5.10
Reasons for leaving home care assistant role

Reason for leaving job	Number
Temporary contract not renewed because client died or service withdrawn	8
Dissatisfied with nature of job or management/organisation	4
Move to 'better' employment	4
Resignation after counselling over suitability	2
Resignation through own ill health	2
Resignation through 'stress' of the job (becoming overinvolved)	2
Temporary contract not renewed because worker unsatisfactory	2
Family commitments	1
Reasons unknown	1
Total number	26

25-hour contracts, as experience had suggested that this might enable more cost-effective use of hours and was more convenient to the employing authority. In the rural areas, a number of assistants were employed on fewer hours as they were organised into a pairing system which had been based on two carers, employed for fifteen hours each instead of 25 hours. Of the 57 home care assistants employed by the health authority, seventeen had been part of the original group of 25 taken on in September 1985. The ages and previous experience of the 57 who were still employed were broadly the same as those of the 26 who left. Of the 57 stayers, all but six had worked in paid domestic or caring work previously, whereas among the leavers a higher percentage had previous work experience in clerical, shop or factory work.

Conclusions

The use of home care assistants, integrating a range of care tasks in one worker and acting as auxiliaries to a range of health care staff, appeared both feasible and effective. As described earlier in Chapter 4, there was no separation of the purchaser/provider roles in the service. Care managers were responsible for home care assistants, held the budget for them and were also the assessors of need. Since the project operated on a small scale and concentrated on a particular target group, these multiple roles did not appear to cause difficulties. However, a larger-scale implementation of this approach might benefit from a degree of separation of the roles of care management and service management. This would involve some staff taking responsibility for the recruitment, training and allocation of home care assistants (the task of service management) and others with responsibility for client assessment, monitoring wellbeing, oversight and support (the task of care management). This theme is examined further in Chapter 11.

From the point of view of home care assistants, they had access to a care manager who provided support, training and other service-related activities. The care managers were able to adapt and vary the styles of provision and support to reflect the different characteristics of the areas in which they worked and the changing needs of clients and care assistants. In general, all saw a need to modify the key carer approach so as to contain the demands made upon the home care assistants.

There was a series of attempts to organise the working patterns of home care assistants in different forms. In some ways, this involved balancing clients' wishes and staff needs, in the main a tension between the keyworker approach on the one hand and the extended team model on the other. The outcome appears to have created a more flexible and client-centred service than is often the case.

There would appear to be a pattern or series of phases in the relationships between home care assistants and care managers. Initially, there would be a high degree of reliance on the care managers when new clients were assessed and accepted, particularly so when the home care assistant was new to the job. This would often be followed by a period of relative stability and, consequently, less reliance upon care managers. However, where client circumstances change and conflicts emerge in the network, the role of the care manager would again become more central. This is considered further in Chapter 10.

6 Organisation and Multidisciplinary Working

There has been a long-term concern in the United Kingdom and elsewhere about processes and practice of coordination and collaboration between health and social services agencies (Aiken et al., 1975; Hokenstad and Ritvo, 1982; Webb and Wistow, 1986). One observer in the United States remarked wryly that, 'Commentators on the effects of coordination are almost universally pessimistic, yet coordination continues to be promoted as a means of providing greater rationality in the delivery of services' (Davidson, 1976, p.118). In the United Kingdom, a great deal of energy and policy analysis was invested in developing collaboration through mechanisms such as joint planning and joint financing during the 1970s and 1980s. This was very much a top-down approach to coordination, with insufficient attention paid to matters of practice, whose difficulties are well summarised in Webb and Wistow (1986). Other commentaries have confirmed the difficulties of implementing a coordinated approach to care (Gray and Hunter, 1983; Audit Commission, 1986; Hunter and Wistow, 1987). In their study of care of the elderly in Scotland, Hunter et al. (1988) described three interconnected levels of joint planning and coordination embracing health and related services: interdepartmental issues at the national level; interagency issues at the intermediate level; and interprofessional issues of joint working at the 'street' level. Whereas the first two levels reflect concerns about structures and joint planning systems, at the third level the attitudes and perspectives of practitioners are crucial. At this third level, behaviour may be determined in ways which formal rules cannot anticipate (Lipsky, 1980). The different levels are interdependent, since day-to-day joint working is critical for the implementation of joint planning strategies and, equally, joint working is most likely to occur where there is coherent interagency planning. Webb (1991) has also stressed this interdependence by identifying the importance of interpersonal relationships or trust as the lubricant for the smooth running of mechanisms for collaboration and coordination.

As described earlier in Chapter 2, four levels of coordination have been examined in this study. First, there is the interagency level. As the Darlington Project was a joint-agency initiative, its impact on interagency cooperation and working is of particular interest. Second, there is the level of inter-professional working, a further area where the project could be expected to have some impact. Third, there is the level of coordination of service inputs to individual elderly people and the role of care management. The intro-duction of the new care manager staff, with a specific responsibility to effect coordination and care management for project clients, would be expected to have a substantial effect on the roles of other service providers and organis-ations. Fourth, at the level of 'hands-on' care, there is the role of the home care assistants as multipurpose workers, and the reactions of traditional ser-vice providers to them and the adjustments that ensued.

This chapter will focus on the first two of these levels — interagency and interprofessional working — and, in particular, on how relationships between the various agencies and professional groups developed during the planning and implementation phases of the project. An attempt is made to identify how the project related to other services and the impact it made on these services, and, in particular, to examine its impact on multidisciplinary working. The sources of the material for this chapter are shown in Box 6.1. The level of care management has been described in Chapter 4 and that of the home care assistants in Chapter 5. The issues arising at all of the four levels during the planning, implementation and consolidation phases are summarised in Box 6.4, at the end of the chapter.

In considering the impact of a new service, it is important to be aware of the service context into which it was introduced and how it interacted with other service providers. In order to do this, the chapter begins by describing the service system prior to the project. Two distinct yet inevitably overlapping phases of the project are then examined: first, the planning and pre-implementation phase; and, second, the implementation and consolidation phase. The particular issues which emerge at each of the two stages can thus

---

Box 6.1
Sources of information

Reports and minutes derived from the joint coordinating group meetings.

Records of project team meetings and a variety of multidisciplinary meetings.

Notes kept by the project manager and the research worker.

Semi-structured interviews conducted by the research worker with a wide range of professionals providing services to elderly people, e.g. general practitioners, paramedical groups, social services staff and wardens of sheltered accommodation.

be viewed in their local context, and the strategies adopted to resolve particular problems in each phase can be compared.

The service system prior to the project

The environment in which agencies operate can be of crucial significance in the development of collaboration. Emery and Trist (1965) suggested that a turbulent environment is particularly likely to encourage collaboration since organisations may cooperate to minimise uncertainty (Cook, 1977). A variety of factors may lead to turbulence, including the development of new programmes, funding and legislation, all of which were manifest in Darlington. Accordingly, the service system prior to the project, which constituted an important part of the environmental context, is examined here.

Acute hospital sector

In the acute hospital sector, in spite of a relatively high level of geriatric bed provision, problems of blocking acute beds by elderly patients waiting for transfer to long-stay beds had led to a re-examination of geriatric hospital provision, which was explored in a series of day censuses of elderly patients in hospital during 1983, 1984 and 1985 (Acquilla, 1986), as described in Chapter 1. The 1984 survey identified 62 long-stay patients who were judged as suitable for support in the community with an adequate level of domiciliary services. This information was used in the plan for developing the project and the subsequent bid for pilot project funding under the Care in the Community Initiative.

In 1983, a review of acute hospital services to elderly people had identified the urgent need for a second consultant with responsibility for geriatric care. Following this appointment, some reorganisation of the acute geriatric services was possible, with a greater priority given to acute treatment, rehabilitation and early discharge, which, in turn, had implications for the kinds of services needed in the community to support elderly people who might otherwise have remained for longer periods on the acute wards. This change in the model of geriatric service (Evans, 1983; Irvine, 1983; Acquilla, 1986) is described in Chapters 1 and 3.

Following these changes, four of the five general practitioners interviewed commented on the improved access to hospital beds and better throughput of elderly patients, while at the same time expressing concern that such a policy would fail if adequate domiciliary services were not developed. This concern was echoed by ward sisters and medical social workers on the geriatric wards, who were anxious that the move to quicker treatment and discharge was in danger of becoming a revolving-door policy, where early discharge was followed in turn by early re-admission for those patients whose care and support needs could not be met in the community. The important linkage role of the medical social worker was stressed by consultants, ward staff and therapists. Interestingly, some difficulties over coordinating care plans were noted by therapy staff also within the hospital setting.

Community health services

As described in Chapter 1, the local care system reflected national problems. General practitioners and district nurses commented on the lack of adequate community support services, particularly the lack of evening and weekend personal care services for elderly people. General practitioners saw their main role in community care as assessment of need and referral, rather than ongoing monitoring. District nurses saw themselves as particularly well placed to assess patient needs, organise other services as necessary, and monitor care. However, they were particularly concerned about the lack of time they felt they were able to devote to the time-consuming task of providing basic personal care. The different therapy and chiropody services all had plans to expand their services, although staff shortages meant that most of their activity was hospital-focused.

Social services provision

In terms of residential care in the district, the local management reported that the supply of long-term care places was comfortably meeting the demand without a waiting list for places, since the supply of beds in both statutory and independent sectors was above both the local authority and national guidelines (see Chapter 3). On the one hand, this was allowing the more flexible use of some of these beds for intermittent and respite care while, on the other hand, the ease with which elderly people could be admitted to residential care was probably acting as a disincentive to the development of domiciliary care services. Additionally, despite the adequate supply of residential care beds, no attempt had been made to enhance the level of personal care offered within the residential establishments. As a result, elderly people with severe incontinence, self-care and mobility difficulties were ineligible for residential care, which further reduced the care options available.

The home help service, like most at the time (SSI, 1987), remained a predominantly domestic care service although finding itself under increasing pressure to provide personal care. The lack of personal care provision from either health or social services was identified by a number of staff as a source of breakdown of community care.

Fieldwork staff, such as medical social workers and field social workers, felt that they could respond only in a crisis, and arrange a variety of services to meet individual needs, but with little opportunity for follow up. Long-term monitoring of needs was seen as infeasible due to insufficient staff. The longer-term monitoring of service inputs was recognised as a real failing of existing services. Social workers did not appear to undertake a long-term role necessary for the development of care management (Hunter et al., 1993).

The service system

Therefore, increased throughput of elderly people from acute hospital beds was increasing the demands on community services which were ill-prepared for the impact of the new discharge policies. There was a lack of clear policy agreements between agencies about who did what, and an inability to follow up very frail elderly people to monitor and coordinate services to achieve effective and efficient care. Thus, the care system in the locality and its pattern of concerns and interactions were similar to those identified in other studies (Goldberg and Connelly, 1982; Sinclair et al., 1990), and discussed in Chapter 1, resulting in a failure to achieve coordinated care at the client level (Glennerster, 1983; Audit Commission, 1986). A number of factors operating in the environment made collaboration more likely to occur. These included a greater degree of turbulence in the environment (Emery and Trist, 1965); a high level of uncertainty about who does what (Cook, 1977; Milner, 1980); a growing interdependence making exchange desirable to achieve mutually beneficial goals, in this case arising from the need to effect hospital discharge (Levine and White, 1961; Aiken and Hage, 1968; Glennerster, 1983); and externally-induced interdependency (Reid, 1969) arising from the central government Care in the Community Initiative.

Interagency working

Planning and pre-implementation phase

Given the preceding picture of service provision there was clearly a need to enhance collaboration in community care provision, although the objectives of the agencies differed. Reid (1965) has indicated that, for significant interagency coordination to occur, the organisations must have shared goals, complementary resources and efficient mechanisms for controlling the exchange process. The first of these required a degree of 'domain consensus', or agreement over areas of responsibility (Levine and White, 1961). This is dependent upon agreement on organisational goals; compatibility of goals and philosophy; and agreement among professionals on their respective roles and positions (Van de Ven, 1976). In the light of this, how was the proposed new project perceived by those in the locality and how did interagency working proceed?

Health services. The health authority was quite clear about the benefits it expected from the project, reflected in the objectives presented in Chapter 2. It expected to be able to discharge elderly people from acute wards who would normally be transferred to long-stay beds, or who would otherwise block acute beds through lack of adequate domiciliary support services at home. The expected benefit from reducing inappropriate acute care utilisation has been an important goal of a number of care programmes in the USA (Kane et al., 1992). Some reduction of demand for beds was essential in order to continue to finance the project after central funding ceased, as two long-stay geriatric wards had to be closed to release the required finance. Allocation of the Care in the Community monies was conditional on this continued funding, as explained in Chapter 1. Indeed, this initiative was one manifestation of the prevailing central policy of reducing reliance on long-stay provision. The increasing focus upon acute care responsibilities within the National Health Service has continued this process.

Some general practitioners expressed concern over the possible increase in workload created by the increased number of elderly people being discharged to the community. Information was obtained on the number of home visits made by general practitioners to project clients during September 1986, in order to establish whether this was the case. However, in the event, this revealed that the average amount of time spent on each project client was five minutes per week. There were also several occasions during the early phase of the project when issues about individual clients needed to be resolved by discussion with general practitioners. One example of this was where certain general practitioners, who were, in the words of one senior partner, 'hospital-oriented', would be more likely to request a hospital admission for certain problems where they felt that domiciliary services were not adequate. In the case of clients who were already being supported in their own homes, it was important to demonstrate to these general practitioners that the project would be capable of maintaining elderly people who might ordinarily have been admitted to hospital in a crisis. The two geriatricians involved with the project were supportive in educating general practitioners about the potential of the project. In many ways, at this stage of its implementation the possibilities being offered by the project to general practitioners were acts of faith, and could not be demonstrated, of course, unless former patterns of behaviour were modified.

Social services. Local social services management expressed concern that the initial aims of the project might lead to a hospital-oriented, health-dominated service, which could offer no benefit to people on the margins of residential care and could place greater demands on relatives and friends by not recognising the wider needs of frail elderly people. As can be seen from the later developments, discussed in Chapter 10, this tension was always evident. It was recognised, however, that the project had to have an impact on the hospital services for the practical financing reasons outlined above. This illustrates the underlying tensions which the project and its managerial arrangements had to negotiate, one area of disagreement between the agencies being the concern to provide for the needs of different groups. This long-standing problem has since become more evident. Although the current community care policy for older people has tended to focus upon diversion of inappropriate admissions from long-stay hospitals, nursing and residential care homes, the greater efficiency saving might be generated from reductions in acute hospital care (Davies, 1993). This concern has also been evident in Australia's Aged Care Reforms (DHHCS, 1991).

Housing. During the initial planning phase of the project, the local authority housing department had made a verbal commitment to support the project and provide housing for those elderly people on the long-stay wards who had no accommodation to return to. This commitment formed part of the submission for central funds. However, as noted in Chapter 4, the political composition of the housing committee was altered following council elections in May 1985, and the commitment to provide housing could not be honoured. At this point it was feared that the original proposals could not be implemented at all. It was decided, however, to continue on the basis of identifying those patients who would normally need long-stay care but who still, for one reason or another, had accommodation. At the same time, it was also decided to make contact with voluntary housing associations to discuss with them the possibility of being allocated a number of tenancies for potential project clients who did not have accommodation. Only limited support for the project was offered by allocating tenancies on a case-by-case basis. As noted in Chapter 4, if more housing had been made available, either by the local borough council or by voluntary housing associations, there would have been more scope for moving other elderly people from the long-stay wards and, inevitably, the composition of the initial cohort supported by the project would have been different. In the event, the majority of project clients returned to their own homes from acute wards, following rehabilitation and assessment. The nature of the available accommodation therefore inevitably exerted a selection effect on the people supported by the project. The importance of the housing dimension for community care and care management is clearly evident, as was experienced in the Wakefield Project (Richardson and Higgins, 1991, 1992).

Private nursing home sector. During the implementation phase of the project, there was continued, rapid growth of the private nursing home sector (Darton and Wright, 1993). Therefore, it was increasingly possible for elderly people with no personal finances to be supported by social security payments in private nursing and residential care homes. It is also important to note that such placements could be made by members of the geriatric multidisciplinary team with no reference to any other party, and it became a powerful and much-used discharge mechanism at no extra cost to the health authority, thus reducing pressure on the acute hospital sector.

Implementation and consolidation phase

Project accountability. The inevitable outcome of the processes of change that were occurring within the agencies, such as the move towards more targeted home care (SSI, 1987), meant that in some ways the agencies were becoming more tightly linked, and traditionally murky boundaries were becoming more unclear. The process has been described as 'structuration' (DiMaggio, 1983). Management coalitions may arise in such a context. The management structure which developed, covering both agencies, is the sort of managerial arrangement which might be expected where this process is occurring (Evans and Klem, 1980; Kaluzney and Fried, 1985). The fact that the project team were managerially accountable to the social services department, yet were simultaneously accountable to the joint coordinating group for the implementation of policies and practices agreed by that group, resulted, at times, in conflicts of accountability, although only when the project was operational. Even though the local social services senior manager was chairman of the joint coordinating group, some difficulties arose, in particular over whether and when decisions made by either the group or the normal line management arrangements should predominate. Since the joint coordinating group met only bi-monthly, more urgent decisions could not await these meetings, and necessary ad hoc decision-making processes resulted. For example, after the first nine months, it was agreed between the project manager and the chairman of the joint coordinating group that there should be a temporary halt to referrals, in order for some consolidation to take place. Ideally this decision should have been made by the joint coordinating group, but it was felt that the decision could not await the next meeting in several weeks time.

Geriatric service. Once the project was established, some geriatric beds were closed in order to release funds to maintain the project after the end of the pilot stage. The introduction of general management into the health service occurred not long before the implementation of the project, and the decision to close the two long-stay wards was one of the first major decisions made through the general management structure. It could be argued that the new structure facilitated the release of the funds to ensure the continuation of the project beyond the three-year pilot phase as the decision-making process was now more clearly defined. The newly-appointed district general manager of the health authority supported the project and had been closely involved during the planning phase.

The consultant geriatricians noted the impact of offering a real choice to patients who might normally need continuing hospital or private nursing home care. Once beds started to close in parallel with the numbers being supported by the project, both consultants expressed considerable concern at this loss of geriatric provision. They were aware that substantial savings were being made by the health authority during the pilot phase, yet they were seeing none of these savings being reinvested in their services. Clearly there was little incentive for the geriatricians to support bed closures at this stage. Wickings et al. (1983), reviewing clinical budgeting and costing experiments, point out the superiority of budgeting systems that both involve clinicians and allow them to control the resources for which they are accountable. Such systems offer incentives for clinicians to identify economies to be redeployed to finance improvements in their services that otherwise would not have been funded.

A further concern expressed by one of the consultants was over the longer-term impact on the remaining long-stay wards of discharging the 'better' and more mentally alert long-stay patients (that is, a creaming-off effect), leaving a hard core of heavily dependent elderly people who were less responsive and rewarding, and who subsequently would create greater demands on the staff, with possible adverse effects on morale (Health Advisory Service, 1982). This could result in rising unit costs of the remaining long-stay patients: an issue that received scant regard at the time (Challis, 1992c). A comparison of dependency characteristics from the annual ward censuses (Acquilla et al., 1987b,c) and detailed assessments of project clients would suggest that the average long-stay ward patient was more dependent than the average project client. However, it is impossible to tell from the census data to what extent the dependency was ward regime-induced and to what extent it reflected the capabilities of the patients.

A related issue was that of the allocation of scarce therapy staff. As more therapy time was devoted to early rehabilitation and pre-discharge planning, less time was available either to maintain the mobility of long-stay patients or to provide recreational activities. This risked increasing the dependency levels of such patients.

Social services. As the project became one of the available options when patients were being assessed for discharge, it also permitted several clients to be discharged earlier, with rehabilitation being continued at home. A few of these clients were eventually discharged to the home help service, as decreasing dependency no longer necessitated the degree of intensive input offered by the project. At this point the question of payment for services became an issue, as project clients had been receiving a free service and were now being assessed to pay for the home help service. This interface between means-tested social services and free health care is a conflict which remains unresolved not just at a local level, but represents a disincentive to the reduction of barriers between services (House of Commons, 1992). To resolve misunderstandings, clients were given a letter on discharge from hospital to the project explaining that at some time referral to the home help service might be necessary, depending on their needs as assessed by the multidisciplinary team.

The project service. It was during this consolidation phase, when the project had begun to be accepted and its impact had become clearer, that a number of service providers said that relationships between hospital and community services had been substantially improved. The district physiotherapist, keen to expand the physiotherapy service into the community, saw the project as having provided a 'bridge' between hospital and community services, through the employment of a physiotherapist and occupational therapist as members of the project team, while retaining their hospital base and their professional accountability. These members of the team also acted as advocates of the project within their own staff groups.

The process of interagency working

There were several specific features that appear to have predisposed the health authority and the social services department to collaborate in the planning and implementation of the project. These are discussed below and are summarised in Box 6.2.

A consensus had developed over time between key people in both health and social services, who wanted to develop domiciliary services for frail elderly people as an alternative to both long-stay hospital and residential

---

Box 6.2
Features that encouraged interagency cooperation

Nationally-led initiative to promote central government policy.

Large sum of Care in the Community funds for the project which meant that in terms of size it could be expected to have a significant impact.

Agreement over aims and philosophy of the project which built on existing services rather than requiring an abrupt shift.

Opportunity to implement existing plans that had stalled for lack of money.

Commitment of senior staff in health authority and social services department.

Met the need to provide a greater level of domiciliary care for patients to be discharged earlier from hospital.

Presence of general management decision-making for the project.

Relatively short planning phase.

High profile of the project both nationally and locally:
- Health Advisory Service cited the project as an example of 'Excellence in Practice'.
- Published articles/research.
- Winning 1986 *Health Service Journal* management award.

---

care. There existed a small group of committed health and social services staff who believed in the concepts of community care and who at the time were actively trying to influence other key people within their organisations to develop services. Most of the planning for the project in its early stages was undertaken by a senior nurse manager and two social services staff, one a senior manager and the other, previously a senior social worker, who became the project manager. This group was able to influence the management networks within their own organisations and thereby build up a commitment for the project which grew out of the perceived shortfalls in existing services. The Audit Commission (1992a) has described such shared commitment and good relationships as the key to improved collaboration. The group were able to produce the basis for a domain consensus (Levine and White, 1961; Van de Ven et al., 1979) across organisations and across occupational groups for the project, at least at management level. This was an important pre-condition because, whatever problems arose at the different phases of the development of the service, there was rarely any dissent from the fundamental aim of the project which was to enhance existing community services and give elderly people the choice to remain at home, which had not previously been available to them. The experience is similar to the preconditions for change described by Hadley and Hugman (1992), who identified three important factors: getting appropriate backing from key stakeholders such as nursing managers and social services; securing the necessary resources; and creating a suitably qualified team to lead the change. Similar factors have been shown to be effective in other settings, for example, in the establishment and continuation of community health care centres in the United States (Sardell, 1988). In considering how services come to be established and whether or not they survive and in what form, Sardell points out the need to pay attention to the relationship between the existence of conflict around the aims of the service in question; the nature of the service concerned; whether and what kinds of interest groups are participants in the policy process on which the service is founded; the incentives or disincentives for supportive behaviour on the part of bureaucrats and policy-makers; and the ways these incentives or disincentives are affected by changes in the larger political environment.

The additional central funding was particularly influential, since it was set in a context where planning for interagency collaboration had commenced, and it made development possible in an area of activity where goals had already been defined. At this stage, therefore, there was agreement over the basic philosophy of the project, and both sides stood to gain from it by being able to implement ideas on a scale that might not normally have been possible within existing resources. It was one of the conditions of the Care in the Community funding that there should be strong evidence of collaboration and cooperation between health and social services. The initiative was therefore an example of what has been termed an 'authoritative strategy' (Benson, 1975) or 'mandatedness' (Hall, R., 1982). In such a case, an external body — in this case the former Department of Health and Social Security — allocates specific sums of money for clearly-defined purposes with strict conditions attached. However, while in the short term this may produce collaboration, there is the risk of conflict in the longer term since agencies may be forced to interact in conditions of domain dissensus and even interpersonal acrimony (Hall et al., 1977, 1978; Molnar and Rogers, 1979).

The actual size of the funding was also a significant factor. First, it provided an incentive to collaboration by, at least in the short term, reducing any additional costs that either agency might experience. It meant an overall net gain in services. Second, the size of the project that could be implemented with the agreed funding was seen as being capable of having a significant impact on services for frail elderly people in the locality. It was therefore seen as worthwhile and significant. Third, from the point of view of influential parties, such as the trades unions, the prospect of creating at least 30 additional full-time posts contributed to the successful agreement that was effected. Another important factor was the high profile that the Care in the Community Initiative had at the time, which was an added incentive for many of the key people to want to be a part of a significant development. Therefore, in planning and developing the project during the period of central funding, both agencies stood to gain a lot from the pilot project at little cost to themselves.

Interprofessional working

To focus upon interorganisational collaboration, without examining the individuals involved, would be to provide only a partial picture. Despite the advent of general management (Griffiths, 1983), interprofessional relationships are still likely to be as important as interagency relationships in influencing the pattern of services (Hall, 1986). Perrow (1970) suggests that it is individuals within organisations, and not the organisations themselves, who pursue goals which may or may not facilitate collaboration. Organisations are shaped by their internal culture, to which occupational groups may substantially contribute (Zucker, 1988). Indeed, it has been argued that the presence of multiple organisational groups and their associated cultures constitute a barrier to service coordination (Harrington and Newcomer, 1982). Friedson (1970) has argued that the occupational structuring which characterises health care organisations militates against coordination. In the context of care management this is particularly important, since one of its functions is to span traditional agency boundaries (Challis, 1994b). Miller and Rice (1967) have argued that such boundary-spanning activities are complex and any attempt to create new boundaries, such as by creating new 'task-centred' roles, may result in clashes between these and the old, or 'sentient' systems. The creation of care managers represents a 'task-centred' system that cuts across a 'sentient' system caused by long-standing professional loyalties and roles.

In this section, as previously, the perspective of different interest groups is considered at two different phases of the project; the planning and pre-implementation phase, and the implementation and consolidation phase.

Planning and pre-implementation phase

Therapy services. The senior therapy staff all reported difficulties arising from staff shortages, as a result of both existing workloads and recruitment problems. The project was seen as requiring extra resources beyond current provision, and anxieties were expressed that there might not be sufficient time to provide the necessary support. At this time the physiotherapy service was piloting a community service, taking referrals from a number of general practices, and the project was seen as having the potential to reinforce this move into the community. Similarly, the introduction of increased occupational therapy support to the project took place in a context of good links between the hospital and social services occupational therapy departments. The new development was also seen as a way of encouraging the use of auxiliaries by the chiropody service. It was hoped that the use of home care assistants to undertake basic foot care of project clients would demonstrate the benefits of such workers. Hence the support of the chiropody service, which had complementary goals to the project, was significant in the planning phase.

However, some concern was expressed by senior therapy staff that changes that were underway at the time, following the implementation of the National Health Service Management Inquiry (Griffiths, 1983), might militate against the flexibility to extend a hospital-based service into the community, since, with acute unit and community unit staff placed under separate management structures and budgets, there was a danger of new boundaries emerging.

Community nursing services. Boundaries over personal care were unclear and, given the de facto involvement of nurses in this area, the discussion of change inevitably led to disquiet. The role of the Director of Nursing Services was crucial in this planning phase, positively influencing community nursing staff regarding the project.

Multidisciplinary assessment. While hospital care was formally coordinated through ward meetings, community care was not. Indeed, there was a general recognition of the problems of individual professions wanting to do their own assessments and being reluctant to accept the assessment of other professionals who may indeed have a more detailed knowledge of particular client needs than themselves. This was compounded by each profession seeing it as good practice to undertake a holistic assessment. The result was that different professionals were making detailed assessments and care plans without coordinating their effects on individual elderly people.

Domiciliary services. The home help service was experiencing an increase in demand for personal care with a consequent increase in demand for evening and weekend work. This made additional demands upon budgets, reflecting a context of targeting services as a means of balancing budgetary constraints with increased demand. As elsewhere, very large caseloads hindered adequate monitoring of the service to ensure it continued to meet the changing needs of clients (SSI, 1987). Home help organisers also reported a lack of clarity over what was or was not permissible in terms of personal care, and which tasks should be done by the district nurse and which should be done by home helps. As nationally (Goldberg and Connelly, 1982; Sinclair et al., 1990), in the absence of clear policy guidelines it was left to individual home help organisers to allocate the service in the light of their own interpretation, thus raising the question of how efficient service delivery could be under such a system of service allocation. So whereas one home help organiser said, 'A home help can just wash clients' hands and faces' and can deal with 'the odd accident of incontinence', another said, 'They're not supposed to deal with regular incontinence, but in practice they often do'. Another said, 'Washing a person is still a district nursing task, but owing to nursing staff shortages it's fallen onto the shoulders of the home help service to do it.' District nurses also expressed uncertainty about what tasks home helps could undertake, this being exacerbated by the lack of a policy framework between agencies and the consequent individual interpretation by staff. This was compounded by the feeling that some of their time was being wasted in performing basic personal tasks not requiring a nurse's skills (DHSS, 1981c).

Sheltered housing. Wardens of sheltered housing recorded the greatest difficulties due to poor relations with other services. Other service providers appeared very uncertain about the extent of their role and whether it was appropriate to provide them with information about their residents. It seemed that they often did not receive information on residents' health and social status unless from the residents themselves, and were often unaware of home help, district nurse or general practitioner involvement with particular residents. As they were required to contact residents daily to ascertain their general wellbeing, they felt they should have some knowledge about their medical and social circumstances to respond more appropriately to their behaviour and conversation. By contrast, wardens reported that at times service providers such as general practitioners assumed that wardens undertook a personal care role for residents, or a more intensive supervisory and monitoring role. Three of the four wardens interviewed felt some resentment that their role was rendered less effective through lack of knowledge and that there was little incentive for them to take on care tasks beyond the official boundaries of their role. This reflects the long-standing confusion about the extensiveness of wardens' roles in sheltered housing (Butler et al., 1983).

Implementation and consolidation phase

Therapy services. Given the staff shortages noted above, it quickly became clear that if the project was to implement the full multidisciplinary nature of the home care assistant role and provide project clients with some of the rehabilitative intervention they required, extra physiotherapy and occupational therapy time would be needed. In the event, project funds were used to finance a part-time physiotherapist and a part-time occupational therapist, each of whom became managerially responsible to the project manager while remaining professionally accountable to their district head of service. These staff were recruited from current employees of the services, who therefore had a good knowledge of local service provision and the aims of the new service.

Therapy services generally reported positive responses to the new development. Both the district physiotherapist and occupational therapist indicated that the project performed a bridge-building role between acute and community services. Their services had established a pattern of working in the community through their staff being members of the project team. Similarly, the district speech therapist commented particularly that trust had been established through the care managers' willingness to respect the professional expertise of other providers and make appropriate use of their services. The importance of trust, gained through day-to-day working, as an influence upon collaboration, cannot be underestimated (Webb, 1991), and similar findings have been observed elsewhere (Dant et al., 1989). The district chiropodist recounted a particularly unexpected additional benefit. Apparently, the district nursing service had requested training from chiropodists in basic foot care skills because of the advantage observed from home care assistants receiving such training.

Geriatric multidisciplinary team assessment. During the planning and pre-implementation phase, it was recognised that multidisciplinary assessments would need to occur at the point of entry to the project service. However, in the early stages, no clearly-defined referral and assessment procedure had been established, referrals came from a variety of sources, and acceptance was dependent upon the quality of advocacy for a particular case, thereby effectively placing responsibility for acceptance solely upon the project team. Ward staff would indicate that their patients were ideal for the service, particularly those who were presenting problems for discharge. This particular problem was resolved by the joint coordinating group, which agreed that referrals should be routed through the geriatric multidisciplinary team. From this point a common assessment procedure and referral route was established, and the geriatric service then became responsible for considering entry to the project. A tension existed as to whether the geriatric team not only screened referrals but also accepted them, or whether the project team could exercise a veto. In practice, such latent conflict was never manifest.

The care managers became a regular part of the geriatric multidisciplinary team, with the senior district nurses also attending the case conference on a rota basis. This was seen as constructive practice by consultants, ward nursing staff, therapists and district nurses, since the care managers were working both in hospital and in the community, and enhancing communication and understanding both within and between settings. Thus, the relationship between health and social services moved from being loose-knit to a more tightly-knit and formalised arrangement (Aldrich, 1979), to constitute what Ovretveit (1986) has called a 'formal' team. There is a long history of difficulty of communication between social work services and medicine, often attributed to differences in perceptions of appropriate timeframes for response, with the former focused more on the long-term consequences of intervention (Goldberg and Neill, 1972; Hallett and Stevenson, 1980; Hunter et al., 1993). Kahn (1974) identifies three prerequisites for effective collaboration between medical and social work staff: first, insight into one's own occupational system; second, insight into the systems of others; and third, a clear definition of and agreement about the reasons, bases and goals of collaboration. These criteria were met in the project. The integration of care managers with the geriatric service ensured that they had their own bounded and understood system within which to operate, namely the project and its specific linkages with the geriatric service and the social services department. They were part of the geriatric multidisciplinary team and were accepted into that system, and their role, function and objectives were clearly understood by the geriatric service. Care managers could also respond more rapidly, since they directly controlled resources for the support and care of patients in the community. Consultants noted better planned and coordinated discharge as one of the major benefits conferred by the care managers.

During this phase several key issues were debated. One of these was the concept of 'readiness for discharge', whether, given the increased level of support available under the new project, the threshold for discharge could be amended to permit the earlier discharge of more dependent elderly people. This led to discussions about the model of care that was being pursued and whether the project was primarily about rehabilitation or maintenance. This has been a continuing debate about services (Kahn, 1975; Brody, 1977b; Davies, 1985), and was not an academic question as there were real differences of opinion at times between care managers and therapy staff, particularly when the care managers perceived the latter as being too rehabilitation-oriented and expecting too much of individual elderly people. Another issue concerned whether receipt of the service was conditional upon the elderly person's positive response to discharge. Such concerns have also been a preoccupation of staff regarding placement in hospital or nursing home care (House of Commons, 1992).

Primary health care services. As frail elderly patients began to be discharged to the project, the issue of defining the boundaries of clinical responsibility emerged. One general practitioner argued forcibly that he should be consulted about the proposed discharge of project clients, as he had knowledge of their circumstances and appropriateness for return to the community. It became policy for potential clients to be discussed with general practitioners prior to discharge. Furthermore, the relationship between the geriatrician and general practitioner would be changed, if the former were to retain some clinical responsibility for discharged project clients. In the event, project clients were treated similarly to day or outpatients, and general practitioners assumed their traditional roles and responsibilities. Although there were discussions about routine medical review by consultants, as described in Chapter 2, this was not introduced. No formal mechanism for the involvement of secondary services in primary health care was developed, although there are several models of how this might be implemented (Strathdee and Williams, 1986; Falloon and Fadden, 1993), which are discussed in Chapter 11. However, the geriatricians were kept up to date regarding clients' progress through the multidisciplinary meetings and retained a 'continuing interest' which could be tapped by the care managers if a problem arose, for example, where the client needed reassessment or a brief hospital admission to give respite to the carer.

Interprofessional roles in the community. For district nurses, the most extensive providers of health care in the community, the advent of the project prompted a considerable reassessment of their role. Whereas for physiotherapy and occupational therapy the project represented an opportunity to expand into the community in a new role, it represented a possible threat to district nurses. Whereas previously they had taken responsibility for making assessments for certain aids, promoting mobility and personal care, they now experienced the competing influences of the project physiotherapist and occupational therapist making home visits and assessments in their place. A degree of 'domain defensiveness' was therefore inevitable (Challis, L. et al., 1988). Boundaries of competence had to be negotiated in a way that had not been so acutely necessary before (Miller and Rice, 1967). The 'who does what', or turf disputes, of service delivery could not be avoided. Such disputes mainly took place over responsibility for dealing with aspects of mobility and activities of daily living, with these three groups of staff having quite markedly overlapping roles. Boundary negotiations had lacked immediacy when the professional input to various clients could take place in greater isolation, having less regard to how their work linked in to that of others. Another related area of concern was whether home care assistants should supervise the taking of medication.

A notable example of where conflict arose during this process of renegotiation of roles was in the home assessment visit. These visits were undertaken initially by the project occupational therapist, physiotherapist and care manager. District nurses felt excluded from their role as assessors and expressed strong feelings. A series of multidisciplinary meetings was arranged to take the heat out of the situation, the outcome of which was the specification of who was responsible for what, based on the different skills taught by the various professional groups during the training period. The previous working relationship of the project manager and senior nurse manager, derived from the planning phase, was influential in negotiating this hurdle. As Seidman (1970) has argued, advances in coordination are rarely neutral: one party advances some interests at the expense of others. From the nurses' perspective, their relative hegemony was reduced by the new arrangements, while that of the physiotherapist and occupational therapist was increased. As Schmidt and Kochan (1977) have argued, interrelationships within the same organisational field can contain both elements of exchange, and power and dependency. Thus, one explanation for the different staff responses is that the therapy staff cooperated with the project development on an exchange basis since it offered them an opportunity to extend their roles, while the nursing staff were more cautious, seeing a potential relative loss of influence.

As the project developed, conflicts over roles in home visit assessments, and over orders for aids and equipment were largely resolved. The view expressed by a senior district nurse that district nurses should be the 'king pin' in community service provision had been modified to some extent. However, the reluctance of some district nurses to accept this shift was demonstrated in the views of one nurse who expressed concern that, if more health professionals were to expand their role into the community, this would threaten the district nurse's role. Similar responses were noted in the Gloucester Primary Health Care Project (Dant et al., 1989). However, other nurses appeared to be coming to terms with a changing identity in relation to project cases where their role was as part of a team and not as 'king pin'. For example, one nurse commented about the home care assistants:

> If we're doing our job correctly, then they're doing what we teach them to do ... we keep our eye on that and assess and re-assess.

Several nurses saw the advent of physiotherapy and occupational therapy in the community as a positive step to enhance services to the clients they visited, and some even sought advice from these therapists to enhance their own skills in the same way as they had chosen to seek expertise from the chiropodist. This reflected the view of several nurses that the project had not only improved linkages between health and social services, but also between hospital and community.

General practitioners, with whom the district nurses had long and close working relationships, observed that, in devolving responsibility for simple caring tasks to home care assistants, the project service was freeing district nurses to make more appropriate use of their specialist nursing skills.

There was also the possibility of conflict between care managers and hospital social workers, given the overlap between the two roles. This was largely avoided, however, mainly due to the heavy workload of the latter, who recognised their inability to follow up elderly people after discharge, while recognising the importance of this for ensuring that care packages did not break down. This reflected the more short-term role of the hospital social worker, who was concerned necessarily with assessment and discharge arrangements, rather than with long-term care (Hunter et al., 1993). The fact that the care managers added to the existing assessment process instead of replacing it was also important, since members of the multidisciplinary team undertook their normal roles and thus experienced minimal change (Scott, 1981).

Home help service. Interviews with three of the four home help organisers indicated that they were more or less indifferent to the advent of the project as it had little relevance to their service. The fourth home help organiser supported the project's aims and felt some regrets that there had not been closer links between the two services from the project's inception. With hindsight, it can be seen that this group was only marginally involved in and consulted about the new service, and consequently expressed indifference towards it. The fact that home care assistants undertook domestic care tasks, principally to minimise the number of people involved in providing care, made overlap more confusing to home help staff.

These views were modified as the project developed, even though the views of home help organisers on the impact of the project remained divided. Clearly the model of care and its implementation had led to an increased awareness of the potential for wider use of home helps. This was particularly the view of area social work staff. Two of the four home help organisers would have liked their home helps to have had more training and taken on more personal care tasks. This reflected a belief that the home help service could provide similar intensive support to the project, although whether it could have done so for more than a few clients with its existing organisational structure is debatable (SSI, 1987; Davies et al., 1990). In the longer term, clearer arrangements about overlapping roles and transfer would clearly have been desirable in the interests of the best use of services.

All of the organisers saw the integration of the two services as more or less inevitable, but not necessarily desirable, a problem experienced in other intensive home care services (Simons and Warburton, 1980). The organisers reported problems over home helps losing former clients to the project on their discharge from hospital and also, when a project client died, leaving a surviving spouse who did not qualify for continuing project support and who was then distressed at the assessed payment for the home help service. The organisers identified this issue of charging or not charging for services as a potential barrier to any future integration of the two services.

One organiser also noted her perception of the over-allocation of home care assistant hours, remarking that time was wasted by sitting and chatting. This may indicate some lack of understanding of the aims and philosophy behind the project, which again suggests that the home help organisers had not been given appropriate information. On the other hand, it might indicate a perception derived from the inevitable lag between the initial recruitment of home care assistants and clients in the early stages of the project.

Sheltered housing. Wardens of sheltered housing expressed mixed views about the impact of the project on them. One warden reported a very good caring service given to a project client. She got on well with the home care assistant and felt able to telephone the home care assistant whenever the need arose. A second warden, however, felt that the project provided an inadequate service for a client in her housing complex. She felt that too many different home care assistants had been involved and that they had failed to take account of the client's sensitivities and need for companionship. She also reported that the main home care assistant was too young, unsuited to the job and, at times, impatient with the client. Furthermore, she was unsure how to contact the care manager to inform her of these inadequacies, having been told of them herself by a friend of the client. A third warden was opposed to the placement of a project client in her housing unit. A place had been allocated to a lady who had spent some considerable time in the long-stay wards, and who was very dependent on help for all activities of daily living. Although the warden was not required to meet these care needs, she saw the placement as inappropriate in a complex of units for independent living. Behind this view appeared to be the fear of having to cope with a highly dependent person who could make considerable demands. This reflects the lack of consensus regarding the role of sheltered housing and who should be suitable (Butler et al., 1983; Clapham and Munro, 1990).

Hospital wards. One ward sister working on an acute geriatric ward objected to the need to transfer elderly people referred to the project from other wards to her ward for assessment and discharge planning. She felt this was an inappropriate use of scarce beds and added to burdens on the ward because of the high dependency of the patients being transferred. She felt that assessments should be carried out on the ward from which the patient was referred. She also felt she was not getting enough feedback about how patients were progressing after discharge to the project, and had some anxiety about bed closures which were now taking place. Her fear was that the recent benefits of not having patients 'blocking' beds while waiting for long-term care might be lost if the ratio of hospital beds to project places changed.

Ward sisters on the long-term care wards felt that the patients who were left appeared to be increasingly institutionalised and unmotivated, and the emphasis on early rehabilitation and discharge had led to a considerably reduced service by physiotherapists and occupational therapists in these wards as they concentrated their efforts in the acute and rehabilitation wards.

The process of multidisciplinary working

A number of factors seem to have contributed to improved interprofessional and multidisciplinary working. These are summarised in Box 6.3 and discussed below. First, there was already a well-established tradition of multi-

---

Box 6.3

Features that encouraged interprofessional working

Commitment from senior managers.

Agreement over the aims and philosophy of the project.

Existing well-established pattern of multidisciplinary assessment in geriatric team.

Chance to implement planned community-based developments in occupational therapy and physiotherapy.

General positive high profile gained by the project.

---

disciplinary working within the acute sector of the health authority. The geriatric multidisciplinary team already met on a weekly basis and referrals to the project came through this team. The care managers, as members of this team, discussed possible referrals and coordinated assessments and care plans. The project was a linked additional service rather than an attempt to change the role and functioning of the existing team, reflecting the greater ease of developing new organisations than changing existing ones (Scott, 1981).

Second, as at the interagency level, there was general agreement among professional groups about the broad aim of the project, of giving elderly people the chance to return home rather than remain in hospital. Thus, a degree of domain consensus was created at the policy level, at least in the short term, despite the existence of gains and losses for different professional groups (Seidman, 1970). Thus the project superimposed a set of linkages between hospital and community upon previously discrete groups.

Third, the project gave both the physiotherapy department and the occupational therapy department the chance to expand their activities into community-based work. Since the physiotherapy department was already piloting general practitioner access to physiotherapy in the community, the opportunity to extend this in a new project was welcomed. Similarly, the occupational therapy department already had close links with its counterpart in the social services department, and the expansion of their service into the community was also viewed positively. The chiropody service, too, was interested in developing the role of aides. On the other hand, the district nursing service probably felt most under threat, in that both community physiotherapy and occupational therapy were relatively new to them, and became involved in areas of work that traditionally were seen as their province. There were also anxieties that the project would increase district nurse caseloads with no extra staff being provided. At the time, the relevant managers judged that no increase in district nursing time was necessary.

Thus, there were elements of both exchange and resource-dependency negotiations occurring simultaneously, in relation to different occupational groups (Schmidt and Kochan, 1977). Furthermore, care management may have been perceived as most threatening to the most numerous and dominant professional group, that is, the community nurses, who otherwise would have seen this role as their territory.

Nevertheless, for all staff groups, it is likely that the chance of being part of an innovative project having a national profile and being scrutinised closely by the Department of Health and Social Security gave added impetus to multidisciplinary working.

The development of the new care management team was influenced by the fact that the care managers were new to the district and were having to develop a new role, as well as gaining acceptance themselves. The fact that these roles had the sanction of senior managers facilitated the process, but this still required much tactful handling by the care managers and their manager. The continuity of involvement of the project manager from planning through implementation assisted in this process. Trust proved to be important and could only be developed slowly (Webb, 1991). The tradition of inertia and the difficulty of changing existing organisations suggests the virtue of developing innovatory services as an easier approach (Scott, 1981). However, new services are likely to offend and transgress normative climates created by groups in agencies and must struggle to legitimate and justify their place.

Conclusion

Davidson (1976) has suggested that organisations may move through a continuum of collaboration from communication through cooperation, coordination and integration towards merger. In Darlington, the agencies moved from a pattern of cooperation towards a degree of integration and teamwork where some accountability to a joint structure was agreed. The framework within which interagency and interprofessional working took place was necessarily flexible. It required the meeting and cooperation of two large bureaucracies, most of whose activities were relatively predictable. The move to develop the project could be seen as representing a move towards a more formally planned approach to coordination, and towards more tightly-coupled arrangements (Aldrich, 1979). A new project required a different range of responses beyond the normal processes and resources of either agency and the context provided the preconditions for collaboration on the several bases of mandatedness (Hall, R., 1982), uncertainty (Cook, 1977) and exchange (Levine and White, 1961; Blau, 1964) and organisational structures had to be developed to manage this. Coping with an unpredictable environment required a degree of both centralisation and professionalisation to be developed within the project (Greenwood and Hinings, 1976). Hall and Quinn (1983) have noted that effective change can occur when there is a 'fit' or congruence between environmental conditions, organisational form and personal style. In conditions of uncertainty, a service such as the project would take the organisational form of an 'adhocracy', characterised as present in an environment of high ambiguity where there is an absence of tradition, an opportunity to shape values and beliefs, and highly devoted intensive effort by members. An external focus, adaptability and discretion are required characteristics with a flexible style of leadership. Such a description is consistent with the operation of the project team.

The various channels of communication that were established during the project phase were vital for providing the means by which problems were identified and resolved. There were, for example, the multidisciplinary team meetings where the care managers played such a vital role in selling the project and explaining its aims and objectives. There were the joint coordinating group meetings where aspects of policy could be discussed, and interagency and interprofessional issues identified and tackled. The project team meetings also acted as a forum for resolving current issues, and the project physiotherapist, occupational therapist and representative of the district nursing service were key links with their own professions and were able to disseminate information about the project and its possibilities to their peers. There were also a number of other meetings with the geriatric nursing staff and with general practitioners which helped to involve a wide range of people in discussions about the project as well as help to resolve problems. As a consequence, a network of communication became established to provide information about the project and consider and resolve issues as they arose.

The different responses of occupational groups might also have been expected from the literature on professionals within organisations, which suggests that, in general, they seek to maintain autonomy (Friedson, 1984). Therefore, decisions about cases and undertaking assessments in a collaborative context requires the maintenance of jurisdiction and authority between different interest groups. With regard to care management, it would be predicted that the most numerous and professionalised agency in the field is likely to assert its right to perform this role. Hence, it is unsurprising that some community nursing staff did so. The care management role is less likely to be perceived as the responsibility of a particular occupational group, the tighter their role definition or the smaller their number. Thus, where the function is specific to a particular bodily system or part, as in the case of a chiropodist, or to a particular activity, such as assessment, in the case of occupational therapists, then the lower the probability that the care management role would be asserted. The nursing staff were probably influenced by concerns about turf and autonomy, whereas the therapy staff were motivated by exchange opportunities and the existing social workers by the then prevalent perception of their involvement as being acute or short-term. It is clear that the effective implementation of care management will require a clearer definition of the role of social services department staff in long-term care in the community (Challis, 1994b). This theme is discussed further in Chapter 11.

Box 6.4
Issues arising at the four levels of coordination during different project phases

PLANNING AND PRE-IMPLEMENTATION

IMPLEMENTATION

CONSOLIDATION

Interagency issues

Geriatric hospital bed provision above national norms. Patient day census carried out.
Residential bed provision above national and local norms — exploration of more flexible use, such as respite care.
Lack of adequate community support services.
No evening and weekend personal caring services in the community.
More highly dependent elderly people needing care in the community.
Second geriatrician appointed.

Care in the Community funding required clients to be discharged from hospital. Social services department feared a health-dominated service offering no benefits to elderly people in the community or at risk of entry to institutional care.
GPs' anxieties over increased workloads resulting from the discharge of frail elderly people into the community.

Difficulties due to split accountability of project team — managed by social services department while policy decisions made by joint coordinating group.
Concern of geriatricians over bed closures and no apparent reinvestment of savings in geriatric provision.
Increased emphasis on rehabilitation and discharge on acute wards led to less staff time for long-term wards.
Patients remaining in long-term care wards more dependent; affecting staff morale.
Less pressure on acute and long-term care beds, also on residential care beds.

Interprofessional issues

Staff shortages leading to constrained services for the range of therapy and chiropody services.
Unclear boundaries between home help and district nursing service in personal care.
Communication and liaison problems between hospital and the community over admission and discharge.
Difficulties arising from different therapists making individual assessments without coordinating the effect on the elderly person.
Wardens of sheltered housing concerned at lack of information and communication about their frail residents.

Extra physiotherapist and occupational therapist employed by project to resolve staff shortage.
Multidisciplinary geriatric case conference assumed increasingly important role in coordinating assessments and care plans for clients.
Need to clarify roles of GPs and geriatricians in relation to clients.
Need to clarify roles and responsibilities of therapy and nursing staff in the community, regarding assessments, mobility and aids.
Little project impact on home help: separate and parallel services.

Improved relations between hospital and community services, with care managers in geriatric multidisciplinary assessment team and therapists working in the community.
District nurses accepting use of HCAs. GPs noted that the use of HCAs freed district nurses to make more appropriate use of their skills and time.
Chiropody service keen to develop aides.
District nursing service interested in foot care training from the chiropody service.
District nurses contributing to multidisciplinary team for clients, but concerned that more professionals working in the community might threaten their role.

Client-level coordination and care management issues

Problems with different services making uncoordinated individual assessments. GPs noted that their role was to assess patients' needs and refer for services, but unable to retain a close monitoring role. Social workers operated in a short-term crisis-driven manner and unable to provide a monitoring or coordinating role.
Home Help organisers unable to undertake a monitoring role.
District nurses asserted that their role incorporated both assessment and ongoing monitoring of elderly people.

Established care manager role:
— negotiations with geriatric multidisciplinary team to incorporate care managers at case conference;
— care managers credibility through liaison and coordination;
— care managers reassured other service providers through use of their expertise;
— clarification of roles in decision-making over discharge and care plans.
Established information exchanges procedure with GPs over discharge and call-out to project clients.

Hospital staff confidence in project team:
— ease of discharge procedure coordinated by care managers;
— enhanced role of geriatric multidisciplinary team in community focus;
— good communication established across boundaries and professional roles respected.
Issue of HCA accountability to different instructing professionals clarified.
Reports of good coordinated care, including for terminally ill clients.
Need for support for care managers in stressful job with many demands.

Care worker issues

Lack of clarity of roles of district nurses and home helps over nursing tasks and social needs.
Home help organisers unable to monitor adequacy of service and changing needs.
Nursing policy moving towards advice/instruction role with less hands-on care-giving.
Physiotherapy and occupational therapy services using aides within hospital setting, therefore receptive to use of auxiliary workers in the community.

Therapy and chiropody services accepted use of HCAs after:
— negotiation of clear accountability;
— agreement that HCAs would be given specific case-related training.
District nursing anxiety over time demands of instructing/monitoring role, and over threats to own role in the community.
Anxiety of hospital staff regarding unqualified care staff supervising use of controlled drugs in the community.
Problems of conflicting advice given by professionals to HCAs.
Stress on HCAs through demands of role.
Integrating HCAs and paid helpers.

Providers noted high-quality care given by HCAs to clients.
Concerns over stress on HCAs through intense involvement and potential problem of creating dependency.
HCA training modified with a greater focus on promoting independence.
Problems of conflicting advice resolved by care managers ensuring a common approach.
District nursing service reported a shift in patterns of provision to more instructing and advising, and less hands-on care-giving.
Growing acceptance noted of chiropody service to use auxiliaries.
Home help service increasingly aware of potential for wider use of home helps through training and example.

This chapter has considered the first two of the four levels of coordination of care which the project was designed to influence — interagency collaboration; interprofessional working; care management and the coordination of care inputs; and the home care assistants as multipurpose workers. The remaining two were discussed in Chapters 4 and 5. The issues arising at all the four levels during the planning, implementation and consolidation phases are summarised in Box 6.4.

7 Clients and the Outcome of Care

This chapter is in two parts. The first part describes the project clients and the comparison group patients, giving details on their personal characteristics, their levels of dependency, the project clients' social networks, and both groups' experience of service support. The second part is concerned with the outcomes of care for both project and comparison groups and covers destinational outcomes, amount of time spent in different care settings, quality of life and quality of care, as well as factors associated with the outcome of care.

The information used in this chapter is based on interviews with elderly people in the project and comparison groups in hospital; interviews with project clients only at four to six weeks after discharge from hospital, concentrating on their social networks; and follow-up interviews with both groups of elderly people at six months after the first interview. The contents of these interviews are described in Chapter 3.

The clients and their experience of care

Descriptive characteristics of the elderly people

As described in Chapter 4, 101 elderly clients were discharged during the pilot project phase. These were compared with 113 comparison patients. Table 7.1 summarises the descriptive characteristics of the elderly people in the project and comparison groups. Approximately two-thirds of both groups were female, while the average age of elderly people receiving the project service was 80 years, and that of the comparison population 81 years. The majority of the patients in both groups had been in hospital for two years or less (96 per cent of the project group and 90 per cent of the comparison group). However, a small number of the comparison group patients had a markedly greater length of stay, of three years or more, and these accounted for a higher mean length of stay for this group. Project patients had a mean

Table 7.1
Descriptive characteristics of the elderly people

	Project group %	Comparison group %	p value
Total number	101	113	–
Gender (%)			
Males	36	36	ns
Females	64	64	
Mean age (years)	80	81	ns
Length of stay in hospital (%)			
Under 1 month	35	12	
1 to 3 months	36	29	
3 to 6 months	18	21	
6 months to 1 year	2	16	<0.005
1 to 3 years	6	14	
3 to 5 years	2	5	
5 years or over	0	3	

'ns' = not significant.

length of stay of 123 days, and the comparison group patients 305 days. This difference was statistically significant (p<0.01). It is possible that this greater length of stay of the comparison group patients might indicate a higher propensity for survival, given that the negative effects often associated with relocation are seen during the first six months of admission to institutional care (Yawney and Slover, 1973). The higher proportion of project clients who had been in hospital for less than one month indicates the subsequent development within the project of taking patients at the point of entry to long-stay care, while they retained their accommodation. Thus, an important part of the difference between the groups at the tails of the distribution is a project effect or outcome, rather than a problem of the research design.

The range of physical disability experienced varied considerably, but the most common cause was stroke, which over one-third of the clients had suffered. Other causes of disability included arthritis, heart and lung diseases, Parkinsonism, cancer, multiple sclerosis, motor neurone disease, fractures, amputations, senile dementia and general frailty. As explained earlier in Chapter 4, despite the original aims of the project to support mentally alert but physically frail elderly people at home, relatively immobile, confused elderly people were considered for the project as long as their disabilities were manageable. Table 7.2 indicates several key health-related characteristics of the elderly people discharged to the project and those in the comparison group. These include depressed mood and the four 'I's of geriatrics — incontinence, immobility, instability and intellectual impairment (Isaacs, 1981). There was no statistically significant difference between the two groups on any of these health-related characteristics. The majority of both groups had severe mobility problems and thus required regular assistance. Only 35 per cent of the project group were reported to be fully continent of urine at the time of discharge from hospital. Similarly, 36 per cent of the comparison group were fully continent of urine, and a quarter of both groups suffered from incontinence of faeces. Just over half of both groups of elderly people experienced severe giddiness; similarly, 45 per cent of the project and 49 per cent of the comparison group were rated as being at severe risk of falling. Given the unpredictability of the latter, it is often a cause of concern to both elderly people and their carers. However, regular visits from the project home care assistants assured that the secondary problem of the 'long lie' associated with falling would be minimised (Hall, M.R.P., 1982; Challis and Davies, 1986). Thirty-seven per cent of the project group and 27 per cent of the comparison group experienced breathlessness. Eyesight and hearing problems were experienced by smaller proportions of both groups. In spite of the number of project clients who had suffered strokes (over one-third), most were able to communicate in some manner, and only six clients could rarely or never make themselves understood, which was the case for four comparison group patients. Five project clients had very little comprehension, which was not a problem for any of the comparison group patients. A significant level of psychiatric disorder, in the form of depression or anxiety, also existed. Using the twelve-item General Health Questionnaire (Goldberg, 1972), 88 per cent of project clients and 94 per cent of the comparison group appeared to suffer from anxiety or depression. It might be unrealistic, however, to describe these high proportions as 'clinically depressed'; rather, the high proportion may be due to physical disorder and disability being closely associated with depression among the elderly (Murphy et al., 1988). As a result, the use of somatic questions to screen for psychiatric disorders is likely to have produced these high proportions of depressed elderly people (McDowell and Newell, 1987; Goldberg and Williams, 1988). Furthermore, as discussed in Chapter 4, the majority of project clients were discharged from acute wards, where their level of dependence precluded prompt discharge. It is possible they could feel discouraged and dispirited as they saw other patients come in, receive treatment, recover and leave. Therefore, it is not surprising to find that 88 per cent of the project clients appeared depressed before their discharge from hospital, particularly if they had been there for several months. Nearly one-third of the project group and over 40 per cent of the comparison group exhibited levels of confusion indicative of the presence of organic brain disease according to the indicators used (Bond et al., 1980).

Fifteen of the clients discharged for project care and support were suffering

Table 7.2
Health-related characteristics of the elderly people

	Project group %	Comparison group %	p value
Mobility			
Unaided/uses aids	30	21	ns
Assisted/chair or bed-bound	70	79	
Incontinence of urine			
Never	35	36	
Sometimes	24	20	ns
Frequently	41	44	
Incontinence of faeces			
Never	75	76	
Sometimes	16	17	ns
Frequently	9	7	
Giddiness			
None	13	24	
Moderate	32	21	ns
Severe	55	55	
Breathlessness			
None	64	74	
Moderate	27	20	ns
Severe	10	7	
Eyesight			
No problem	87	81	ns
Partially sighted/blind	13	20	
Hearing			
No problem	86	87	ns
Problems impairing communication	14	13	
Depressed mood[a]			
Present	88	94	ns
Absent	12	7	
Confusional states[a]			
Present	30	43	ns
Absent	70	57	

'ns' = not significant.
a 69 project cases; losses were mainly due to missing data for initial cases.

from an identified terminal illness and wished to be cared for and die in their own homes (seven women and eight men). Nine were discharged to live with a spouse or family, and six lived alone. Eleven of these clients had been diagnosed as suffering from cancers, including one with leukaemia; two were becoming very frail and deteriorating rapidly; one client had pneumo-coniosis with a severe chest infection as well as advanced Parkinsonism; and the final client diagnosed as terminally ill suffered from motor-neurone disease and, in defiance of all possible prediction and expectation, was still alive two and a half years after discharge from hospital. Only one of the comparison group patients was diagnosed as being terminally ill.

Table 7.3 shows the activities of daily living with which the elderly people needed help. The majority of elderly people in both groups had limited self-care ability. Everyone required help with bathing, and a large majority required help with dressing, toileting and transferring. Two-thirds of each group needed help with maintaining continence. The only significant dif-

Table 7.3
Help required with activities of daily living

Activity of daily living	Project group %	Comparison group %	p value
Bathing			
No help required	0	0	ns
Needs help	100	100	
Dressing			
No help required	14	25	ns
Needs help	86	75	
Toileting			
No help required	22	17	ns
Needs help	78	83	
Transferring			
No help required	14	17	ns
Needs help	86	83	
Continence			
No help required	32	35	ns
Needs help	68	65	
Feeding			
No help required	88	97	<0.05
Needs help	12	4	

'ns' = not significant.

ference between the groups appears to be that more of the project group clients needed help with feeding, which could perhaps be attributed to more than a third of them having suffered strokes. On average, elderly people in both groups needed help with four of the six activities listed in Table 7.3. Although being in hospital at the first interview, the majority of both groups were considered to be fully dependent on help with regular light household tasks, such as making meals, as well as with less frequent domestic tasks, such as cleaning, laundry and shopping.

The Clifton Assessment Procedures for the Elderly Behaviour Rating Scale (Pattie and Gilleard, 1979) was used to compare the two groups as well as to give a broad profile of the project group. This scale generates a set of four subscales in addition to the overall scale. These scales are: physical disability, apathy, communication difficulties, and social disturbance. It can be seen from Table 7.4 that the two groups were similar, except on social disturbance, on which the comparison group appeared to have a higher degree of impairment. This is consistent with the levels of cognitive impairment noted in Table 7.2. This would suggest in part a selection effect, since the project was concerned predominantly with physically frail but mentally alert elderly people, but also the differing pattern of psychiatric services available in the two areas, with consequent effects upon the composition of the geriatric long-stay population. The broad profile of the project group, according to the norms issued by Pattie and Gilleard, would suggest that they were similar to patients on an acute medical care ward. This is not surprising since, as we have described in Chapter 4, the clients selected for the project came predominantly from among patients who were identified as requiring long-stay care, but who were currently on the acute geriatric wards, often awaiting transfer.

Table 7.4
Mean CAPE BRS subscale and total scores

	Project group			Comparison group		
	Male	*Female*	*Total*	*Male*	*Female*	*Total*
Physical disability	6.5	6.1	6.2	5.9	5.9	5.9
Apathy	7.1	6.4	6.6	6.4	6.3	6.4
Communication difficulties	0.6	0.4	0.5	0.5	0.3	0.4
Social disturbance	0.8	0.9	0.8**	1.2	1.7	1.6**
BRS total score	14.8	13.7	14.1	14.0	14.3	14.2
Number of cases	36	65	101	41	72	113

** $p<0.01$.

Table 7.5 shows with whom the project clients were discharged from hospital to live. Of the 101 clients, 38 were discharged to live alone, of whom nine were men. Two of those discharged to live alone were women who had each spent approximately three years in long-term hospital care. They were both allocated new individual housing tenancies by voluntary housing associations and participated in choosing furnishings and decoration for their new homes prior to discharge. The others returned to existing tenancies or privately-owned accommodation. This encompassed the full variety of local authority flats and houses, privately-owned or rented flats, bungalows and houses, sheltered housing and, in one case, a privately-rented house in a poor state of repair. Sixty-three clients were discharged to live with family, relatives or 'others'. Of these, 42 returned to live with a spouse, and 25 of these clients were male. A further fifteen returned to live with family or relatives. Seven of these were women returning to live with sons, and it is interesting to note that only one of these men was married with a family (the remainder were single). Five clients, one of them male, returned to live with daughters, only one of whom had a family. The remaining three women lived with a sister, a sister-in-law and a grandson respectively. One client was discharged to live with her male lodger, who had in the past acted as her informal carer. The remaining five represented a group of long-term hospital patients with no home available. Three of these, one male and two females, were placed with two different families. For the woman placed by herself this arrangement was resoundingly successful, with the effect of considerably enhancing her social life and satisfaction (Braun and Rose, 1987; Oktay et al., 1988). However, in the case of the male and the female client who were placed in a second family, the arrangement broke down, leading to re-admissions to hospital for both. The reasons for the breakdown of care are examined later in the chapter. The other two were severely disabled women who had each spent two years or more in hospital care and who were accommodated in a specially-adapted group living home, each having a private bedroom and sharing communal living areas.

Table 7.5
Living group on discharge for project clients

Living group on discharge	Project group (%)
Alone	38
Spouse	42
Family	15
Family placement	3
Group home	2
Non-family 'others'	1
Number of cases	101

Social networks

Many studies have focused on the importance of understanding social networks. It has been proposed that social support contributes to mental health, as a causal factor in the development of neurotic disorders (Henderson et al., 1980a). In particular, the absence of a confiding relationship has been shown to increase vulnerability to depressive disorders (Brown and Harris, 1978; Murphy, 1982; Champion, 1989). Furthermore, it has been suggested that social relationships may act as a buffer against psychiatric morbidity in the face of adverse life events (Brown and Harris, 1978; Murphy, 1982). A lack of adequate social networks may result in an elderly person being more likely to enter residential care, or place heavy demands on domiciliary services because they are less able to call upon assistance than those with adequate networks (Wenger, 1989). Social integration has also been found to be associated with mortality in the elderly (Blazer, 1982; Seeman et al., 1987; Davidson et al., 1988), particularly in the light of the relationship between depression and mortality (Murphy et al., 1988; Jorm et al., 1991; Dewey et al., 1993).

At the first interview, both groups were asked about the number of children, relatives and friends who visited them in hospital. Few, only 6 per cent of project clients and 5 per cent of comparison group patients, had received no visitors during the previous week, and there was no difference between the two groups in the mean number of visits received (seven for the project clients and six for the comparison group patients).

However, merely knowing the number of a person's social relationships provides only a partial picture. It has been suggested that it is the quality rather than the quantity of social interaction that is the important factor; related to this is the extent to which a person feels content with their amount of social interaction (Henderson et al., 1980b, 1981).

The measurement of social relationships in this study was made using the Interview Schedule for Social Interaction (ISSI) designed by Henderson and colleagues (Henderson et al., 1980b, 1981). The schedule is described further in Chapter 3. This schedule was a development of the conceptual work of Weiss on the provision of social relationships (Weiss, 1974). It was designed to measure what social relationships and support are available to individuals and how adequate the individual perceives this network to be. This schedule was originally designed for use with a general population, and was subsequently adapted slightly for use with an elderly population (Henderson et al., 1986). A set of indices was computed referring to the availability and adequacy of both close relationships and the wider social network. Thus, four scores were computed, two for close 'attachment' networks and two for wider networks:

- The availability of attachment — a score based on eight items ascertaining the availability of close, confiding and emotionally intimate relationships.
- The adequacy of attachment — a percentage score of twelve items based

upon the number of relevant availability questions. This measures the individual's perceived adequacy of these attachments.

- The availability of social integration — a score of fifteen items ascertaining the availability of a wider social network of friends and neighbours.
- The adequacy of social integration — a score of sixteen items measuring the individual's perceived adequacy of this social network.

Although the ISSI information was collected at first interview and follow-up interview for both groups of elderly people, and four to six weeks after discharge from hospital for the project group, the information collected in hospital did not prove to be either valid or reliable given the context in which it was collected, where people's perceptions of contacts would either reflect ward routines or previously remembered patterns. Therefore, the ISSI information used for the analysis in this chapter was that obtained in the interview with project clients only, approximately four to six weeks after their discharge from hospital. Although interviews were undertaken with 82 project clients, it was decided to omit from the analysis those cases where a substantial amount of the information was missing, so as to avoid variability in the numbers of cases for the different scales. This provided information for 59 project clients.

The mean scores for these 59 cases for the four indices are shown in Table 7.6, where they are compared with the most appropriate available data, namely Australian samples in Hobart and Canberra (Henderson et al., 1981, 1986). The Australian samples appear to have a similar number of close relationships to the Darlington clients, but a far greater wider social network, involving at least twice as many people. Furthermore, the Australian samples appear to be more content with what they have. Although the low mean score for the availability of social integration for the Darlington clients may in part be due to the Darlington group being slightly older (mean age 80),

Table 7.6
Social interaction mean scores

	Darlington	Hobart over 65	Canberra over 65
Availability of attachment	4.9	5.6	5.3
Adequacy of attachment	71.6	94.6	85.0
Availability of social integration	2.8	7.8	5.6[a]
Adequacy of social integration	9.4	14.3	13.4[b]
Number of cases	59	268	51

Source for Australian data: Henderson et al. (1986).
a   Based on 16 items instead of 15.
b   Based on 17 items instead of 16.

particularly than the Canberra group (mean age 71), the main reason for the difference is likely to be that the Darlington group had been pre-selected as a frail, dependent group, unlike the community samples of both Hobart and Canberra. Therefore, the Darlington group are likely to have more restricted networks, primarily limited to family members (Bowling and Browne, 1991). Similarly, Gregson and colleagues (1993) found a third of stroke patients lacking wide networks of support on discharge from hospital. Furthermore, Wenger (1986, 1989) found that most members of the support and social networks of elderly people are family members and that, with increasing age and associated dependency, elderly people become more reliant on family members for support. However, it may also be the case that the particularly low score for the project clients represents a group of elderly people who are underestimating the amount and the adequacy of the social interaction they experience due to the presence of depressive disorders and, in some instances, exhibiting neurotic symptoms (Henderson, 1981).

Females obtained higher scores than males on all the indicators. However, this was statistically significantly higher for only the adequacy of social integration score ($p < 0.001$). This reflects the findings of other social network studies, where women generally have larger social networks than men and are more likely to have networks beyond immediate family members (Mugford and Kendig, 1986; Wenger, 1989). As may be expected, the availability of attachment score was statistically significantly higher for those elderly people living with a spouse compared with those living alone and those living with family or with others ($p < 0.001$).

Experience of services

Attitude to hospital care and hospital discharge. At their first interview, project clients were asked about their hopes and concerns about the prospect of being discharged from hospital. Thirty-seven per cent expressed positive hopes about discharge home while a further 54 per cent expressed negative attitudes to hospital care as their reason for wanting to return home. Those clients who anticipated positive gains from going home commented mainly on: wanting to be at home with their family; wanting to exercise more choice and control over their lives; anticipating a fuller life with more social contacts; viewing home as a place to be content as well as more comfortable or better fed; and simply wanting the privacy of their own home. The comments made by those who wanted to go home because of a dislike of hospital care were similar to comments made by the comparison group patients about what they disliked about being in hospital. Both groups commented on: their dislike of the regimentation and set routines of hospital care and the lack of choice; the distress caused by the noise and disturbance both day and night from other patients, especially the confused ones; feeling bored and cut-off from 'real life' and from their family and friends; and feeling depressed, hopeless and that life was empty. These comments reflect the mainly negative attitudes of many elderly people to geriatric hospital care both from those currently in geriatric units and from those living in their own homes (McAlpine and Wight, 1982; Salvage et al., 1988). Other anxieties expressed by the project clients before their discharge home centred on fears of burdening a spouse or other caring relatives (twelve clients). Significantly more of the project clients, 53 per cent compared with 28 per cent of comparison group patients, felt that they were already a burden on their family and friends at the first interview (p<0.01). At the follow-up interview, however, the figures were 43 per cent and 30 per cent respectively. This difference between the groups was no longer statistically significant, reflecting the support of the project to both clients and their carers. Anxiety was also expressed over managing at home in view of their loss of independence and mobility (eleven clients). Several clients also expressed concerns over being alone with nobody to call on during the night. This latter concern is examined in more detail in Chapter 4.

Service support: views at follow-up interview. At the follow-up interview six months later, both groups of elderly people were asked about the contact with or help they had received from health and social services during the previous six months. Thirteen of the comparison group patients had spent some time at home during the six months between interviews. The amount of time spent at home by these thirteen patients varied from four weeks to 24 weeks, out of a maximum of 26 weeks. Eleven of the thirteen received day hospital care, eight received community nursing, five received meals-on-wheels and eight received the home help service. Nine had contact with a social worker and similarly nine had contact with a general practitioner. Of the comparison group as a whole, 33 per cent received physiotherapy and 29 per cent occupational therapy.

Fifteen per cent of the project group received hospital relief care, 87 per cent community nursing, 18 per cent meals-on-wheels and 10 per cent the home help service. Sixty-nine per cent had contact with a general practitioner. Sixty-eight per cent received physiotherapy and 42 per cent received occupational therapy. All clients received support from care managers and all but one client had support from home care assistants. The exception was one of the three clients who were discharged to family placements.

Both groups were asked about what they felt were the good and bad things about being at home or in hospital. For the project clients the main positive comments centred on being able to exercise choice and to have family, friends and their own possessions around them at home. Whereas at the first interview, similar proportions (46 per cent of project clients and 44 per cent of comparison group patients) felt that their life was run too much by other people, at the follow-up interview significantly more of the comparison group patients (49 per cent, compared with 26 per cent of the project clients) felt this to be the case (p<0.01). Others commented on the advantage of being in their own home, with the many memories it contained. Many also commented on the ways in which the project was most helpful to them, which was mainly in providing personal care and being reliable, of a good standard and enabling them to remain at home. Few comments mentioned the negative aspects about being at home, although three clients mentioned being more lonely compared with being in hospital. Several clients observed that the least helpful thing about the project for them was that insufficient time was given for housework and outings, and three clients commented on difficulties caused by new and unfamiliar home care assistants, resulting from inevitable staff turnover.

Twenty-nine of the comparison group patients felt that the main advantage of being in hospital was that they got the care and attention they needed. Other positive comments mentioned the abundance of good food and the kind and good nurses, and the advantages of having companionship and activities to occupy them. Negative comments were similar to those made at the first interview.

The thirteen comparison group patients who had spent some time at home during the six months between interviews also commented on the services they received while at home. Six complained that a ramp or an aid either had not been supplied or was not in use because it was inappropriate. Interestingly, several also commented that the care supplied by services was either inadequate or uncoordinated. A study by Victor and Vetter (1988a) on discharging elderly people from hospital revealed that the elderly person's need for help at home had only been discussed in 55 per cent of cases. An assessment of the use of nursing and social services by elderly people discharged from hospital revealed similar complaints about service provision (Williams and Fitton, 1991). One of the main problems appeared to be insufficient or ineffective services. It was also discovered that elderly people who were subsequently re-admitted to hospital were four times more likely to have experienced multiple problems with services than those who remained at home (Williams and Fitton, 1991). If care management is to be effective, it must address these problems of coordination.

Eighty per cent of the project clients felt that they had been involved to some degree in planning the tasks of home care assistants. Ninety-three per cent felt that they were better off at home and only three per cent felt that they would be better off in hospital. Elderly people were asked if they had been able to discuss any difficulties or confide in any service providers. There was an overall significant difference between the two groups in those who confided in no one compared with those who confided in a service provider (p<0.001). Whereas only one-quarter of the comparison group said that they had confided in a service provider, 63 per cent of project clients said they had done so. Forty-one per cent of the project clients named a home care assistant as being the main person with whom they could discuss problems. This indicates the quality of relationships which had developed between some clients and their home care assistants, which sometimes also included the involvement of members of the home care assistant's family:

Mrs R. was an 81 year old widow, living alone in a socially isolated old property. From time to time she became confused, heard voices and disturbed neighbours by knocking and shouting at night. Her key home care assistant, who lived nearby, developed a close supportive relationship with Mrs R. which went far beyond the paid care role. Mrs R. was regularly taken on outings by the home care assistant and her family, and had made friends with the home care assistant's own elderly mother.

As described in more detail in Chapters 4 and 5, care managers sought to match clients and care assistants to facilitate good relationships wherever possible.

The outcomes of care

Destinational outcomes

Table 7.7 indicates destinational outcomes at six and twelve months after discharge for both the project and comparison groups. About two-thirds of the project group were still in their own homes after six months, and only three people were in institutional care, the remainder having died during the period. After twelve months, over 50 per cent were still at home. Although there was a significantly higher death rate in the project group after six months (X^2=13.38; p<0.001), this was not evident at twelve months (X^2=1.75; ns). One possible explanation for this is that fifteen of the 101 project cases were identified as requiring terminal care, whereas only one such case was identified in the comparison group. However, even excluding those people identified as terminally ill, the death rate in the project clients remains significantly higher at six months (X^2=4.77; p<0.05), although at twelve months the difference between the death rates of the two groups was no longer

Table 7.7
Destinational outcomes at six and twelve months

Location	Project group		Comparison group	
	6 months %	12 months %	6 months %	12 months %
At home	66	56	12	9
Institutional care	3	4	78	60
Dead	31	40	11	31
Number of cases	101	101	113	113

Overall chi-squared tests: at 6 months X^2 = 123.96 (p<0.001); at 12 months X^2 = 89.80 (p<0.001).

statistically significant. After excluding the terminal illness group, 30 per cent of each group had died after twelve months.

It is interesting to compare these figures with survival patterns in the Darlington long-stay wards which would have been the alternative form of care for most project clients. Patient deaths in the long-stay wards are difficult to calculate in a comparable way. If it is calculated as a proportion of those patients who had been resident in those wards through the year, a measure of the relative frequency of this form of turnover (Levine and Wright, 1957), the death rate in the long-stay wards was 32 per cent. This compares with 30 per cent for the project and comparison group when the terminally ill patients are excluded from the calculation.

Another explanation of the difference in death rate at six months may be that within the comparison population is a 'survivor' group effect which, as described earlier in this chapter, may also partly explain the greater length of stay in hospital for the comparison group patients. A further influence on mortality could be that the closer supervision and treatment of even minor ailments of patients in hospital may tend to increase their longevity. Nonetheless, mortality rates in such a vulnerable group must be expected to be high. A similar figure emerged in the study by Harwood and Ebrahim (1992) for hospital patients. In a further study of individuals aged 75 and over discharged to a care attendant scheme, 20 per cent of patients had died after twelve months. However, this group was less dependent than the project clients (Townsend et al., 1988). This is not dissimilar to the estimated mortality rate of 17 per cent per annum of residents in homes or long-stay hospital wards made by Jagger and colleagues (1993), again for a less dependent population.

A comparison was made between the destinational outcomes of those project clients who had been referred from long-stay wards, and those who had been discharged from other wards. The wards of referral to the project have been described in Chapter 3 and are shown in Table 4.1. It is possible that patients from long-stay wards might experience different outcomes from other patients, perhaps due to the effects of relocation. There has been a long-standing debate about the effects of relocation. Much of the early work seems to have focused upon the effects of relocation from an elderly person's own home to institutional care (Lieberman, 1961; Yawney and Slover, 1973; Tobin and Lieberman, 1976; Schulz and Brenner, 1977). The findings on the effects of transinstitutional relocation or relocation from institutional to home care is less conclusive, and some work suggests there is little relationship between relocation and mortality (Borup, 1983; Robertson et al., 1993). In a study of relocation of elderly people from one hospital to another by Harwood and Ebrahim (1992), 29 per cent were dead at six months, which is similar to the 31 per cent of the project cases. However, this was a group of elderly people with a much higher length of stay in hospital and slightly higher dependency levels. This study also found little evidence of a relocation effect and furthermore suggested possible beneficial effects from improved environmental circumstances (Haddad, 1981; Harwood and Ebrahim, 1992). A randomised controlled trial evaluating nursing home and long-stay geriatric hospital care reported that 32 per cent of those who entered two new nursing homes had died after a year, compared with 25 per cent of those who were randomly allocated to long-stay hospital care. This difference was not significant and, although the nursing home residents tended to deteriorate more rapidly in terms of their overall mental and functional ability and to experience a higher accident rate, there was clear evidence that quality of life in the nursing homes was superior to that on the wards (Bowling et al., 1991). Other studies have suggested that variations in relocation effects may be associated with subgroups within a relocated population, although the characteristics of such subgroups are difficult to identify (Pattie and Gilleard, 1978).

At least two other possible factors may cause the outcomes for long-stay patients to be different to those discharged from other wards. First, long-stay patients may have been admitted at an earlier period when admission criteria were less stringent. As such they might have lower morbidity which would work through to lower mortality levels. Second, a survival effect could be present along with the possible relocation effect. If acutely ill patients die relatively soon after admission and relocation effects are most potent in the first six months after admission, then those surviving more than six months may well be more hardy individuals. In this study, 26 of the 101 project patients were from long-stay wards, of whom ten had been there for more than six months. The destinational outcomes, in terms of institutionalisation, survival and remaining at home, were no different for those patients from long-stay wards compared with other patients at six and twelve months. Perhaps this is unsurprising since to some extent the boundary and the point of transfer between acute ward and long-stay ward are arbitrary. However, there did seem to be an indication that, for those project patients who had been in long-stay wards for more than six months, death rates were lower than for the other project patients: of the ten such patients, only one had died within twelve months. This effect was markedly different from the 39 out of the 91 other patients — a difference between a 10 per cent death rate and a 43 per cent death rate over twelve months ($p=0.08$, exact chi-squared, StatXact, 1989).

It is surprising, however, that a similar survival effect was less, if at all, evident for the comparison group. At six months, 13 per cent of those in hospital for less than six months, compared with 7 per cent of those in hospital for more than six months, had died. This was not a statistically significant difference. At twelve months, the death rates for these subgroups were almost identical at 30 and 33 per cent respectively.

Looking at these figures, there is no evidence to suggest any negative impact of relocation on the project patients. The higher death rate at six months in the project group is as likely to be attributable to a higher proportion of shorter-stay patients, as well as to the terminal illness factor discussed above.

Table 7.8 shows the average number of days per case spent in different settings for the first six months for each elderly person in the project and comparison groups (182 possible days). The average number of days that project clients were at home was 137, and the number of days in any form of institutional care was small. Overall, only 38 project clients experienced any form of institutional care during the six months. Following discharge, 23 clients had episodes of acute hospital care, fifteen had episodes of long-stay hospital care (eight for respite care), one person spent a period of time in a residential home and one person entered a private nursing home.

Table 7.8
Average number of days in different care settings

Setting	Project group		Comparison group	
	Days	*Range*	*Days*	*Range*
At home	137	3,182	12	0,166
Acute hospital	3	0,40	<1	0,14
Long-stay hospital	6	0,145	155	15,182
Private residential home	0	–	<1	0,40
Private nursing home	<1	0,24	3	0,110
Local authority home	<1	0,8	3	0,167

As noted above, thirteen of the comparison group patients spent some time at home during their six-month evaluation period. Nine of these spent more than half of this period at home, which accounts for the surprisingly high average of twelve days for the group as a whole. A few patients also spent some of this time in other care settings. One patient was discharged from hospital to a private residential care home, five to private nursing homes and three to local authority residential care homes, one of whom subsequently went home. Two patients were re-admitted for acute hospital care, one from a private nursing home and the other from a private residential home, and both subsequently died in hospital.

Thus, in line with the goals of the project, vulnerable elderly people were enabled to remain and be supported at home. Incidentally, it is worth noting that these data indicate the importance of a study design which uses a comparison group, since, despite being patients on a long-stay ward, an average of twelve days were spent at home over the six months by the comparison group. This indicates that the 'days at home gain' of the project was 125 (137-12) and not the 137 which might be concluded in the absence of a comparison group.

Quality of life and quality of care outcomes

The outcomes of the project for elderly people were measured by examining the differences between interview data collected before hospital discharge and six months after discharge. Equivalent measures were derived for comparison group patients. Comparisons between change scores were made using analysis of variance, and the initial difference in the levels of social disturbance in the two groups was statistically controlled using covariance analysis. The individuals identified as terminally ill were excluded from this analysis. The information from the Interview Schedule for Social Interaction (Henderson et al., 1980b, 1981) was omitted from the analysis of change, due to missing information on a large proportion of cases, especially at the follow-up interview at six months and due to the unreliability of the information collected in hospital, as noted earlier in the chapter.

Subjective wellbeing outcomes. Table 7.9 compares changes in subjective wellbeing indicators for elderly people followed up in the project and comparison groups. There was a statistically significant improvement in overall morale (Lawton, 1975; Challis and Davies, 1986) and a nearly statistically significant improvement in a measure of satisfaction with their current life situation, and a greater reduction in depression for those elderly people receiving the project compared with the comparison group. There was also a significant reduction in loneliness for the project clients. An example of the effects of the move from hospital to home on change in mood state was Mrs S.:

Mrs S. was a mentally alert, 88 year old widow who suffered from chronic arthritis and leg ulcers. In hospital she had suffered from sleeplessness,

Table 7.9
Subjective wellbeing indicators: mean change scores over six months

	Project group	Comparison group	p value[a]
General satisfaction	0.79	0.08	0.056
Satisfaction with life development	0.18	0.10	ns
Morale	1.74	0.21	0.037
Depression	-2.88	-1.05	<0.01
Loneliness	-0.84	0.23	<0.001
Number of cases (minimum)[b]	38	72	

a F-test. 'ns' = not significant.
b Minimum number of cases for which a comparison could be made, due to variable non-response to individual questions, losses due to deaths and missing initial data for project clients who entered the project at the beginning.

loss of interest in life and anxiety over other members of her family. She spent two months in a hospital ward before being discharged home with support from the project. After six weeks at home she reported a re-kindling of interest in reading a newspaper, listening to the radio and involving herself in what was happening in the outside world; she was sleeping well, feeling stronger and talked of her delight in having her own belongings around her which reinvolved her in control of her life and helped to restore her feelings of self-worth. She was a strong-willed independent person who was able to accept help as long as she felt it was 'on her terms'. She reported that the project help was able to adapt to her needs and was thus proving acceptable to her.

The only subjective wellbeing indicator which showed no improvement for the project group was the indicator of satisfaction with life development, which is based upon the person's perception of their experience of life as a whole. It is unlikely therefore that current situational changes, however valued or positive, would lead to a re-evaluation of previous life experience. The situationally-determined elements which are more amenable to change do appear to have moved in a positive direction for recipients of the project. This effect has also been observed in other studies (Gilleard et al., 1981).

Health and behavioural outcomes. Table 7.10 shows the health and behavioural change scores for both groups. Not surprisingly, there was little change in the score for the activities of daily living with which elderly people needed help over time and no significant difference between the groups. Although the change scores show a slight improvement, given the frailty of the elderly people

Table 7.10
Health and behavioural indicators: mean change scores over six months

	Project group	*Comparison group*	*p value*[a]
Activities of daily living	-0.19	-0.08	ns
CAPE BRS — physical disability	0.19	0.17	ns
CAPE BRS — apathy	-0.62	0.12	0.014
CAPE BRS — communication difficulties	0.07	0.11	ns
CAPE BRS — social disturbance	0.60	0.09	ns
CAPE BRS — total score	0.33	0.56	ns
Number of cases (minimum)[b]	57	99	

a F-test. 'ns' = not significant.
b Minimum number of cases for which a comparison could be made, due to variable non-response to individual questions, losses due to deaths and missing initial data for project clients who entered the project at the beginning.

it would be unlikely for there to be much, if any, improvement in a measurement of health over time. An analysis of the individual activities of daily living revealed that the majority remained at the same level of ability over time, and there were no individual statistical differences between the groups.

In the main, on most of the behavioural indicators derived from the CAPE BRS (Pattie and Gilleard, 1979), no marked changes were observable, as might be expected. However there was a significant reduction in apathy for project clients compared with those remaining in hospital. This was clear when clients were discharged and could exercise greater control over their environment. Thus, for example, clients would sometimes respond positively to the opportunity to influence the minutiae of everyday life. For example:

> Mrs T. was a 78 year old married woman who had suffered a major stroke which left her without speech, mobility, continence or even apparent comprehension. Her early rehabilitation progress was limited and she was transferred to a long-term care ward. However, her husband and family refused to accept this outcome and argued strongly for her right to be discharged and cared for at home. Within weeks of her discharge to her home in a small village, and to care by the project, she began to make progress. Over the next months, even without speech, she resumed control of her household — able to indicate approval or disapproval of all that went on around her. She received regular visits from family, friends and neighbours, and by the time of the follow-up interview at six months after her discharge she was able, by gestures and non-verbal responses, to reply to the majority of the questions. Clearly, much of this progress and reduction in apathy can be attributed to a gradual rehabilitation after her stroke, but this client appeared to lack the motivation for any successful rehabilitation until she was returned to her home environment with an adequate level of individual care and attention.

It is not perhaps surprising that most of the CAPE indicators do not show significant changes. It is probably unlikely that changes in social disturbance, communication difficulties or physical disability would arise as a result of discharge from hospital, although the greater degree of social activity and control over their own lives could account for the change in project clients' apathy level.

Quality of care outcomes. A number of different indicators of quality of care were considered. These included a measure, judged by the assessor, of the amount of care required in four areas of daily living — activities associated with rising and retiring; personal care such as toileting and transfer; daily domestic care such as meal preparation; and weekly domestic care such as laundry, shopping and heavy housework. Indicators of the client's perception of the 'reliability' of help received in each of these domains, the 'effectiveness' of that help (whether help was provided in the way in which it was needed) and the 'sufficiency' of that help (whether they received enough help) were derived from the relevant question across the four domains. These factors have been seen as important facets of community care from the client's perspective (Bayley, 1973; Challis, 1981).

From Table 7.11 it is clear that project clients experienced a significant gain in the number of social activities in which they participated, compared to long-stay patients in hospital. This latter finding supports other evidence of a low level of social activities in long-stay geriatric care (Wade et al., 1983; Neill et al., 1988). Using summary measures of client state from the Older Americans Resources and Services (OARS) (Duke University Center for the Study of Aging and Human Development, 1978), only the social resources indicator showed significant change. Whereas the project clients experienced improved social resources through time, the comparison group experienced an overall level of decline in their social resources.

Table 7.11
Quality of care indicators: mean change scores over six months

	Project group	Comparison group	p value[a]
Social activity level	6.48	2.08	0.011
Social resources	0.18	-0.15	0.017
Need for improvement in level of care	-4.94	-0.22	<0.001
Reliability of help	2.26	-0.33	<0.001
Effectiveness of help	2.93	-0.74	<0.001
Sufficiency of help	2.64	-0.38	<0.001
Adequacy of help — rising and retiring	2.11	-0.33	<0.001
Adequacy of help — personal care	2.30	-0.30	<0.001
Adequacy of help — daily domestic care	1.38	-0.38	0.002
Adequacy of help — weekly domestic care	1.69	-0.30	<0.001
Number of cases (minimum)[b]	42	76	

a F-test.
b Minimum number of cases for which a comparison could be made, due to variable non-response to individual questions, losses due to deaths and missing initial data for project clients who entered the project at the beginning.

Improvements in quality of care could involve environmental changes as well as personal help:

Mrs U. was an 80 year old widow who was physically frail and also at times mentally confused. Prior to her hospital admission she had lived alone in an old, neglected, privately-rented property, where she had been prone to falls, accidents, self-neglect and night disturbance. After a three-month hospital stay she continually refused to consider nursing home care and was eventually discharged home with project support. The care manager took the necessary steps to ensure house improvements were made while the key home care assistant set out to establish an acceptable routine of supervision, physical care, emotional support and social activity. Over the next months, good diet and reliable individual care led to physical improvement in Mrs U.'s health and less confused behaviour. She no longer spent long periods alone with consequent loss of night/day orientation, and her social isolation was reduced by the home care assistant's regular visits and by regular outings. Her physical environment was also improved by adaptations to her home.

For some clients, changes in social participation could be quite marked:

Mrs V. was a 75 year old widow who had spent nearly four years in a long-stay hospital ward following a severe stroke. She was wheelchair bound but mentally alert with no communication difficulties. Before her years in hospital she had been in residential care, so the prospect of discharge to a flat in sheltered accommodation meant a totally new start in independent living. She set out to maximise the opportunities of life in her new environment; she attended coffee and bingo sessions, received regular visits from another resident and from a Task Force visitor, and took particular pleasure in regular outings with her son or her home care assistant to collect her pension and purchase new furnishings or ornaments for her flat. In particular, Mrs V. commented on her pleasure in being able to offer her visitors a cup of tea, even if they had to make it themselves. Being able to offer hospitality did much for her sense of self-respect.

In terms of the more practical indicators regarding overall quality of care shown in Table 7.11, the project clients appeared to experience greater benefits than comparison group patients. The overall rating of need for additional care was significantly reduced, indicating a marked reduction in the shortfall between need and what was provided for the project clients. When the elderly people were asked about the reliability, effectiveness and the sufficiency of the help they received in the four areas of daily living activities, their perceptions of project services were that they were more reliable, effective and sufficient throughout. In all of these areas the project group showed a significant improvement over time, shown by the positive increase in the score, compared with the comparison group. The evidence thus suggests that the care provided to project clients was more adequate in each domain. Similar effects were found in a study in the USA, comparing nursing home support with community-based care (Braun and Rose, 1987).

Factors associated with the outcome of care

Social networks and project client wellbeing. Tables 7.12 and 7.13 present the results of the relationship between the four measures of social interaction, derived from the Interview Schedule for Social Interaction described earlier in this chapter, and outcome indicators for project clients. Table 7.12 shows the correlations between the social interaction scores and the level of client wellbeing at the follow-up interview at six months, and Table 7.13 shows the correlations between the different social interaction scores and client wellbeing change measures. The client wellbeing indicators included were the CAPE BRS subscores and total score, depression, PGC morale score, need for improvement in the level of care, social activities and a measure of organic disorder. Only those indicators where a correlation coefficient reached 0.2 or above are shown on Tables 7.12 and 7.13.

In Table 7.12 the number of social activities at follow-up interview was positively correlated with three of the measures of social integration. This could be attributed to those with more extensive social networks having greater opportunities for social activities, and those able to take part in social activities making more friends. There was a statistically significant association between inadequacy of attachment score and a measure of the need for improvement in the level of care, suggesting the important role played by close social relationships in the care of these elderly people, both in filling care gaps and in providing surveillance and support.

Table 7.12
Social networks correlated with project client wellbeing at follow-up

	Correlation coefficient
Availability of attachment	
Social activities	0.35*
Adequacy of attachment	
Need for improvement in care	-0.29*
Availability of social integration	
CAPE — apathy	-0.34*
CAPE — total score	-0.33*
Social activities	0.31*
Adequacy of social integration	
Depression (GHQ)	-0.26
CAPE — apathy	-0.26
CAPE — total score	-0.25
Social activities	0.31*

* $0.05 \geq p > 0.01$

Table 7.13

Social networks correlated with project client change measures

	Correlation coefficient
Availability of attachment	
CAPE — physical disability	-0.31*
CAPE — total score	-0.33*
Availability of social integration	
CAPE — social disturbance	-0.40**
CAPE — total score	-0.32*
Adequacy of social integration	
CAPE — social disturbance	-0.25
CAPE — total score	-0.32*

* $0.05 \geq p > 0.01$; ** $0.01 \geq p$

The negative association between the level of apathy at follow-up interview and the availability of social integration suggests a possible link between the opportunity for wider social activity and its impact upon mood state. Since opportunity for social integration is likely to be greater for those at home than in hospital, it is possible that this may account for some of the reduction in apathy for project clients over time. However, it is also the case that those individuals with a personality disposition to more apathetic behaviour would be likely to have less extensive social relationships.

The CAPE BRS total score at follow-up interview was also significantly negatively correlated with the availability of a wider social network, perhaps demonstrating the limitations imposed by severe frailty on the ability to take part in a wider social network (Jorm et al., 1991). Similarly, the CAPE BRS mean change score was significantly negatively correlated with the three measures of social interaction shown in Table 7.13, associating higher levels of social interaction with a lower decline in health status. The negative correlation between physical disability and the availability of attachment implies again that increasing physical ill health may affect an elderly person's ability to keep up with even close contacts (Wenger, 1989, 1992). There was a significant association between social disturbance and the availability of a wider social network, suggesting how adverse behaviours associated with cognitive impairment may impinge upon an elderly person's ability to continue relationships beyond close family members (Wenger, 1994).

These analyses appear consistent with the view that those elderly people with more extensive and adequate social networks may experience an improved quality of life, and even aspects of their health and wellbeing may be protected (Brown and Harris, 1978; Murphy, 1982). However, there is also the possible confounding effect that some aspects of an elderly person's personality, or specific behavioural problems, may affect their ability to take part in, and thus benefit from, social networks. Although the causal direction may work in both ways, it is likely that project intervention, through hospital discharge, permitted a greater degree of social integration than otherwise would have been the case, and thereby led to some positive effect of social integration upon wellbeing.

Factors associated with the breakdown of project care. During the monitoring phase of the project, thirteen clients receiving the project services (nine women and four men) were re-admitted to long-stay institutional care. For some clients, however, this may be seen as the end of a successful period of project support rather than the breakdown of care, given that many had been cared for at home by the project for some time prior to this re-admission. Seven of these thirteen clients had carers and these cases are described further in Chapter 8. Of the thirteen cases, two women had been receiving project services for more than two years; four clients (three women and one man) for more than one year; three clients (two women and one man) for more than six months; and four clients (two women and two men) for less than six months. Of the clients supported at home for between six and twelve months, one woman entered a nursing home because, despite their best efforts, the project was unable to fulfil her needs for stimulating companionship. She was lonely, having been socially active with the church and other activities when younger. Her care manager commented how this indicated the importance of understanding a client's needs by looking at the person in the context of their life pattern and expect-ations, and not only focusing upon the here and now.

The project appeared to be less of a success for the four clients who had received the project service for less than six months before re-admission became necessary. Of these, one man who had been discharged to a family placement exhibited behavioural problems and was described as behaving in a sexually inappropriate way. This necessitated his re-admission to hospital after thirteen weeks. The remaining three clients were supported by the project for less than six weeks. None had carers, and two (one man and one woman) were discharged to live alone and the third (a woman) to a family placement. A factor common to these four cases appears to be features assoc-iated with the problems of depressive mood states (Lindesay and Murphy, 1989). Their depression scores, as measured by the General Health Question-naire (Goldberg, 1972), were generally higher than the average for the group as a whole. It is interesting that one of these clients lacked any motivation in hospital and nursing staff were not too hopeful that this patient could be cared for successfully at home. She remained unmotivated once back in hospital and died soon afterwards. Another was hostile to the project help and he was re-admitted when he became depressed and threatened to commit suicide. The last client exhibited a number of problems, including demanding behaviour and reluctance to do anything for herself, which led to her re-admission from a family placement. This suggests that, given the high prevalence of psychiatric problems among frail elderly people, psychiatric assessment may be helpful for some individuals before discharge to such a scheme (Bergmann and Eastham, 1974; Tench et al., 1992; Ardern et al., 1993). Interestingly, of these four cases, two had been discharged to family placements where managing problems of mood state may have been particularly difficult.

Factors associated with non-survival of project clients. It has been shown in Table 7.7 that 31 per cent of the project clients had died by the end of six months. Given this relatively high death rate, it is interesting to explore whether any factors appeared to be systematically associated with non-survival. The presence of such general predictions could be helpful in planning for the utilisation and turnover of people using such a service. The influence of terminal illness upon death rate has already been noted, and here the influence of several client-related factors (sex, age, dependency, presence or absence of carer, and continence) upon the probability of survival over six months are also explored. The method used was logistic regression analysis, which is a multivariate technique designed to predict the probability of a binary outcome, in this case survival or non-survival. The results are shown in Table 7.14.

Factors which proved to be associated with non-survival have a positive coefficient and those associated with survival a negative one. Thus, in effect,

Table 7.14
Factors predicting non-survival of project clients

Variable	Coefficient	Std error	Wald statistic[a]	p value
Constant	-24.39	7.98	9.34	0.002
Terminal illness	4.70	1.20	15.43	<0.001
Physical disability (CAPE)	0.55	0.31	3.12	0.077
Male/physical disability (CAPE)	0.92	0.38	5.85	0.016
Apathy (CAPE)	5.68	2.18	6.80	0.009
Apathy (CAPE), squared	-0.34	0.14	5.71	0.017
Male/apathy (CAPE)	-0.82	0.36	5.20	0.023
Incontinence	-1.34	0.71	3.58	0.059
Carer	-2.31	0.78	8.72	0.003

Correct predictions = 87%
Goodness of fit chi-squared = 84.73
p value = 0.665
df = 91

a The Wald statistic is the coefficient divided by the standard error, squared. Under the hypothesis of a zero coefficient, it has a chi-squared distribution with one degree of freedom.

the equation predicts the probability of death over a six-month period given the characteristics of the elderly person in hospital. The p-value, p=0.665, is associated with the goodness of fit chi-squared, 84.73, which indicates that the model does not differ significantly from the best possible model. Not surprisingly, given our earlier observations about the effect of a diagnosis of terminal illness, this proved to be a powerful predictor of non-survival. In addition, the greater a person's physical disability, the greater the probability of their death within the six-month period (Jorm et al., 1991). This effect was much stronger for male clients. Apathy, probably associated with depression, was also associated with non-survival, in this case particularly for female clients. Given the association between the presence of physical disorders and depressed mood (McDowell and Newell, 1987; Goldberg and Williams, 1988), these findings are again perhaps not surprising. The negative quadratic term for apathy indicates that although there is a positive relationship between levels of apathy and non-survival, this relationship increases more slowly at higher levels of apathy. Other factors associated with survival include the presence of a carer and whether the elderly person suffered from incontinence. Although this effect of incontinence may seem surprising, it must be remembered that this prediction is only over a short period of six months and many of the elderly people in this study with chronic disorders, particularly of bladder function, survived beyond six months.

Effects on the case-mix of elderly people. Having examined the effects of the project on those elderly people who received it, it is interesting to consider whether the project had any effect on the hospital system as a whole. The project, unlike many attempts to discharge long-stay patients, was operating from a mainly acute hospital and therefore closures of beds, or wards, would not automatically lead to the closure of the hospital but only to sectors within it. In fact, during the life of the project, two long-stay wards in the main hospital were closed. These savings made funding available for the continuation of the service after the project phase, which is described in Chapter 10. However, there may be more subtle system effects of the project, detectable in changes in the nature of the patient population over time, as much as the more crude indicator of numbers of beds closed.

Annual censuses were held of the hospital population aged 65 and over between 1983 and 1987 (Acquilla et al., 1987c). The number of patients in long-stay wards declined from 162 in 1983 to 145 in 1986, and then dropped to 124 in 1987 as a result of the closure of one long-stay geriatric ward in the Memorial Hospital. The second ward closed in 1988. However, the declining numbers of long-stay patients in hospital in the context of a geriatric home care service like that developed in Darlington, may be less significant than changes in the nature of the patient population itself. Bed-blocking and the inappropriate placement of patients in hospital wards have been long-standing concerns within geriatric medicine (Rubin and Davies, 1975; McAlpine, 1979; Seymour and Pringle, 1982). There appears to have been a noticeable reduction in median lengths of stay in the hospital as a whole between 1983 and 1987. Median lengths of stay in 1986 (25 days) and 1987 (28 days) were much lower than in 1984 (36 days) and 1985 (50 days). In the long-stay wards too, median lengths of stay declined from 508 days in 1984 to 461 days in 1985, 455 in 1986 and 415 in 1987.

Table 7.15 shows the main reason why patients remained in hospital for each of the five censuses. It appears that there was a decline in the proportion of patients recorded as requiring long-stay care in hospital. At the same time, a higher proportion of patients were remaining in hospital for rehabilitation or continuing treatment. These changes appear to have taken place around the time that a substantial number of patients were being discharged to the project, and it would not be unreasonable to attribute at least some of this decline in patients requiring long-stay care, and the increase in the proportion of patients remaining in hospital for health care related reasons, to the existence of the project. Following the start of the project in 1985, only one patient could be identified who had been in a medical, surgical or orthopaedic ward for more than three months and who required long-stay care. The comparable figure in 1984 was nine. Of course, such a process of decline in long-stay beds was occurring in many geriatric settings. Based upon two censuses of long-term patients in Canterbury over a similar period, one in 1984 and one in 1989, Jenkinson and colleagues (1992) report a decline in beds from 127 to 66. Patients in the 1989 census were more physically dependent according to the Barthel index (Collin et al., 1988), and showed a higher degree of cognitive impairment using the Abbreviated Mental Test (AMT) (Hodkinson, 1972) than those in 1984. The authors suggested that this more dependent group represents a core of patients who are difficult to place outside hospital.

The Darlington census data permitted such a comparison only between 1985 and 1987, when bed numbers decreased from 133 to 99, where the underlying trend might have insufficient time to make an impact. Individual

Table 7.15
Main reason why patients are still in hospital by year of census

Main reason why still a patient	1983 %	1984 %	1985 %	1986 %	1987 %
Rehabilitation/treatment	46	47	44	52	50
Requires long-stay care	44	42	45	32	36
Social reasons	9	5	3	5	5
Holiday/short-term care	0	4	6	7	5
Other/not known	1	1	2	3	4
Number of patients	392	425	333	351	347

Source: Acquilla et al. (1987)

activities of daily living and a nurse rating of cognitive impairment were obtained instead of the continuous measures used by Jenkinson and colleagues (1992). There was no individual difference which reached a satisfactory level of significance. However, comparing the 1987 group with the 1985 group showed that the 1987 group were more impaired with regard to washing, dressing, transferring, toileting and incontinence, while the 1985 group were more impaired only with regard to mobility. It may be the case, therefore, that the lack of evidence of significant change in physical dependency or cognitive impairment over time in the Darlington hospital long-stay population was due to the relative insensitivity of the measures used.

Conclusions

Overall the evidence suggests that those patients who were discharged to the Darlington Project were better off by most criteria than comparison group patients remaining in long-stay hospital care. Few project clients spent time in other forms of care. Despite a higher death rate at six months for project clients, in the main they also experienced significantly greater wellbeing in terms of their quality of life, significantly greater social activity, and better quality of care compared with the comparison group.

Although there would seem to be good reasons for suggesting that the impact of the project service upon patients was a direct consequence of the type and style of service received, it would also be possible to suggest that some of these gains were mediated through project clients' social networks, albeit if access to such networks was itself a consequence of project intervention.

Furthermore, it appears that the project may also have had an effect on the use of long-stay beds in the hospital which discharged the clients for the project. Both the reductions in the number of long-stay beds and the number of patients occupying long-stay beds in inappropriate departments of the hospital could be attributed in some part to the provision of the project.

8   The Experience of Carers

Research into the experiences, needs and problems of informal carers is by no means new, although in recent years there has been a substantial increase in the amount of research and review literature in this area. It has been calculated that about one adult in seven is involved in looking after an elderly or disabled relative. Overall, 15 per cent of adult females (3.5 million in all) and 12 per cent of adult males (2.5 million in all) defined themselves as carers in a study of informal carers based upon General Household Survey data (Green, 1988). This represents about six million carers in all, and the majority (75 per cent) were looking after a person aged 65 and over. Most carers — three out of four — are women, usually daughters, wives and mothers of their dependants. Most are in middle or late middle age, and growing numbers are themselves elderly (Hicks, 1988). In recent years it has become clear that more men are involved in providing care than was previously thought to be the case. This is largely accounted for by the numbers of elderly male spouse carers (Arber and Gilbert, 1989). Informal care has become recognised as playing a central role in the provision of community care. Recent policy documents in the United Kingdom and overseas have recommended that carers' views and needs should be taken into consideration (Griffiths, 1988; Thorslund and Parker, 1994) and the White Paper on community care (Cm 849, 1989) affirms that practical support for carers should be one of the six key objectives for service delivery (para. 1.1). Underlying this view of the centrality of informal care is the perception that public support for carers represents a long-term investment. Such a view is also evident in other countries (Kraan et al., 1991). Given the extent and importance of the role of informal carers in the provision of care and support to elderly people, it was important to establish the effects of the project on the carers of those elderly people who received it.

As explained in Chapter 3, research interviews were carried out with three groups of carers. The first group were those who were carers of a client of the Darlington Project; this group is referred to as 'project carers'. These carers were interviewed on two occasions: about two weeks after discharge of the elderly person and again at six months. A second group of carers in Darlington, whose elderly relatives attended the local day hospital but otherwise received traditional service support at home, have been compared with the project carers. This was designed to provide a picture of the experience of caring for a frail elderly person at home receiving the usual range of services. This group is referred to as 'day hospital carers'. The third group were carers of elderly people in long-term hospital care in a neighbouring health authority, these elderly people formed part of the client 'comparison group'. This third group of carers is referred to as 'hospital carers'. The hospital and day hospital carers were interviewed on one occasion since it was not appropriate to collect measures of change. It will be remembered from Chapter 3 that a before-and-after measurement of the effects of the service on the project carers was not feasible, since it was impossible to see carers before they were apprised of the discharge of the elderly person from hospital. Interviews were undertaken with 75 project carers, 27 hospital care carers and 30 day hospital carers. Thus a comparison was made between the experience of carers of elderly people receiving the services of the project, carers of elderly people receiving the usual home care services and carers of elderly people receiving long-stay hospital care.

This chapter is in two parts. The first concentrates on the three groups' experiences of caring: the tasks they performed, the elderly person's behaviour, and the burdens of caring as well as the distress associated with these experiences (Platt, 1985). It also examines the informal and formal support received by the three groups as well as the perceived benefits of caring. The second part of this chapter examines the factors that were associated with the breakdown of care in the project group, the indicators of burden and stress, the individual factors that were associated with variation in the levels of stress and, finally, an attempt is made to explain which factors appear to have had the greatest influence on carer stress for the three groups of carers.

The experience of caring

The elderly people

There were relatively few differences between the three groups of elderly people with identified carers. Full interviews were not undertaken with the elderly people who attended the day hospital, although the Clifton Assessment Procedures for the Elderly Behaviour Rating Scale (CAPE BRS) was completed (Pattie and Gilleard, 1979), which provided information on their level of dependency. Table 8.1 shows the mean CAPE BRS subscales and total scores for those elderly people with carers in the three groups. Dependency, as measured by the CAPE BRS, was graded by Pattie and Gilleard

Table 8.1

Mean CAPE BRS subscale and total scores for elderly people with carers

CAPE BRS scales	Project	Hospital	Day hospital
Physical disability	6.5	6.5	6.6
Apathy	6.5	6.7	6.1
Communication difficulties	0.5	0.6	0.9
Social disturbance	0.8[a]	2.0[a]	2.6[a]
BRS total	14.4	15.7	16.2
Number of cases	75	27	30

a   Overall analysis of variance, $p<0.001$.

(1979) into five categories, ranging from independent to maximum dependency. The total scores for the three groups fall into the fourth, or high dependency, category. This category represents marked impairment and such people are usually institutionalised and need considerable help with daily living. This category also contains the greatest overlap between those in social services accommodation and those in hospital care (Pattie and Gilleard, 1979). The only significant difference between the groups was on the measure of social disturbance, where the mean score was significantly lower for the project group compared with the hospital and day hospital groups. This may suggest in part a selection effect, since the project was mainly concerned with physically frail but mentally alert elderly people. However, at the second interview the mean score on this measure for the project group had increased significantly from 0.8 to 1.4 ($p<0.05$), similar to the trend within the project group as a whole, as noted in Chapter 7, which may suggest that at initial interview social disturbance was less evident due to the elderly people being located in the relatively restricted environment of acute wards with busy routines. There were no significant sex differences between the three groups, although there were more females in the project group (63 per cent, compared with 52 per cent of the hospital group and 50 per cent of the day hospital group). The sex distribution, and the relationship between the elderly people and their carers, are shown in Table 8.2.

Carer characteristics

Table 8.3 describes the three groups of carers. There were no statistically significant age and sex differences between the three groups. The mean age of the three groups of carers ranged from 59 years for the hospital carers to

Table 8.2
Relationship of carer to the elderly person by sex

| | Elderly person | | | | | |
| | Project | | Hospital | | Day hospital | |
Carer	Male	Female	Male	Female	Male	Female
Male spouse	–	14	–	3	–	6
Female spouse	20	–	6	–	13	–
Son	2	5	0	2	0	0
Daughter	2	15	3	8	1	4
Other male	2	3	2	0	0	0
Other female	2	10	2	1	1	5[a]
Total number	28	47	13	14	15	15

a   This includes one carer who was caring equally for her mother-in-law and father-in-law, although only the mother-in-law attended the day hospital.

66 years for the day hospital carers. Not surprisingly, the proportion of female to male carers was higher for all three groups. Approximately two-thirds of the project carers, three-quarters of the hospital carers and four-fifths of the day hospital carers were female. Although there was a greater number of married carers in the day hospital group, there was no statistically significant difference between those who were married and those who were not across the three groups.

A larger percentage of the day hospital carers were spouse carers compared with the other two groups, also shown on Table 8.2, although again this was not a statistically significant difference. For the hospital carers there was a larger percentage of daughter or son carers. However, this may be due to a larger number of daughters and sons visiting the elderly person in hospital, and thus being selected for interview. However, there was no significant difference in the proportions of spouse carers, daughter or son carers, and carers with another relationship to the elderly person between the three groups.

In fact, the only significant individual difference between the groups was that a greater number of the day hospital carers were living with the elderly person (p<0.01). This is due to the combined effect of there being more spouse carers in this group than in the other two groups, and a greater number of elderly people living with relatives. The selection of more spouse carers in this group may be due to the pattern of utilisation of day hospital provision, since an elderly person living on their own before a hospital admission may be more likely to be discharged to residential care whereas they may be more

Table 8.3
Characteristics of the carers

	Project	Hospital	Day hospital	p value
Number of carers	75	27	30	–
Mean age in years	63	59	66	ns
Sex (%)				
Male	35	26	20	
Female	65	74	80	ns
Marital status (%)				
Married/co-habiting	75	85	90	
Single	13	4	3	
Widowed	7	7	3	ns [a]
Separated/divorced	5	4	3	
Relationship to elderly person (%)				
Spouse	45	33	63	
Daughter/son	32	48	17	
Daughter-in-law/son-in-law	1	7	10	
Niece/nephew	1	–	3	ns [b]
Sister/brother	1	7	–	
Sister-in-law/brother-in-law	3	–	–	
Other	16	4	7	
Living with elderly person/lived with before admission (%)				
Yes	65	56	93	
No	35	44	7	< 0.01

'ns' = not significant.
a Two categories: married/cohabiting *v* three remaining categories.
b Three categories: spouse *v* daughter/son *v* five remaining categories.

likely to be discharged home with the provision of the day hospital service if there is a carer at home. The lack of informal support in the community has been found generally to be a precipitating factor in the application of elderly people for local authority homes. This is especially the case when there is no supporting spouse (Bland and Bland, 1985; Neill et al., 1988; Booth, undated). Under 10 per cent of new admissions have been found to be married (Booth, undated). A third of the residents of local authority homes have been found to have been admitted direct from hospital, and in these cases it appears that their own home had already been given up, thus limiting their options (Bland and Bland, 1985).

Care tasks performed

Table 8.4 shows the frequency with which care tasks were undertaken and the distress that was associated with the performance of these tasks. Hospital carers were excluded from these comparisons, as they were not routinely performing 'hands-on' care tasks for their relatives, since they received such care from the nursing staff.

The table shows the percentages of each group that performed each task daily (that is at least once a day) and weekly (that is, less often than daily but at least once a week). The percentage of each group experiencing moderate or severe distress associated with the performance of these tasks and the percentage of those describing themselves as resigned to the performance of these tasks have also been included. Resignation has been acknowledged as a form of distress for carers, although in another study resignation was treated as synonymous with no distress (Levin et al., 1989). As Chapter 3 explains, the category was included to cover distress over problems that had existed for some considerable time (Platt et al., 1980), and it was felt that a response of resignation was a form of distress for the carers, albeit of a more chronic kind. Thus there are indicators of the amount of activity performed by the different groups of carers and also of the degree of distress of those performing the activity. In some ways, the aggregate wellbeing of the two groups of carers could be seen as a combination of the two, care and stress, a multiplicative relationship between the overall amount of activity and level of distress. The project carers would appear to have benefited particularly on such an indicator, although we have not used it here.

The project carers were receiving regular daily support from the home care assistants, who performed many of the personal and domestic care tasks. As a consequence, fewer of the project carers performed the majority of these tasks on a daily basis compared with day hospital carers. Whereas 77 per cent of the day hospital carers helped the elderly person in and out of bed each day, only 32 per cent of the project carers did so. Fewer project carers spent time supervising the elderly person (p<0.06), and equally were less distressed by this. Although the greater amount of time spent by the day hospital carers in supervising the elderly people may be explained by the majority of these carers living with the elderly persons, their greater amount of distress reflects the findings of other studies that providing constant supervision is stressful (Gilleard, 1984). On the whole, those project carers who were performing these tasks appeared to experience less distress and feel less resignation about the performance of the tasks than the day hospital carers. Whereas 39 per cent of those day hospital carers who helped the elderly person in and out of bed said that they were distressed by it, and 25 per cent said they were resigned to it, this was the case for only 17 per cent and 2 per cent of the project carers respectively. Although a similarly large proportion of each group spent time daily with the elderly person for companionship, a far higher proportion of the day hospital carers (67 per cent)

Table 8.4
Care tasks and associated distress for carers

| | Frequency performed | | | | | Associated distress for carers performing task | | | | |
| | Daily[a] | | Weekly[b] | | p value[c] | Distressed | | Resigned | | p value[d] |
Tasks	Project %	Day hosp. %	Project %	Day hosp. %		Project %	Day hosp. %	Project %	Day hosp. %	
Helping in and out of bed	32	77	7	7	<0.001	17	39	2	25	<0.001
Personal care/heavy lifting	63	73	11	13	ns	27	50	10	23	<0.01
Regular pop-in checks	84	97	12	3	ns	24	45	18	35	<0.01
Supervision	65	90	8	3	ns	24	38	23	45	<0.01
Preparing meals	73	97	7	0	<0.05	2	7	2	17	<0.01
Light housework	77	93	9	7	ns	3	23	3	17	<0.01
Managing soiled linen	24	10	8	27	<0.05	17	23	3	13	<0.001
Tasks outside the home	12	3	79	90	ns	10	10	17	30	ns
Time for companionship	81	90	15	7	ns	25	67	15	17	ns
								15	10	<0.001

'ns' = not significant.

a At least once a day.
b Less often than daily but at least once a week.
c Significance of difference between the groups in frequency of tasks performed (exact chi-squared test, StatXact, 1989).
d Significance of difference between the groups in associated distress/resignation (exact chi-squared test, StatXact, 1989).

than project carers (25 per cent) felt distressed about spending time this way. The project carers had the support of the home care assistants and therefore experienced fewer demands on their time from the elderly person, and this may explain why they found devoting time for companionship less distressing:

> The carer of a project client, a married daughter caring for her mother, commented that before her mother's admission to hospital she had been visiting her four times a day to perform these care tasks and was finding the distress and tiredness levels high at that stage. But now, with the project's help, she visited once a day and found this quite an acceptable and manageable level of care and therefore was able to enjoy the time she spent with her mother.

Home care assistants could also, by negotiation or request, take the elderly client on outings, or sit with them to give the carer some personal time. Overall, the help and support of the home care assistants gave the carers more choice about the kinds of task they would perform and enabled them to avoid any that they found difficult or distasteful. It also enabled the carers to perform fewer care tasks and allowed them greater choice over the times they performed the tasks. Given these circumstances, it is likely that these carers would experience less burden from care tasks:

> By contrast, the nature of distress experienced by some of the day hospital carers can be illustrated by the experience of a 79 year old woman caring for her 83 year old husband after his stroke. She was routinely coping with washing, bathing, dressing, lifting and transferring her husband, as well as dealing with meals, laundry and nocturnal disturbance. As he was unable to stand unaided, she had to kneel to wash and dress him and found this, combined with the difficulty of lifting him in and out of his chair, caused her exhaustion and severe back pain, especially as she was herself suffering from glaucoma and circulatory problems.

Behaviours experienced

The impact on the carer of individual aspects of the elderly person's behaviour were examined. These included features such as underactivity, night disturbance, forgetfulness, misery, overdependence, withdrawal, indecisiveness, odd ideas, embarrassing behaviour and incontinence. Such behaviour problems have been found to be poorly tolerated by carers in many studies (Isaacs, 1971; Sanford, 1975; Greene et al., 1982; Gilleard, 1984; Argyle et al., 1985; Morris, R.G. et al., 1988; Levin et al., 1989). The common features that emerge from these and other studies are that, in general, problems of incontinence, night disturbance, demanding behaviour and apathy are frequently reported as causing distress to carers. This may be due mainly to the difficulty for carers in coming to terms with these problems, particularly when they may be perceived as deliberate attempts to upset the carer (Gilleard, 1984). The psychological and physical aspects of the elderly person's behaviour and the distress for carers associated with these are shown in Table 8.5. The table shows the percentages of the three groups of carers who experienced these behaviours and their associated distress.

Overall, certain aspects of the elderly person's behaviour associated with psychological or mental health problems appear to have been experienced by a greater percentage of the day hospital carers than the project carers. This is consistent with the higher mean CAPE BRS social disturbance score for elderly people in the day hospital group (see Table 8.1). Apart from the risk of falling, similar proportions of each group experienced physical problems.

The extent to which some individual behaviours were experienced by the carers varied among the groups. Elderly people in hospital were seen as being at a lower risk of falling than the other two groups. Unsurprisingly, they were also seen as causing less nocturnal disturbance ($p<0.01$), and much less distress was evident for their carers over this. As would be expected, this appeared to be a far greater problem for the day hospital carers, most of whom lived with the elderly person, and for project carers. A larger percentage of the day hospital attenders also exhibited uncooperative behaviour ($p<0.05$), indecisiveness ($p<0.05$), and embarrassing behaviour ($p<0.05$), again reflecting the higher mean CAPE BRS social disturbance score for this group. For some of these behaviours which are particularly associated with psychological or mental health problems, such as exhibiting odd ideas and indecisive behaviour, the hospital carers seemed more resigned to and less distressed by the presence of these behaviours than the other two groups. For these carers it appears that the hospital setting may render such problems less distressing.

Other problems experienced by the carers which have not been tabulated include aggressiveness and speech difficulties. Aggressiveness was experienced by only 3 per cent of the project carers, but by 11 per cent of the hospital carers and 17 per cent of the day hospital carers. Speech difficulties were encountered mainly by the day hospital carers, 37 per cent compared with 20 per cent of the project carers and 22 per cent of the day hospital carers.

There is, of course, a problem in separating the apparently 'objective' elements of behaviour from the 'subjective' elements of distress. An unsupported carer, experiencing heavy demands in caring for an elderly person, might be more likely to report a problem as present than one receiving more support.

Table 8.5
Elderly person's behaviour and associated distress for carers

| | Present | | | | Associated distress for carers experiencing behaviour | | | | | | |
| | | | | | Distressed | | | Resigned | | | |
Aspects of behaviour	Project %	Hosp. %	Day. hosp. %	p value[a]	Project T %	Hosp. hosp. %	Day %	Project %	Hosp. hosp. %	Day %	p value[b]
Psychological problems											
Slowness	77	77	97	ns	41	35	41	29	35	48	ns
Underactivity	76	92	93	<0.05	22	50	57	42	38	32	<0.01
Nocturnal disturbance	62	35	77	<0.01	51	0	35	24	33	57	<0.001
Forgetfulness	61	73	77	ns	30	32	35	25	37	52	ns
Misery	59	81	73	ns	77	57	73	10	38	27	<0.05
Overdependence	55	58	73	ns	56	40	50	31	47	36	ns
Complaints about aches and pains	50	65	67	ns	39	71	30	27	12	45	ns
Uncooperative	41	42	70	<0.05	67	46	62	19	55	38	ns
Worry	41	54	43	ns	52	21	39	11	57	39	<0.05
Withdrawal	35	39	53	ns	61	50	50	9	20	19	ns
Indecisiveness	33	46	63	<0.05	27	8	32	23	83	58	<0.01
Odd ideas	33	46	37	ns	27	8	73	41	50	27	<0.05
Irritability	27	35	33	ns	72	33	30	28	56	60	ns
Embarrassing	14	27	40	<0.05	78	100	75	22	0	25	ns

Physical problems

Risk of falling	91	69	90	<0.05	49	39	63	20	28	30	ns
Requiring physical or nursing care	85	81	93	ns	21	14	21	29	38	54	ns
Incontinence — urine	80	77	60	ns	40	40	11	21	45	61	<0.05
Incontinence — faeces	48	40	40	ns	45	40	50	36	40	33	ns

'ns' = not significant.

a Significance of difference between the groups in presence of behaviour (exact chi-squared test, StatXact, 1989).

b Significance of difference between the groups in associated distress/resignation (exact chi-squared test, StatXact, 1989).

The burdens of caring

While community care has at times been seen as a cheap option compared with the cost of institutional care, it may be argued that this merely represents the transfer of economic cost from the formal sector to a variety of costs for the informal sector. Informal carers experience a variety of costs in economic terms, through loss of employment or restricted employment (Nissel and Bonnerjea, 1982; Wright, 1983), as well as effects or burdens on their social lives and leisure time, on the household as a whole, and on both their physical and mental health. These costs have been directly or indirectly attributed to caring for a dependent person (Grad and Sainsbury, 1965, 1968; Gilleard et al., 1984; Levin et al., 1989; Parker, 1990).

The burdens which have been examined include the effects on children in the household, such as their physical and emotional health, their behaviour and school performance. They also include effects on the carer's own physical and emotional health, social life, leisure time, income and expenditure, time off work, household relationships, as well as effects on the lives of others both within and outside the household.

Few of the carers had children under school leaving age living in the household. This was the case for only seven project carers, six hospital carers and four day hospital carers. Consequently, few carers identified problems affecting children. Two children in each group were experiencing some emotional health problems, which the carers felt were related to the elderly person's ill health. One project carer, two hospital carers and one day hospital carer were experiencing disturbed behaviour from a child which was attributed to the elderly person's ill health.

Table 8.6 shows the main burdens experienced by the carers in each group, the effects on their physical and emotional health, their social life and leisure time. It shows the percentage of each group which experienced problems in these areas and the distress associated with these. The majority of individuals, ranging from 66 to 100 per cent in the three groups who experienced these burdens, attributed this to their caring role.

The prevalence of physical ill health was similar for the three groups of carers. The symptoms reported were varied and included chronic conditions such as angina, bronchitis, glaucoma and Parkinson's disease, as well as symptoms most frequently linked to carer stress such as back pain, blood pressure, headaches, sleeplessness, ulcers and vertigo. Given the link between physical symptoms and psychological wellbeing, it has been argued that it is difficult to determine whether there is in fact a causal link between caring tasks and the physical health of a carer (Parker, 1990). Furthermore, since many carers are past middle life, symptoms of ill health may be a consequence of the ageing process (Leff, 1993). Whether a direct or indirect result of caring, however, it has been argued that carers do experience a greater than average amount of physical exertion in their daily lives which restricts their lives in many ways (Parker, 1990). Furthermore, poor physical health has been

Table 8.6
Burdens experienced and associated distress for carers

Burdens	Burden present				Associated distress for carers with burden						
					Distressed			Resigned			
	Project	Hosp.	Day hosp.	p value[a]	Project	Hosp.	Day hosp.	Project	Hosp.	Day hosp.	p value[b]
	%	%	%		%	%	%	%	%	%	
Physical health	81	89	80	ns	44	91	54	36	9	38	<0.01
Emotional health	64	89	80	<0.05	77	75	79	19	25	21	ns
Social life	58	70	83	<0.05	23	53	56	39	16	16	<0.05
Leisure time	42	63	70	<0.05	54	29	33	21	41	62	<0.05

'ns' = not significant.

a Significance of difference between the groups in presence of burden (exact chi-squared test, StatXact, 1989).

b Significance of difference between the groups in associated distress/resignation (exact chi-squared test, StatXact, 1989).

associated with carers ceasing to provide care for their elderly dependants (Levin et al., 1989). The distress associated with physical ill health was higher for the hospital carers, perhaps reflecting in part the demands of frequent travel to and from the hospital.

However, significantly fewer of the project carers experienced emotional health problems compared with the two other groups. This is particularly important given that it is generally agreed that the greatest cost to carers is in terms of their psychological health (Grad and Sainsbury, 1965; Isaacs et al., 1972; Gilleard, 1984; Gilleard et al., 1984; Levin et al., 1989).

Project carers also experienced significantly fewer restrictions on their social life and leisure time, although similar proportions of those experiencing problems in the three groups felt that they were related to caring for the elderly person. Comments made by the carers help to explain these differences, in particular observations made about the quality of personal care given to elderly clients by the home care assistants, the flexibility of the service to adapt to changes in circumstances, relief from the sole responsibility of caring, and the reliability of the service. A number of carers particularly valued the accessibility of the local home care assistant who could be contacted easily in the event of an emergency:

> For one woman caring for her terminally ill mother-in-law, this meant that when her own mother became ill and needed to be visited in hospital every evening, the home care assistants were able to alter their routine and stay with the client until 10 p.m. when the carer returned home.

By contrast, day hospital carers experienced the greatest burden on their social life and leisure time, which led many to comment on the unrelentingness of the caring role. As one woman said of life with her elderly mother-in-law, 'she is always there'. There was no privacy for herself and her husband.

Whereas more project carers appeared to be resigned to the lack of a social life, fewer appeared to be resigned to the lack of leisure time. The explanation for this may lie in the difference between social and leisure activities. The former implies interaction, the latter time to oneself. Thus, it is possible that those project carers lacking leisure time were more distressed by this, given the recent discharge of their elderly relative from hospital, whereas the reduced social life gave little distress since it was compensated for by the return of the elderly person from hospital.

A few carers in each group had experienced financial difficulties in the previous month: ten project carers, nine hospital carers and eight day hospital carers felt that these financial problems were related to the elderly person's ill health. The costs incurred by the day hospital carers were similar to those incurred by the project carers. For these people caring for an elderly person at home, the most frequently recorded cost was that of extra fuel to maintain an adequate temperature. Interestingly, all three groups incurred costs due to the elderly person's laundry. For the hospital carers this was often due to their concerns about the hospital laundry service, which for some imposed an extra cost of clothing. One carer recorded her husband's need for nine pairs of trousers to cope with the vagaries of the hospital laundry service. Travel costs were incurred by the three groups of carers due to visiting the elderly person in their own home, in hospital, or taking the elderly person out. Food required for special diets was an additional expense for the carers of elderly people at home. For the hospital carers, the cost of food took on a particular significance as they invariably chose to take favourite foods, fruit, cigarettes or even brandy on most visits, rendering each visit a non-trivial expense. A number of the carers of the hospital patients found some hardship in meeting these outlays since many had lost pension and other benefits on the elderly person's entry to long-stay hospital care, while the pension allowance for the elderly person in a long-stay hospital was, at the time, under £8 per week. The extent of the financial costs incurred by the carers are examined further in Chapter 9.

One problem, albeit experienced by few carers, was that of difficulty in combining employment with caring. Five project carers and three day hospital carers had recently experienced some work difficulties which they felt were related to the elderly person's ill health:

> One day hospital carer commented on how she had to give up her part-time job and much of the time she would have devoted to her teenage children to care for her 90 year old mother-in-law. She found that her resentments over this were leading to family friction and guilt, yet there appeared to be no prospect of relief, or even a family holiday.

Thirteen project, five hospital and thirteen day hospital carers experienced some household disruption in the form of arguments or friction between family members which they felt was related to the elderly person's ill health. It is notable that for the day hospital carers this was the case for almost half of the group, although this may be explained in part by a high proportion of these carers living with the elderly person, thereby exacerbating stresses and conflicts within the household. In part it could be attributed to inadequate support from services. For the hospital carers, these conflicts appeared to be mainly between siblings over the sharing of duties and responsibilities towards the elderly person.

Informal and formal support received by the carers

The extent of informal support received by the three groups of carers from relatives, friends and neighbours, as well as their different experiences of the health and social services were examined. Table 8.7 shows the informal support the carers received. Each group maintained a high level of contact with relatives, although the project carers received slightly less practical support from them. This was not surprising, given the practical help provided by the home care assistants. For all three groups, the contact with friends and neigh-

Table 8.7
Informal support received and associated relief for carers

Support	Support received				Associated relief for carers receiving support			
	Project %	Hospital %	Day hosp. %	p value[a]	Project %	Hospital %	Day hosp. %	p value[b]
Support from relatives								
Contact (telephone or face-to-face)	91	93	97	ns	87	64	83	<0.05
Practical help	61	74	77	ns	96	95	96	ns
Support from friends/neighbours								
Contact (telephone or face-to-face)	71	63	80	ns	60	35	67	ns
Practical help	40	19	43	ns	93	100	92	ns

'ns' = not significant.

a Significance of difference between the groups in support received (exact chi-squared test, StatXact, 1989).

b Significance of difference between the groups in associated relief (exact chi-squared test, StatXact, 1989).

bours was less than with relatives and, not surprisingly, the practical help received was noticeably less for the carers of the hospital group. For such carers, the range of practical help that could be given was small, and social contact rarely gave rise to practical assistance. Although the level of contact was similar for the three groups, the carers of the hospital group appeared to experience less relief from contact with relatives ($p<0.05$), and relief from contact with friends and neighbours was almost significantly lower ($p<0.06$). It is possible that friends and neighbours are less likely to understand the carer's feelings of ambivalence about the elderly person being in hospital, and this contact may therefore provide less relief for these carers. For the three groups of carers as a whole, it is clear that practical help was greatly valued. The relief experienced from practical help appeared to be far greater than that obtained by social contact alone.

Given the differing experiences of statutory services for the three groups, each group is described separately.

Project carers. As well as support from the care managers and the home care assistants, the majority (87 per cent) of these carers had received regular support from the community nursing service in the last month. Only two carers said that they themselves had not received any practical help from the health and social services in that period. The majority (88 per cent) felt that they had been involved in planning the care of the elderly person, nearly all felt that service providers understood their position and needs, and all of these carers thought that the elderly person was better off at home than in alternative forms of care.

Many positive comments were made by carers at the first interview conducted two weeks after the discharge of the elderly person from hospital and commencement of care at home. The positive comments made about the project service included the quality of the care provided, particularly the personal care; the caring nature or personal qualities of the home care assistant; the flexibility of the service to adapt to changes in circumstances; relief from the burden of physical care; relief from the single-handed responsibility of caring; the accessibility of the home care assistant who could be contacted easily in case of emergency; the quality of the relationships which developed between the home care assistant and the client and carer; the benefit to others in the family; and the reliability of the service. Most (84 per cent) of these carers felt that confiding in a service provider had provided them with some feeling of relief. This was much higher than in the other two groups.

Some negative comments were also made about the project service, most often arising from changes in home care assistants and care managers. These comments mainly concerned the introduction of new home care assistants for holiday and relief cover. It was clear that many found it hard to accept relief home care assistants who had different ways and were not familiar with regular routines. Carers sometimes found it difficult to cope with the number of different service personnel who visited the elderly person soon after discharge to instruct and monitor the home care assistant's activity. Thus, despite the reduction in 'hands-on' caregivers, they still experienced a number of different professional contacts. Some carers commented that they felt insufficient time was devoted to domestic house cleaning tasks, although this may have been due to a misunderstanding of the aims of the project. One woman caring for her husband commented on missing having a home help who used to prepare meals and give the house a thorough clean. A few carers found it difficult to get on with the home care assistant. In some instances this appeared to be related to the carer not being prepared to relinquish some of the care burden, and in others there was simply a personality clash. On a few occasions problems were caused by the home care assistant failing to turn up on time. Other concerns were expressed over the lack of a night care service; confidentiality, such as a fear that the home care assistants would be making the families' 'private business' known to others; and some carers expressed the need for further relief from caring.

From further information gathered at the second interview with these carers six months later, it was clear that almost all were still pleased to have the elderly person at home and found reward and satisfaction in seeing the elderly person more content. In the words of one man caring for his mother who had spent several years on hospital wards, the best thing was to see her 'live a normal life again'. For many of the spouse carers, the project enabled them to continue to share their life as a married couple in the marital home. As one man said, 'She is my wife; we want to be together after 60 years of marriage'. In many instances, close, confiding relationships developed between the home care assistants, their clients and the caring relatives.

For carers who had felt alone and struggling for long periods, the relief of having someone with whom to share the burdens and responsibilities was immense. One woman caring for her mother said that she felt as though 'a great load' had been lifted from her shoulders. She particularly valued the peace of mind of knowing that her mother was receiving the care she needed while at work herself.

It appeared that the most valued features of the service were reliability, flexibility and the quality of care and associated relationships. These factors enabled carers to come to trust the project staff, and thereby to feel relief from some of the stresses of caring and experience satisfaction in having their frail relative at home.

Hospital carers. Given that the elderly person was in hospital, it is not surprising that 74 per cent of these carers received no practical help from the community health and social services. Approximately one-third of these carers felt that service providers did not understand their position. However, only 15 per cent thought that the elderly person would be better off at home, indicating that most saw the placement as appropriate, at least given the alternatives available.

Hospital carers commented on the extent of loneliness without the elderly person, distress caused by the evident unhappiness of the elderly person in a hospital ward, and dissatisfaction with the quality of care given to the elderly person. They also expressed feelings of being torn between the competing demands of the needs of the elderly person and other demands in the carer's life, such as work or family, coupled with feelings of powerlessness to change or influence the situation. Spouses were the people most frequently suffering from loneliness as a result of their partner's hospitalisation. As they were usually in poor health themselves, they felt powerless to change the situation. One husband described his life as pointless and empty now. He said, 'it's almost like she's dead', and yet this was a bereavement without recovery as the pain was renewed every time he went to visit. Several of this group had complained about the quality of care given to their spouse or had attempted to try to alter the situation, and had then felt they had been labelled as troublemakers, which made their situation more lonely and difficult. Although all of these carers had contact with hospital staff, just under half experienced no relief from being able to confide their anxieties about the elderly person and any problems about the care received.

Daughters and sons most often reported feelings of guilt and of being torn by the competing demands of care responsibilities and other family or work commitments. Many of this group were aware of the importance their parents attached to their visits, yet at the same time found the visits upsetting because of their parent's evident unhappiness. In particular, they were often distressed by parents being dressed in clothing that was not their own, or appearing unkempt, or seeming understimulated or withdrawn. The stressful nature of these visits was increased by the lack of privacy in a ward or day room, and the frequently-reported difficulty in finding an opportunity to discuss concerns about the elderly person with appropriate hospital personnel, who usually appeared hard-pressed and overworked. Since almost all of these caring relatives visited the hospital more than once a week, and sometimes daily, every visit was likely to rekindle any ambivalence about the elderly person's situation.

Day hospital carers. Apart from the day hospital, the main service received regularly by these carers to help them care for the elderly person was the community nursing service (received by 63 per cent). Few received other domiciliary services. The home help service was provided to only 13 per cent and meals-on-wheels to 10 per cent of this group, perhaps reflecting the high proportion of these carers living with the elderly person. It has been suggested that domiciliary services often discriminate against carers (Bebbington, 1979; Parker, 1990) and that a large proportion of service provision is directed at dependent people living alone rather than those living with carers (Green, 1988; Neill et al., 1988). Several carers had chosen not to continue with the home help service as they found the amount of time allocated or the nature of the tasks performed benefited them little. A higher proportion (37 per cent) were receiving social work support, mainly from the social worker at the day hospital.

However, 38 per cent said that they experienced no relief from confiding in a service provider and 70 per cent said that they had received no practical help from services, other than day hospital attendance, in the last month. Thirty-five per cent felt that providers of services did not understand the carer's position and their needs. However, 28 of the 30 carers thought that the elderly person was better off at home, and only two carers thought that the elderly person would be better off in hospital care.

For many of the day hospital carers, their greatest need was for time to call their own, a break from the caring role. They were often deeply grateful for any help they received, but a recurring problem was the unreliability and unpredictability of services. Almost all the carers whose relative went to the day hospital placed great importance on the time off but, owing to the vagaries of the ambulance service, their relative's time of departure and return could vary by up to two hours, and this left them quite unable to make advance plans to use the time constructively. They were also aware that the service was for rehabilitation rather than for carer relief and could be terminated at any time. In a number of cases, the elderly person had refused to consider a period of respite care in hospital or residential care, with the result that the carer had no prospect of a holiday break.

Several carers reported problems with access to services, promises made about help which was not forthcoming, aids which were unavailable or unsuitable when delivered, and confusing red tape over applications for attendance allowances or badges for disabled car users. A number of carers found the unpredictability of district nursing visits undermined the routines which they relied upon to make their task manageable.

A number of carers, whose relatives had tried out the day care service which was available in local authority homes, all reported that this had proved unacceptable to the elderly person owing to the lack of stimulation and interest shown in them. In the words of one carer, she felt that her husband was 'just dumped' and then ignored.

Many of the carers felt that the services were not adapted to meet their needs. As one daughter said, 'If only you could get the help you want instead of having to take what they offer', a comment that was echoed by a wife who said of service providers 'They can only really see things from their point of view'. Some carers also commented on the lack of preparation, advice and instruction for undertaking the role of carer. A 69 year old man whose wife had suffered a severe stroke when relatively young was eager to do what he could to assist her progress to greater independence, but he felt he had been left to flounder without the instruction he needed to assist in her rehabilitation. However, it is noteworthy that in spite of the many difficulties reported by these carers, 21 (two-thirds) had given no thought to the possibility of ceasing to care at home.

The benefits of caring

Despite the emphasis in the literature on the stresses and burdens experienced by carers, it has been found that it is possible for rewards and feelings of satisfaction to co-exist with these (Grant and Nolan, 1993). A more formalised version of the items developed by Qureshi et al. (1983, 1989) was used in this study to establish in what ways the carers perceived that caring had been a positive experience for them and their household as a whole. Similar items were used to examine benefits identified by the home care assistants in Chapter 5. To measures of subjective feelings were added items normally conceived of as burden-related, such as effects on lifestyle, in order to capture the range of the carers' experiences, identifying burdens, stresses and also any positive features which they considered important. Only the items which were relevant to a significant number of carers are shown in Table 8.8. Items which were not relevant in the analysis of burdens, such as effects upon children, were similarly not relevant in the analysis of benefits.

Among the subjective factors it is noticeable that a feeling of reciprocity, derived from exchange theory (Gouldner, 1960; Blau, 1964); that is, giving in return for the support earlier received from the elderly person, was experienced by those supporting someone at home but not by those whose relative was in hospital where the scope for exchange was necessarily reduced. Nonetheless, it is noticeable that hospital carers were undertaking activities not

Table 8.8

Positive benefits to carer of type of care received

Benefit	Project %	Hospital %	Day hospital %	p value[a]
Subjective feelings				
Reciprocity	41	19	47	ns
Empathy	49	0	33	<0.001
Social obligation	51	19	83	<0.001
Usefulness	58	33	67	<0.05
Caring altruism	87	67	80	ns
Lifestyle of carer				
Income	18	4	13	ns
Physical health	53	74	23	<0.001
Household routine	57	33	60	ns
Mental health	61	59	50	ns
Companionship	69	11	50	<0.001

'ns' = not significant.

a   Exact chi-squared test (StatXact, 1989).

normally required or expected when a person is in institutional care, such as preparing food and undertaking laundry. Many project and day hospital spouse carers commented on how they saw caring as a reciprocal part of married life, which led one project carer to comment, 'She would have done the same for me if things had been the other way around'. Similarly, a day hospital carer, a woman caring for her mother, said, 'I can repay her for all the years she looked after me'. Again, the level of empathy, an understanding of and identification with an elderly person's feelings, was not noted as a benefit by the hospital group, which is probably explained in part by their lack of prolonged day-to-day contact, and in part by their concern at the care received. Similarly, social obligation and usefulness would be less relevant benefits to carers whose relative was hospitalised, since they would consider themselves to be neither undertaking an obligation nor contributing as much to the person's welfare as they would if the person were at home. Conversely, a high proportion (83 per cent) of the day hospital carers felt that they were performing a social obligation. However, caring altruism, a desire to help others which gives the carer a degree of satisfaction, was noted as a benefit by a high proportion of the hospital group, compared with the other subjective factors. It would be reasonable to assume that these carers felt they had given as much as they could to the elderly person prior to hospitalisation rather than at the present time. Nonetheless, caring altruism was experienced by fewer hospital carers than other carers. For many of the project carers, their greatest satisfaction was to see their elderly relative content and settled in their own home, as a woman caring for her aunt said, 'She is content at home and is beginning to take an interest in life again.'

With regard to lifestyle factors, many carers experienced a reduction in income when the elderly person entered hospital care, as described later in Chapter 9. This is reflected in the lower reporting of any financial benefit by the hospital carers than by the other two groups. In terms of physical health, carers whose elderly relative was hospitalised saw this as a particular benefit to them. Many commented on the relief from the physical burden of care, reflecting the poor health of many of the carers themselves. Surprisingly, there appeared to be little benefit to the household routine from the elderly person being in hospital rather than being at home, perhaps reflecting the considerable time and effort some of these carers put into travel to and from the hospital. There appears to be no difference between the groups in terms of the carer's mental health, although the loss of companionship for the hospital group was particularly evident and many of the spouse carers commented that loneliness was the worst thing about the situation. Companionship was of greatest benefit for project carers, where many had clearly shared a close relationship for many years One man described his greatest reward as 'being together still after 47 years of marriage'. A woman caring for her father commented, 'It will be a very different world when I don't have him — nothing can make up for what I shall lose.'

There is evidence that as well as burdens and costs, all three groups of carers were able to experience some benefits from the form of support they were receiving, although the perception of benefits differed according to the caring situation.

The effects of caring

Factors associated with the breakdown of project care

As explained in Chapter 7, during the monitoring phase of the project, the care of thirteen individuals receiving project services broke down, requiring their re-admission to long-stay institutional care. Seven of these clients had carers: one client entered long-stay hospital care, one entered a residential home and five were admitted to a nursing home. Given the small number of cases, only a brief analysis of these data is appropriate. Although the mean malaise score at first interview was marginally higher for those carers whose elderly relative was subsequently re-admitted for long-stay care (6.8 compared with 6.0), this was not statistically significant, and thus there was no clear relationship between carer stress and the breakdown of care. On a larger scale, other studies, mainly of dementia sufferers, have found that the amount of stress experienced by the carer is the factor most likely to determine the breakdown of care (Zarit et al., 1986; Gilleard, 1987; Jerrom et al., 1993). Upon examination of the individual case histories, it appears that, in four of the five cases where fuller information was available on the breakdown of care, there was a poor relationship between the carer and the elderly person. Two cases involved aggression, and in one case the carer was suffering from mental illness. In the remaining case the major problem associated with the breakdown of care appeared to be the poor physical health of the carer. As explained in Chapter 7, however, many of these clients had been receiving project services for some time. Of the seven clients with carers, two had been receiving project support for more than two years, three for more than one year and the remaining two for more than six months. Hence, for most of these individuals, what has been described as breakdown could equally be seen as the end of a successful period of project care.

The overall levels of burden and stress

Table 8.9 presents summary indicators of, first, the numbers of tasks performed and the behaviours and burdens experienced by the carers and, second, the carers' subjective feelings associated with these (Platt et al., 1983; Platt, 1985), and the levels of malaise or stress experienced (Rutter et al., 1970). The individual care tasks, behaviours and burdens have been described earlier in the chapter. The measure of psychological stress, or malaise, consisted of 24 items designed to assess the presence of symptoms associated

Table 8.9
Behavioural, burden and stress indicators: mean scores

Variables	Project	Hosp.	Day hosp.	F^a	p value[a]	Sig. group diffs[b]
Behavioural and burden indicators[c]						
Care tasks undertaken	6.7	na	7.9	4.72	<0.05	na
Elderly person's behaviour	13.6	14.8	18.4	2.63	ns	–
Burdens experienced	4.4	5.3	6.3	3.46	<0.05	–
Minimum number of cases	63	25	28			
Subjective indicators[c]						
Distress — care tasks	4.7	na	9.8	12.41	<0.01	na
Distress — behaviour	12.9	17.6	24.1	9.00	<0.001	§, †
Distress — burdens	4.5	5.6	7.3	3.92	<0.05	§
Malaise score[d]	6.1	8.9	7.2	4.3	<0.05	‡
Minimum number of cases	62	27	26			

'na' = not applicable.
a   Analysis of variance. ns = not significant.
b   Key to paired comparisons (Newman-Keuls test):
     §   Project *v* Day Hospital significant at 0.05 level.
     †   Day Hospital *v* Hospital significant at 0.05 level.
     ‡   Project *v* Hospital significant at 0.05 level.
c   Platt (1985).
d   Rutter et al. (1970).

with psychosomatic stress (Rutter et al., 1970). The higher level of social disturbance in the hospital group has been controlled for statistically using covariance analysis. Following a significant overall statistical test of differences among the three groups of carers using analysis of variance, individual comparisons were made using the Newman-Keuls procedure (Snedecor and Cochran, 1980).

It can be seen that the project carers had to undertake significantly fewer care tasks than day hospital carers, and were significantly less subject to distress associated with the performance of these tasks. Hospital carers were excluded from these comparisons as they were not routinely performing care tasks for their relatives. The three groups of carers experienced behavioural problems to a similar extent. It is clear that the day hospital carers were significantly more distressed in their reactions to the elderly person's behaviour than either of the other two groups:

The nature of this distress was evident from the experience of a 50 year old woman caring for her 70 year old husband. She recorded her feeling that whatever she did for him was taken for granted and unappreciated by him, which in its turn caused her anger and resentment, to the extent that their strong marital relationship was undermined, and she felt that her own health and wellbeing were being sacrificed to an increasingly unrewarding role.

Some commented on the destruction of a meaningful relationship with the elderly person, due to personality change, the effects of illness or through resentments engendered by the disability and care tasks. Thus one wife commented on changes in her husband's behaviour since his stroke and said, 'He is like a child now, not a husband.'

The fact that the project carers were noticeably less distressed by the elderly person's behaviour can be attributed, at least in part, to the regular and reliable support of the home care assistants and of the care managers, which ensured the ready availability of someone with whom to discuss and share difficulties:

The 72 year old wife of a 75 year old man suffering from a muscular wasting disease, said of the home care assistants and the care manager, 'They allow you to talk ... they are always prepared to listen'.

Indeed, many of the project carers commented favourably on the personal qualities of home care assistants and on the quality of relationships that developed between them and their clients as well as with carers themselves.

Although there was an overall difference in the burdens of daily living experienced by carers in the three groups, differences between individual groups did not reach a conventional level of statistical significance. The overall apparent difference between the groups could, however, be due to more distressed carers reporting more burdens. When the subjective distress associated with these care burdens is compared, it can be seen that project carers were significantly less distressed than the day hospital carers. The different experiences of the services and degree of support received by these two groups of carers, described earlier in this chapter, may help to explain this.

A cut-off point between four and five on the malaise scale, out of a possible score of 24, was used to identify carers experiencing significant levels of stress (Rutter et al., 1970). This revealed that 60 per cent of the project carers, 82 per cent of the hospital carers and 67 per cent of the day hospital carers were experiencing a high level of stress, although this was not a statistically significant difference between the groups. However, comparing the malaise scores of the three carer groups, as shown in Table 8.9, indicates that psychological stress was significantly lower for project carers than for those carers whose elderly relative remained in continuing hospital care. At first this finding may seem paradoxical, especially in the light of the findings of Levin et al. (1983, 1989, 1994) and McKay et al. (1983) that both short-term and long-term hospital or institutional care reduced stress levels among carers of elderly people. It does, however, confirm the observations of other studies which suggest that, although admission to institutional care may markedly reduce the practical burdens experienced by carers, it does not necessarily reduce the feelings of anxiety and guilt associated with such an admission (Dobrof and Litwak, 1977; York and Calsyn, 1977; Smith and Bengtson, 1979; Brane, 1986; Challis and Davies, 1986; Stephens et al., 1991). Many carers reported feelings of depression and anxiety, and sleep problems which were frequently attributed to guilt and conflicts of duty and responsibility within their lives and to distress at their elderly relative's condition in hospital. Spouses who were left alone at home recorded feelings of loneliness, grief and emptiness in their lives.

In conclusion, it appears that there is no evidence that improvements in elderly people's wellbeing after discharge from hospital to project care were purchased at the cost of higher levels of distress for their caring relatives. Indeed, the level of carer wellbeing in the project group was higher than that of a group of carers receiving the standard range of services and of a group of carers of long-stay hospital care patients. Follow-up interviews with carers of project clients, after the elderly person had been discharged for six months, indicated no significant change in the levels of the tasks performed and the behaviours experienced by the carers, the burdens or subjective distress they experienced, or their level of malaise, compared with these initial observations. Thus, the relative positive benefits observed for carers of the project clients appear not to be attributable to some kind of honeymoon experience following the early discharge of the client from hospital. Whatever benefits carers experienced appear to have continued over a relatively long period.

Factors influencing variation in carer stress

In this section we examine the extent to which different factors influenced variation in carer stress. These analyses are based upon a series of comparisons of the effects of individual factors on the level of carer malaise (Rutter et al., 1970). Tables 8.10 to 8.13 show how the mean malaise score varied according to the caring situation and a range of variables which may be likely to cause problems for the carers. Three propositions were tested here using two-way analysis of variance. Given the unequal sizes of the three groups, the hierarchical or 'stepdown analysis' method was used (Overall and Spiegel, 1969). First, it was established whether there was a group or service effect on the mean malaise score; second, whether there was a possible problem effect, for example whether the mean malaise score varied according to the extent to which individual burdens were experienced; and third, whether there was an interaction effect between the previous two phenomena on the mean malaise score. The range of factors examined included the personal characteristics of the carers and the elderly people, the care tasks which were undertaken, the perceived behaviour of the elderly person, and the burdens experienced by the carers.

Descriptive characteristics. Table 8.10 examines the effects of individual characteristics of the carers and Table 8.11 those of the elderly people with carers. Some information on the day hospital group was not available for Table 8.11 as shorter interviews were conducted with this group. It is clear from Table 8.10 that female carers tended to be more stressed in general than male carers, although the female project carers experienced less stress than those of the other two groups. The level of stress experienced by the male carers appears to be similar for the three groups. Table 8.11 shows that the only elderly person characteristic that appears to have had an effect on carer stress is sex, where those caring for a male elderly person experienced a significantly greater degree of stress across the three groups. Since most of these would be women, this relates to the earlier observation about the stress levels of female carers. Perhaps surprisingly, confusional states were not significantly associated with malaise, although the mean malaise score was lower where no confusion was evident.

Table 8.10

The effects of type of service and characteristics of carers on carer malaise

Characteristics	Mean malaise score			Tests[a]	
	Project	Hosp.	Day hosp.	Service	Character.
Sex					
Male	5.32	4.57	5.83	<0.05	<0.01
Female	6.45	10.40	7.50		
Marital status					
Married	6.49	8.61	7.56		
Single/widowed/separated divorced	4.84	10.50	3.67	<0.05	ns
Does elderly person live with carer?					
No	5.38	8.17	6.00		
Yes	6.43	9.47	7.25	<0.05	ns
Relationship to elderly person					
Spouse	7.00	10.11	7.47		
Daughter/son	5.43	8.23	9.60	<0.05	ns
Other	5.00	8.40	4.17		

'ns' = not significant.

a Two-way analysis of variance (hierarchical method).

Table 8.11
The effects of type of service and characteristics of the elderly people on carer malaise

Characteristics	Mean malaise score			Tests[a]	
	Project	Hosp.	Day hosp.	Service	Char-acter.
Sex					
Male	8.59	11.54	8.07	<0.01	<0.001
Female	4.53	6.43	6.27		
Living group					
Alone	5.60	7.00	4.00		
Spouse	7.20	9.92	7.47	<0.05	ns
Family/other	4.71	9.17	8.14		
Risk of falling					
None	6.14	7.25	–		
Moderate	5.61	10.50	–	<0.01	ns
Severe	6.41	8.47	–		
Incontinence of urine or faeces					
Never	6.24	9.33	8.00		
Sometimes	5.76	9.70	7.15	<0.05	ns
Frequently	6.15	8.21	6.83		
Confusion					
None	5.64	9.20	4.56		
Mild	6.05	9.33	9.40	<0.05	ns
Severe	9.33	6.00	7.90		

'ns' = not significant.

a   Two-way analysis of variance (hierarchical method).

Although not tabulated, the CAPE BRS scores were also examined. The only positive correlation between the malaise score and the CAPE BRS scores was for the day hospital group where the CAPE BRS total score was significantly correlated with the malaise score ($p < 0.05$), as was the CAPE BRS social disturbance subscale ($p < 0.01$). For the hospital group the CAPE BRS social disturbance subscale was significantly negatively correlated with malaise ($p < 0.01$). Hence, the higher the level of disturbed behaviour, the lower the level of carer stress. This may be explained by these carers being somewhat protected from the effects of the aspects of the elderly person's behaviour measured by this subscale, or that the presence of the behaviours was likely to make hospital care seem more appropriate and therefore be experienced as less stressful.

Care tasks undertaken. In the main, there appeared to be no relationship between the frequency of performing particular care tasks and the level of carer stress in either the project or day hospital group. Of course, the direction of causal relationship is unclear for these tasks. The general lack of relationship between level of care given and stress may be explained by this unclear causal relationship. It may be that the presence of stress reduced the frequency with which these tasks were undertaken, as much as that the frequency with which certain tasks were performed caused a higher level of stress. Thus, for most of these tasks, this equilibrating process may explain why little difference was evident between the groups in the influence of tasks upon stress levels. However, for tasks which were undertaken outside the home, such as shopping, there appeared to be a higher level of stress for project carers when they were doing these tasks more frequently, reflecting the effect of greater demands upon them.

Behaviour of the elderly person. Table 8.12 indicates that a greater degree of underactivity and withdrawal by the elderly person were significantly associated with higher levels of stress across the three groups. Forgetfulness and indecisiveness both produced significant interaction effects as a result of a lower level of stress and a greater degree of indecisive and forgetful behaviour for the hospital group. Although not statistically significant, some other behaviours associated with cognitive impairment, such as expressing odd ideas and exhibiting embarrassing behaviours, appear to have been experienced differently by those carers whose elderly relative was in long-stay hospital care. One possible interpretation of this might be that carers experience a greater reduction in their stress where the elderly person transferred to hospital is confused and exhibiting associated behaviours (Levin et al., 1989, 1994). That is to say, the carer of a confused person in hospital may feel less guilt, since they may feel that this care setting is the most appropriate with the onset of cognitive impairment. The distress of an elderly person without cognitive impairment in hospital care appeared to be more difficult for carers to tolerate. However, the relative acceptability to the carer of hospital care has to be weighed against the desirability of a familiar environment for a confused elderly person (Netten, 1993). There would therefore appear to be some consistency in these findings. Specifically, the way in which behaviours of a confused elderly person impact upon carer stress is qualitatively different for an elderly person living at home compared with an elderly person in long-stay hospital care. Similarly, Levin and colleagues (1989) found that many problems which were associated with the elderly person's mental state affected their carers' willingness to accept admission to residential care. This applied both to carers living with and not living with the elderly person.

Despite the findings of Sanford (1975) that physical care problems were poorly tolerated by carers, there was no evidence in this study that problems

Table 8.12
The effects of type of service and behaviours experienced by carers on carer malaise

Behaviours	Mean malaise score			Tests[a]	
	Project	Hosp.	Day hosp.	Service	Behaviour
Psychological problems					
Slowness					
None	4.23	8.67	7.00	<0.05	ns
Some	6.24	8.85	7.17		
Underactivity					
None	3.60	8.00	7.00	<0.05	<0.05
Some	6.51	8.88	7.18		
Nocturnal disturbance					
None	5.88	9.12	5.57	<0.05	ns
Some	5.80	8.22	7.65		
Forgetfulness					
None	5.35	10.29	3.57	<0.05[b]	ns
Some	6.16	8.26	8.26		
Misery					
None	4.92	5.20	8.63	<0.05	ns
Some	6.45	9.67	6.64		
Overdependence					
None	5.11	9.09	6.88	<0.05	ns
Some	6.39	8.60	7.27		
Complaints about aches and pains					
None	6.55	7.44	6.20	<0.05	ns
Some	5.06	9.53	7.65		
Uncooperative					
None	5.24	8.53	6.00	<0.05	ns
Some	6.63	9.18	7.67		
Worry					
None	5.57	8.58	7.88	<0.05	ns
Some	6.19	9.00	6.23		
Withdrawal					
None	5.29	7.06	5.93	<0.01	<0.01
Some	6.78	11.60	8.25		

Table 8.12 (continued)

Behaviours	Mean malaise score			Tests[a]	
	Project	Hosp.	Day hosp.	Service	Beha-viour
Indecisiveness					
None	5.69	9.71	4.00	<0.01[b]	ns
Some	6.09	7.75	9.00		
Odd ideas					
None	5.62	9.21	6.84	<0.05	ns
Some	6.23	8.33	7.73		
Irritability					
None	5.65	9.12	6.75	<0.05	ns
Some	6.28	8.22	8.00		
Embarrassing					
None	5.35	9.00	5.72	<0.01	<0.05
Some	8.78	8.29	9.33		
Physical problems					
Risk of falling					
None	5.33	7.63	6.67	<0.05	ns
Some	5.88	9.33	7.22		
Requiring physical/nursing care					
None	4.90	7.40	4.50	<0.05	ns
Some	6.00	9.14	7.36		
Incontinence — urine					
None	4.58	7.33	7.42	<0.05	ns
Some	6.20	9.25	7.00		
Incontinence — faeces					
None	5.06	8.53	7.17	<0.05	ns
Some	6.55	8.70	7.17		

'ns' = not significant
a   Two-way analysis of variance (hierarchical method).
b   Significant interaction effect.

such as risk of falling, need for nursing care, or incontinence were associated with higher levels of stress for carers. However, behaviours associated with cognitive impairment did influence carer stress in different ways in different care environments.

Burdens. Table 8.13 shows that for all three groups an increase in the extent of the burden led to a greater degree of stress, although the level of stress was generally lower for the project carers. Where carers had physical health care problems, although not shown as significant on the table, this was almost significantly associated with greater stress for the three groups ($p < 0.06$). This was particularly so where the carer was in receipt of treatment for a particular health care problem. Receipt of treatment itself may be an indicator of the degree of severity of the carer's health care problem and, if so, the argument would be that the worse the carer's physical health, the greater the stress they experienced in their caring role. As would be expected, the greater the emotional problems reported by the carer, the greater the degree of stress as measured by the malaise scale, particularly where carers were in receipt of treatment for these problems. This observation is not surprising since one would expect a measure of emotional health to be correlated with the level of malaise and so the finding is also indicative of the degree of concurrent validity in the measures. For all three groups of carers, impairments in social life were associated with higher stress.

Table 8.13
The effects of type of service and burdens on carer malaise

Burdens	Mean malaise score			Tests[a]	
	Project	Hospital	Day hosp.	Service	Burden
Physical health					
No problems	4.00	9.67	5.17		
Some — no treatment	5.14	7.60	7.00	<0.05	ns
Some — treatment	6.87	9.11	8.00		
Emotional health					
No problems	3.70	2.33	3.17		
Some — no treatment	6.64	9.16	7.00	<0.01	<0.001
Some — treatment	10.78	11.80	12.60		
Social life					
No impairment	4.35	6.25	5.80		
Some contacts	6.27	9.85	6.72	<0.01	<0.01
No contacts	8.11	10.33	9.29		
Leisure time					
Spare time daily	5.13	8.50	5.00		
Spare time some days	6.11	9.13	8.13	<0.01	ns
No spare time	8.29	9.00	8.00		

'ns' = not significant.
a   Two-way analysis of variance (hierarchical method).

That is, the more restricted a person's social life, the greater the level of stress. The presence or absence of leisure time did not appear to be so clearly associated with the degree of stress, although again the project carers appeared to have lower levels of stress than the other two groups. Clearly, however, restrictions on a carer's personal life can be distressing, an association that has been found in other studies (Bebbington et al., 1986; Stephens and Christianson, 1986).

Regression analysis of factors influencing carer stress

The previous analysis examined the individual effects of personal characteristics, care tasks, behaviours and burdens upon carer stress. In these subsequent analyses, each group of carers was investigated separately to examine the joint influence of factors upon carer stress. Multiple regression analysis was used to explore the relationship between a range of client and carer factors and carer stress. The dependent variable was the malaise score. The independent variables included characteristics of the carer (sex, marital status, relationship to the elderly person and whether or not they lived with the elderly person); characteristics of the elderly person (sex, CAPE BRS scores and confusion); and the behaviours and burdens experienced by the carers (as shown in Tables 8.5 and 8.6). The results of this analysis are shown in Table 8.14.

Project carers. For these carers, higher levels of stress were associated with caring for a male elderly client, the presence of socially embarrassing behaviour and the presence of confusional states. These results are not surprising. Those caring for a female have been generally shown to experience higher morale and better mental health than those caring for a male (Gilhooly, 1984; Gilleard, 1984; Morris et al., 1991). The literature on carer stress has found that problems associated with the care of confused elderly people, and particularly the presence of behavioural problems, cause the greatest stress for carers and are the least well tolerated (Isaacs, 1971; ; Greene et al., 1982; Gilleard, 1984; Argyle et al., 1985). Levin et al. (1989), in their study of confused elderly people and their carers, found that the carers were much more likely to be distressed about disturbed behaviours than about giving practical help and time to an elderly person. This may be a consequence of such disabilities having greater consequences in terms of changes in the carer's lifestyle (Horowitz, 1985) and the disruption of the relationship between the carer and the elderly person (Morris, L.W. et al., 1988). Furthermore, it has been suggested that whereas physical disabilities may be easier to manage and are viewed more easily as an actual illness, disturbed behaviours may be perceived as being used deliberately by the elderly person in order to upset the carer (Gilleard, 1984) and are less predictable.

Hospital carers. For the carers of elderly people in long-stay hospital care, higher levels of stress were associated with caring for a male elderly client, having

Table 8.14
Factors influencing carer stress

Variable	Coefficient	Std error	t value	p value
Project group				
Constant	3.26	0.61	5.34	<0.001
Male elderly person	4.35	0.86	5.09	<0.001
Embarrassing behaviour	3.30	1.14	2.89	0.006
Confusional state	1.73	0.87	1.99	0.052
$F = 12.55$				
p value < 0.001				
$R^2 = 0.40$				
Adj. $R^2 = 0.37$				
Number of cases = 60				
Hospital group				
Constant	5.25	1.51	3.48	0.002
Male elderly person	5.32	1.30	4.10	0.001
Carer's social life disrupted	3.84	1.40	2.74	0.013
Male carer	-3.51	1.44	-2.43	0.025
Irritable behaviour	-3.08	1.35	-2.28	0.034
$F = 10.76$				
p value < 0.001				
$R^2 = 0.68$				
Adj. $R^2 = 0.62$				
Number of cases = 25				
Day hospital group				
Constant	2.27	1.49	1.52	0.140
CAPE social disturbance	0.91	0.40	2.29	0.031
Forgetful behaviour	3.63	1.70	2.14	0.042
$F = 7.62$				
p value = 0.003				
$R^2 = 0.37$				
Adj. $R^2 = 0.32$				
Number of cases = 29				

a restricted social life, being a female carer and experiencing less irritating behaviour on the part of the elderly person. Other studies suggest male carers in general have been found to have a higher morale than female carers (Gilhooly, 1984; Levin et al., 1983), while women report higher levels of burden and psychological distress associated with caregiving (Zarit, 1982). This has been ascribed to a lower level of emotional involvement on the part of male carers (Zarit et al., 1986) and their greater willingness to leave their dependant unattended (Gilhooly, 1984). This may be indicative of differential role expect-ations in relation to caring (Zarit, 1982). It has also been argued that men cope more effectively with life stresses in general and with caregiving in particular (Billings and Moos, 1981). Again, male carers have been shown to receive more domestic domiciliary support (Hunt, 1978; Bebbington and Davies, 1983; Charlesworth et al., 1984), as well as more informal support (Noelker and Wallace, 1985). Restrictions on the social lives of carers, attributable to caring, have been found to be a severe burden for many carers (Sainsbury and Grad de Alarcon, 1971). This may be particularly the case for spouse carers (Levin et al., 1989). More surprisingly, however, the absence of irritating behaviour appeared to be associated with higher malaise. If these elderly people had been cared for at home, then it is likely that this behaviour would have been positively associated with malaise. This group of carers however, because of hospital care, may have experienced a buffering effect from this and other behavioural prob-lems which in general appear to be stressful for carers. As noted earlier, the presence of problematic behaviours associated with cognitive impairment may make the acceptance of hospital care easier. Where such behaviours are absent, the feelings of guilt about hospitalisation may be greater, leading to higher levels of stress.

Day hospital carers. Higher levels of stress for these carers were associated with higher levels of the CAPE BRS social disturbance score and the presence of forgetfulness in the elderly person. Again, these results are not surprising. The CAPE BRS social disturbance subscale includes behaviours which have been shown to be the least well-tolerated by carers, such as being objectionable to others during the day and during the night, falsely accusing others of violence or theft, and not sleeping at night (Sanford, 1975; Argyle et al., 1985). Surpris-ingly, the sex of the elderly person did not enter this equation as it did for the other two groups. However, it may be that sex is less a determinant of malaise in caring for a spouse, and a higher proportion of this group were spouse carers.

Conclusion

On the whole, the three groups of carers appear to share not dissimilar characteristics, although their experiences of caring were clearly different. However, given that the comparison data were cross-sectional, it is not pos-sible to infer causality or to measure outcomes for the carers. It is clear, however, that in all respects project carers were at least no worse off than the carers of elderly people in long-stay hospital care and those receiving the usual range of domiciliary care services. The factors influencing carer stress for the day hospital and project groups would seem to reflect the findings elsewhere that confusional states and behavioural problems cause the greatest stress for carers, while for the hospital carers these effects seem to be mitigated by the elderly person being in hospital. However, the hospital carers had the highest carer malaise score, whereas the project seemed able to reduce the distress associated with caring for frail elderly people by providing relief from some of the practical care tasks and greater peace of mind that their elderly relative was being well cared for. On the basis of the equations, it is clear that the complexity of factors which determine carer psychological wellbeing do not permit any simple judgement of the appropriacy of any one care environment for frail elderly people as a means of providing carer relief.

9 The Costs of Care

This chapter examines the costs of care for the project and the comparison group. Cost data were collected on flows of resources over the six-month period from the time at which an elderly person first received care from the project until the six-month follow-up date, and for a similar period for comparison group cases. The price base used in calculating the cost figures is 1986/87, the first full year in which the project was in operation. The first part of this chapter contains a brief description of the principles on which the examination of costs was based. The second part examines how individual unit costs were calculated. The third section presents and compares the costs to different parties for both the project and comparison groups. The final section examines the factors which influenced variations in costs to major interest groups (society as a whole, the main agencies, community service providers), and those which influenced variations in the amount of time provided by home care assistants. Such analyses can help to tease out some elements which consistently influence the use of services.

Costing principles

The approach used in costing care reflects one used in previous evaluative studies in Kent and Gateshead (Challis and Davies, 1986; Challis et al., 1990). Three concerns underlay this approach. The first was to examine what costs were incurred by a range of potentially interested parties; the second was to focus not only upon revenue costs but also to estimate the economic effect of placing resources into community support rather than hospital care (the concept of opportunity cost); and the third was, where appropriate, to discount current costs to reflect their future benefits. These principles are summarised below and are discussed in more detail in Netten and Beecham (1993), which examines some of the approaches and difficulties involved in costing community-based care.

A range of different parties

A decision to provide community-based rather than hospital care, in this case by the health and social services authorities, has implications beyond the boundaries of those agencies. Individuals, families and other agencies will incur costs and benefits as a result. In order to present a broad picture of the effects on different interest groups, cost estimates have been made for six 'accounts' or sectors which bear costs. These are: the project, the social services department, the National Health Service, the private sector of residential and nursing homes, the public purse, and society as a whole. The latter includes the expenses of the elderly people as well as financial costs to informal carers.

Revenue costs and opportunity costs

The financial accounts of agencies usually give average cost information, and the conventions employed in the collation of these accounts tend to vary. As a consequence, these accounts may not always adequately reflect the consumption of real resources (Sugden and Williams, 1978). For example, the accounts for the National Health Service did not make provision for capital costs while those prepared by social services departments did.

An attempt has been made to ensure that the cost estimates represent a reasonable approximation to opportunity cost: that is, based on the judgement that the value of a resource represents the benefit forgone by using it in one way rather than in an alternative way. Of course, in practice such an approach may have to utilise the available cost information, but, in making assumptions about capital elements, consideration of opportunity costs can be helpful to ensure that different 'accounts' are treated similarly (Knapp, 1984, 1993).

Discounting future costs

Costs and their associated benefits may occur at different times and, to make any comparison between alternative styles of service, account has to be taken of these time lags. For example, provision of an expensive set of aids and adaptations may promote independent living over a considerable period of time, or a detailed multidisciplinary assessment may yield benefits over a period. Both therefore can be seen as 'investment goods', the costs of which should not be seen as being borne only at the point at which they were incurred. Such current costs need to be discounted at an appropriate rate, akin to an interest rate, over an appropriate time period, in the same way that the construction costs of a building are often discounted over a period of 60 years (Knapp, 1984).

Unit costs

The costs examined in this chapter are the costs to the project, the social services department, the National Health Service, private residential and nursing homes, the public purse, and society as a whole.

The project

As described earlier, the project team consisted of a project manager, three care managers, a part-time physiotherapist, a part-time occupational therapist and a number of home care assistants. A care budget was also available for additional expenditure. The components of the costs to the project include not just expenditure on particular services, such as home care assistant time, but also allow for the time of the care managers, the project manager, administrative costs and overheads.

Care managers/project team. The costs of the three care managers and the project manager have been estimated from information on salary costs, employer's contributions, travel expenses, administration and clerical support. To estimate a cost per case, caseloads of 20 and 25 cases have been assumed. These two caseload sizes were then considered in two different scenarios: first, held by the care managers alone; and second, held by the three care managers, with the project manager holding a caseload of 50 per cent. The former assumes that the project manager was entirely concerned with administrative and supervisory duties. A cost per hour of the project team has also been estimated. The costs based upon these assumptions are shown in Table 9.1.

Table 9.1
Project team costs: price base 1986/87

Project team costs	£ per week
Three fte[a] care managers	
Caseloads of 20 per case per week	14.84
Caseloads of 25 per case per week	11.87
Three and a half fte[a] care managers	
Caseloads of 20 per case per week	12.74
Caseloads of 25 per case per week	10.24
Cost	
Three care managers with caseloads per hour	9.38
Three and a half care managers with caseloads per hour	8.04

a fte = full-time equivalent.

The most costly assumption, relating to a caseload of 20, of £14.84 per case per week has been used as the fixed cost component and added to each client, multiplied according to the number of weeks they were alive during the six-month period of evaluation. For the analysis, this represents the more conservative assumption since it provided the highest level of cost to the project. Furthermore, given the development costs associated with establishing the project and the limited number of available cases, this proved closest to what actually occurred, as shown in Chapter 4, and represented the planned numbers for the project.

In a normal situation, reflecting CIPFA (1987) assumptions, an additional charge of 10.3 per cent for overheads on top of the above costs would need to have been added if this project had been situated in a social services department; this has not been included in the project team costs due to the administrative organisation peculiar to the project.

Physiotherapist and occupational therapist. The project employed a physiotherapist and an occupational therapist on a part-time basis. These health authority staff were costed as the other health authority physiotherapy and occupational therapy staff, since they were all employees of the National Health Service. These unit costs, which are described later in the chapter with the National Health Service staff, provided an hourly rate of £10.68 which allowed for travel and overheads.

Home care assistants. Full information was available on the wages and number of home care assistants, as well as on the number of hours worked and at what rate for each client. There were four rates of pay, allowing for weekend and evening work. An allowance was made for holiday and sickness cover, employer's contributions, administration, equipment and clerical support. This gave an hourly rate which was increased for unsociable hours to give the amounts shown in Table 9.2.

Table 9.2
Home care assistant costs: price base 1986/87

Home care assistant costs	£ per hour
Normal time weekday	4.22
After 8 p.m. weekday	5.28
Normal time weekend	5.81
After 8 p.m. weekend	7.40

Care budget. A flexible care budget was deployed in the purchase of additional support for elderly people from the community and for the provision of additional items. Discretionary payments were made by care managers to individual members of the community acting as 'helpers' for visiting and supporting the elderly people. These were costed at the amount paid for that help. A substantial amount was spent on incontinence pads. In most cases, information was available on the amount spent on individual clients, but, where the amount was unclear, an average cost was assumed.

Social services department costs

Costs to the social services department included provision of care by social services other than the activities undertaken by the project team and the home care assistants. This provision included the time of home helps, day care, meals-on-wheels, residential care and social workers. These unit costs are described below and are shown in Table 9.3.

Table 9.3
Social services department unit costs: price base 1986/87

Social services department unit costs	£
Home help per hour	4.22
Meals-on-wheels per meal	1.05
Day care in a purpose-built centre (revenue costs) per day	7.56
Day care in a purpose-built centre (5% capital allowance)/day	8.93
Day care in a residential home per day	2.55
Residential care (revenue account with capital) per day	17.41
Residential care (5% capital allowance) per day	18.43
Social worker per visit	5.46

Domiciliary services. The estimates of the unit costs of home help and meals-on-wheels were obtained from CIPFA 1986-87 Actuals for Durham County Council and from local authority accounts. The cost estimates include management and administration.

Day care. This was provided both in purpose-built day centres and also in residential care homes. The cost of day care in a day centre was obtained from local authority accounts. The unit cost includes both capital and running costs, travel and meals. The opportunity cost of day care in a purpose-built day centre was also calculated, allowing for land and building costs at a discount rate of 5 per cent over a 60-year period.

The cost of day care in a residential home was estimated from previous work to be about a third of that in the day centre, including meal and travel costs (Challis and Davies, 1986).

Residential care. Data from local authority accounts provided information on the cost of residential care, and the unit cost includes capital and loan repayment costs. The opportunity cost of residential care was also calculated with a capital allowance of 5 per cent, allowing for rebuilding and the price of land over 60 years.

Social workers. The estimated cost of a home visit by a social worker was obtained from a national study (Knapp et al., 1992). This estimate was based upon an average visit of 35 minutes and allowing for overheads. None of the clients in the project received extensive social worker input since this role was undertaken by the project care managers.

National Health Service costs

National Health Service costs included episodes of hospital inpatient care, day hospital care, outpatient treatment and community health services such as district nursing and physiotherapy (including travel time, equipment and an allowance for overhead costs). Also included in the cost to the National Health Service was an estimate of general practitioner and medication costs for elderly people living in the community. An estimate was also made of the initial setting-up costs of the project in terms of extra assessment time and case conference time devoted to the formulation of rehabilitation plans for project clients by staff in the geriatric team, over and above that which would be undertaken for any patient in hospital.

Hospital services. Two different cost estimates have been made for the hospital costs, based on two assumptions for the cost of inpatient care. As described earlier, the elderly people in the study were discharged from Darlington Memorial Hospital, a district general hospital containing both acute assessment facilities and — less common in a district general hospital — long-stay inpatient beds. In view of the mainly acute status of this hospital, the hospital costs for a long-stay geriatric care facility have also been estimated as an alternative scenario, so that comparisons of the potential cost of implementing the approach in other settings can be made. The hospital used for these estimates was the main hospital for the comparison group patients.

The first cost estimate was based upon care in the hospital from which the project clients were discharged. However, given the mainly acute status of this hospital, it provided a wide range of different medical specialties. Obviously these will vary quite significantly in the amount of medical, nursing and other demands they make upon the hospital facilities, making the average cost per bed day markedly higher than that of other long-term hospital care for elderly people. Therefore an attempt was made to apportion costs in a way that reflected the demands made on facilities specifically for the care of elderly patients. The first estimate for inpatient care was based on the hospital costs of the Department of Medicine for the Elderly, from where the project clients were discharged. Table 9.4 summarises the components of the cost of hospital care for this estimate.

The most expensive component of long-stay care for elderly patients is likely to be the nursing care, which in the geriatric care hospital made up 52 per cent of the cost per inpatient day. Hence an attempt was made to estimate nursing costs, including overhead and administrative costs, for the Department of Medicine for the Elderly by apportioning the total nursing costs of the hospital according to the number and grade of nurses within each department. Using this formula the total nursing cost was £5.68 million, of which the weighted proportion for the Department of Medicine for the Elderly was 16.66 per cent. This gave a unit cost for nursing per inpatient

Table 9.4

The components of the cost of hospital care: price base 1986/87

The components of the cost of hospital care	£
Direct treatment services and supplies	
Medical/dental	147,554
Nursing	946,377
Medical and surgical equipment	82,164
Drugs	41,277
Subtotal	1,217,372
Medical and paramedical support	
Radiology, pathology, physiotherapy, occupational therapy and other paramedical support	115,140
Patient-related general services	
Catering, laundry, linen	359,468
Non-patient-related general services:	
Administration, medical records, training and education, staff catering, domestic and cleaning, porter services, transport, engineering, energy and utility, building maintenance, grounds and gardens, miscellaneous services and expenses	1,227,672
District headquarters overheads at 4.75%	138,683
Overall total	3,058,335

day of £18.55. This compares with the nursing cost per inpatient day for the hospital as a whole of £31.34, reflecting the higher costs of services such as intensive care in the overall average. To this were added the costs to the elderly wards of medical and dental services, medical and surgical equipment, pharmacy, paramedical services, patient catering, laundry and transport, as estimated by the district health authority. Non-patient-related costs such as maintenance, medical records and administration were based on regional health authority accounts and were also included. An allowance for district headquarters overhead costs of 4.75 per cent was made based upon district health authority costings. With a total number of elderly inpatient days of 51,028, an average of £59.93 was estimated per elderly inpatient day. This is shown in Table 9.5 with the other unit costs to the National Health Service. This average of £59.93 compares with the cost in the regional health authority accounts of £80.15 for the hospital as a whole, reflecting the higher cost of other services such as intensive care. It does not allow for capital expenditure and is based upon revenue costs alone.

Thus this first cost estimate assumes that the cost of a bed for an elderly patient in the Department of Medicine for the Elderly in Darlington represents the cost of hospital care. This opportunity cost is a relatively high one compared with much long-stay hospital care, and arises because long-stay beds for elderly people in Darlington were provided in a hospital which offered mainly acute facilities. This provides the best 'opportunity cost' estimate of the cost of not investing in project services in that health district.

In other districts such long-stay beds would be in a lower cost setting, and in the second cost estimate the cost of hospital care is based on the costs of the geriatric hospital which cared for the comparison group patients. The regional health authority accounts provided a cost for this of £36.50 per inpatient day. For reference, the other unit in the comparison area, a mainly long-stay facility, had a slightly higher cost of £41.62 per inpatient day. In these three different settings, the nursing cost as a proportion of total cost ranged from 31 per cent at Darlington Memorial Hospital, to 43 per cent at the mainly long-stay hospital, to 52 per cent at the geriatric hospital. The hospital costs have been based on two different types of hospital setting: the Department of Medicine for the Elderly at Darlington Memorial Hospital and a geriatric hospital facility, representing the highest and lowest available figures respectively. The amounts are shown in Table 9.5 with the other unit costs to the National Health Service.

Capital costs. As noted earlier, capital cost elements are usually omitted from the National Health Service costings, unlike costings in social services. Therefore this element needed to be estimated in order to make the costs comparable. Based upon estimates of the cost of refurbishing hospital buildings, three possible costing assumptions may be made (Wright et al., 1981). These are: to improve existing buildings without structural alteration; to upgrade buildings with structural alterations; or to construct new buildings. Reflecting the need

Table 9.5

Unit costs to the National Health Service: price base 1986/87

Unit costs to the National Health Service	£
Hospital inpatient — Darlington Memorial Hospital (revenue) per inpatient day	59.93
Hospital inpatient — Geriatric Hospital (revenue) per inpatient day	36.50
Hospital inpatient — Darlington Memorial Hospital (5% capital allowance) per inpatient day	63.00
Hospital inpatient — geriatric hospital (5% capital allowance) per inpatient day	39.57
Day hospital — Darlington Memorial Hospital (revenue) per day	27.57
Day hospital — geriatric hospital (revenue) per day	28.47
Day hospital — Darlington Memorial Hospital (5% capital allowance) per day	30.64
Day hospital — geriatric hospital (5% capital allowance) per day	31.54
Hospital outpatient — Darlington Memorial Hospital per visit	22.82
Medication (at home) per day	1.09
District nurse per hour	11.04
Physiotherapy (in hospital) per hour	7.63
Physiotherapy (home visit) per hour	10.68
Occupational therapy (in hospital) per hour	7.63
Occupational therapy (home visit) per hour	10.68
Speech therapy (home visit) per hour	8.58
General practitioner per visit	7.92
Chiropody per visit	5.13

to upgrade many long-stay facilities, the capital assumption of upgrading buildings with structural alterations was used, inflating the figures of Wright and colleagues by means of the Public Sector Building Tender Price Index (Department of the Environment, 1987). It can be seen from Table 9.5 that, at a 5 per cent discount rate over a 60-year period, this provided an additional cost of £3.07 per inpatient day.

Day hospital. The cost of a visit to a day hospital was obtained from the regional health authority accounts for both the Darlington Memorial Hospital and the geriatric facility. These prices do not include a capital element. Therefore, in the estimation of social costs, a capital element has been applied to the day hospital, equivalent to the inpatient capital element of £3.07.

Outpatient appointment. Regional health authority accounts provided an estimation of an outpatient appointment at the Darlington Memorial Hospital. This did not include a capital element. The geriatric hospital did not have an outpatient facility.

Medication at home. From the regional health authority accounts the following amounts were estimated, based upon medication/pharmacy costs per inpatient day: Darlington Memorial Hospital £3.70, the mainly long-stay facility £3.03, and the geriatric facility £1.09. The unit cost for the geriatric facility was used as the closest approximation of the cost of medication for these elderly clients while at home.

Other National Health Service personnel costs. A calculation was made of costs to the National Health Service of home visits and hospital contact by community-based staff. These included the district nurse, the physiotherapist, the occupational therapist, the speech therapist and the chiropodist. Data were available on the amount of time spent by each of these staff with each patient, save for the chiropodist where an average visit of half an hour was assumed. Cost estimations have taken account of salaries, travel, subsistence and overheads where appropriate and were based upon figures used in a national study (Knapp et al., 1992).

General practitioner. It was assumed that an average visit made by general practitioners lasted fifteen minutes and the unit cost of this was again derived from a national study (Knapp et al., 1992).

Aids and adaptations. Aids and adaptations for the clients were provided by Durham Health Authority Home Equipment Loan Service. The cost of most aids was attributable to both health and social services and was thus divided equally between the two. Other equipment costs attributable to a single agency were costed accordingly. The costs of aids were discounted over an estimated lifetime of five years at a rate of 5 per cent.

Setting-up costs. There were certain costs incurred in setting up a package of community care for each client. These consisted of the involvement of various staff in case conferences specially convened for assessment and referral to the project, and also in additional assessments in hospital and at home. These costs are over and above the usual assessment time received by all patients which is included in the hospital costs. The concern here is with the extra or marginal costs incurred by the project clients. The setting-up costs to the project include the time spent introducing the home care assistants to clients, both with the care manager and other professionals present, and also time which care assistants spent alone with clients prior to hospital discharge. The setting-up costs are shown in Table 9.6.

A cost for the case conference, which usually considered each client twice prior to discharge, was estimated by assuming a total time spent on each client of fifteen minutes, and estimated the cost of those present: a consultant geriatrician, a junior hospital doctor, a ward sister, a physiotherapist, an occupational therapist, a senior ward sister and a social worker. The cost of the additional assessment in hospital was estimated by calculating the cost of the time spent by the professionals involved or closely consulted. These were a senior ward nurse, a physiotherapist, an occupational therapist, a general practitioner and a care manager. The time of the care manager spent on coordinating meetings with the client and with the client's family, collating case notes, as well as time spent at assessment has been included, since they performed an overall coordinating role. Approximately 50 per cent of the clients received a home assessment and this was costed according to the time spent by those involved in the visit, travelling and writing up the assessment, on average taking about two hours. In most cases this involved the care manager, a physiotherapist and an occupational therapist. Finally, there was the cost to the project of introducing the home care assistant to the client in hospital which was calculated by adding together the cost of the time of the home care assistant (estimated to be three hours), the care manager (estimated to be one and half hours) and other professionals involved.

Although the care manager's time has been costed (see Table 9.6), it has not been included in the total setting-up cost per case as it has already been included as one of the costs to the project.

Table 9.6
Setting-up costs: price base 1986/87

Setting-up costs	£ per case
Case conference	20.36
Hospital assessment (not including care manager)	8.13
With care manager — 25 cases add £41.46	
With care manager — 20 cases add £35.54	
Home assessment (not including care manager)	21.36
With care manager — 25 cases add £18.76	
With care manager — 20 cases add £16.08	
Home care assistant (not including care manager)	14.77
With care manager — 25 cases add £14.07	
With care manager — 20 cases add £12.06	
Total cost	64.62

The total setting-up cost of £64.62 per case was discounted over the six-month period for which each client was monitored or over the amount of weeks clients lived if this was less than the six months. This was a relatively short period over which to discount the 'investment cost' of assessment and initial care planning, but in view of the frailty of the elderly people in question it seemed appropriate. Of course, many individuals remained at home for longer than six months, and if no formal team review were initiated this would inevitably further reduce this cost.

Private establishments

Unit costs for private residential and nursing homes were obtained by using the corresponding supplementary benefit limits introduced in July 1986 (House of Commons, 1987). The rates were £17.86 per day for a private residential home and £24.29 per day for a private nursing home. While it is recognised that currently many establishments charge more than these rates, this was less often the case in 1986 and for that reason those rates have been treated as a guide to the cost of private care. Thus, outside London in the same time period, the mean daily charge was £27.86 for nursing home care (Darton and Wright, 1992).

The public purse

The estimated public expenditure includes revenue costs to the National Health Service and the social services department, pension and benefits, including housing benefit and attendance allowance. This was based on information from interviews and client records in order to ascertain flows of benefits over the six-month period which were adjusted for individual changes in circumstances, such as entry to other forms of care. Where appropriate data were not available, an average level of expenditure was applied based upon national data (DHSS, 1988).

Society as a whole

Costs to society as a whole have been calculated as an estimate of all the resources consumed in providing care. In order to calculate these costs to society, the opportunity costs of services, when applicable, were used. This included: agency costs described earlier in the chapter, with a capital element of 5 per cent added to National Health Service and social services department costs; costs to private residential and nursing homes, based upon the supplementary benefit limit for each category; the opportunity cost of housing, again discounted at 5 per cent; the personal expenditure of the elderly person; and costs to informal carers. Pensions and benefits, as transfer payments rather than flows of real resources, have not been included.

Housing. Elderly people in hospital necessarily receive accommodation as well as care and treatment. An estimate of the housing cost of those discharged from hospital was necessary in order to make realistic cost comparisons between an institutional and a domiciliary care setting. In opportunity cost terms, this considers the housing forgone by the rest of society in maintaining elderly people at home. In order to assess the opportunity cost of housing, the value of individual project clients' housing was estimated from Nationwide Building Society figures (Nationwide Building Society, 1986), where the type of housing was known. For a small number of the comparison group who spent a part of the monitoring period at home, the type of housing was not always known and the value of housing was estimated by using the weighted average house price for the project group. The estimated value of the house was then discounted at a rate of 5 per cent over an estimation of its lifetime, taken to be 60 years, to give a weekly cost for each unit of housing.

The actual cost to society of housing is influenced by whether a person lives alone or with others, and whether the space would be put to alternative use were the person to leave. Thus, if an elderly person was living alone and entered long-stay hospital care, their housing would be likely to become available for alternative use. On the other hand, if they were living in their children's home this is unlikely to be the case. Hence if the client lived with others, the weekly cost of housing was divided between the client and any others concerned: thus, for example, living with a spouse halved the amount. If, however, the client was living with other family members in the family home, the opportunity cost of housing for that client was taken to be zero.

It was assumed that housing costs were only incurred during the actual time the elderly person was at home and occupying the house. This applied to both project clients and comparison group patients.

Other expenditure. Elderly people in hospital incur food and fuel costs as part of the cost of hospital care. Again, making a realistic comparison between the cost of hospital and domiciliary care requires account to be taken of the fuel, food and other living expenses of a person remaining at home. In addition, a person in hospital will spend money on sundry items in addition to those provided by the hospital. These expenditures have been labelled personal consumption.

Personal consumption for both groups for time spent at home was estimated using information from the 1986 Family Expenditure Survey (Department of Employment, 1987), where the expenditure for single person retired households was used, deducting the housing element, which had been estimated separately and described above, to give £41.40 per week for elderly people living alone. A similar method was used for shared retired households where the amount of household expenditure was halved to give £36.57 per week for a person sharing a household.

Personal consumption in local authority residential homes and in hospital was taken to be the pension personal allowance of £7.75 per week, and in private nursing and residential homes to be £9.05 per week (DHSS, 1988).

Informal carers. Although costs to informal carers have been examined for the three groups of carers in Chapter 8, this chapter concentrates on the differential costs to carers of the project clients and the carers of the hospital comparison group. Therefore this chapter does not include care costs which cannot differentially be attributed to receipt of the project or to the fact that an elderly person was in hospital, such as carers having given up work to care in an earlier period. Nobody in the project or comparison group gave up work to care during the six months of the evaluation period, although some carers had given up their job or reduced their working hours prior to this period. Therefore it would be wrong to infer that the costs presented here are the only costs borne by carers. Rather, the cost data indicate the differential financial costs borne by carers of elderly people in receipt of the project and of elderly people in hospital care. There are other costs which will have been incurred equally by both groups of carers prior to the provision of the project service. Information was available for costs to 74 of the 75 carers of the project group and to a sample of 27 of the comparison group carers. The average cost to this subgroup was then generalised to all carers in the comparison group for the purpose of calculating a total cost to society.

As described in Chapter 8, a variety of costs were borne by both groups of carers. The main extra costs to carers which could be attributed to caring for the elderly person either at home or in hospital were those of fuel, food, clothing and laundry.

The extra cost of fuel was obviously only a problem for project carers, 56 per cent of whom spent extra money on heating due to caring for the elderly person. With information on the heating bills many of them paid, an attempt was made to calculate how far this was above the average money spent on fuel, light and power from the 1986 Family Expenditure Survey (Department of Employment, 1987), but this information did not provide regional differences and it appeared that project carers, even when they felt that they were spending more money than usual in this area due to caring, appeared to spend less than the average for the country as a whole. Since these carers identified real additional costs, the supplementary benefit addition for extra heating at the higher rate of £5.45 was used as a weekly extra cost.

Additional money was spent on food by both groups of carers. In order to calculate the cost to carers of providing additional food for the elderly person, the 24 per cent of project carers who said they spent extra on food were subdivided into two groups according to whether they lived with the elderly person or not. Of those carers who lived with the elderly person, many said that they spent more on food due to providing special diets for the elderly person; therefore the supplementary benefit addition for a special diet allowance at the middle rate of £3.70 was used as a weekly extra cost for these carers. For those project carers who did not live with the elderly person, it was assumed from the information available that on some occasions they took full meals to the elderly person and at other times they provided snacks. An allowance of 75 pence was made for each time they took food to the elderly person. Forty-eight per cent of the comparison group said that they spent extra money on food due to the elderly person being in hospital. This ranged from taking in fruit and sweets to taking in sandwiches and cake for an elderly person's tea every day. Based on this information an allowance of 50 pence was made for each time they took food to the elderly person in hospital.

Clothing was another area which led carers to incur additional expense. Twenty-two per cent of the project carers and 37 per cent of the comparison group carers said that they spent extra money on clothing for the elderly person. This may seem rather high for the carers of those elderly people who were in hospital, but of these ten carers, six said that they needed to buy extra clothing because of their experience with the hospital laundry, where much clothing appeared to get lost. They needed enough clothing to manage between the laundry being taken away and returned. One carer said that her husband needed nine extra pairs of trousers in hospital, due to the vagaries of the hospital laundry service. For those hospital carers who said they spent extra on clothing, an amount of £100 was allowed over the six-month costing period, based on carers' responses. For project carers, a lower amount of £70 was allowed for replacement over the six-month period, assuming that clients would be wearing their day clothes most of the time, and garment loss rates would be lower, again based on carers' responses.

Laundry was also an added expense for both groups of carers. Sixty per cent of the project carers and 37 per cent of the comparison carers said that they spent more on laundry due to caring. For the comparison group carers this reflected their concerns with the hospital laundry service and ranged from some carers doing no laundry at all for the elderly person to some visiting most days and taking laundry on each visit. The supplementary benefit allowance addition for laundry at £2.24 per week was allowed for these carers. This was a burden experienced by more of the project carers, and this amount was doubled to £4.48 to allow for the fact that they would also have some additional heavier items to wash, such as bedclothes, and to allow for extra expenditure on soap powder.

Despite its more frequent mention by project carers, there were also some comparison group carers who said they spent extra money on sundry items such as toiletries for the elderly person in hospital. Project carers also spent extra money on telephone calls to arrange relief cover, arranging private chiropody and buying extra bedding for the elderly person.

Although a substantial amount of information had been collected on the kinds of extra costs carers experienced in these two different settings, the information was not adequate in many cases on the extent to which some or all of these costs were offset by transfers of money to the carer from the elderly person. It can be assumed that for carers of the hospital group who had been in hospital for a year, when the elderly person would only be receiving the personal allowance of £7.75, this may have been insufficient to recompense carers for their extra expenditure. All of the project cases were

Table 9.7
Main cost components: price base 1986/87

	Project cases		Comparison cases	
	Over 6 months £	Per week alive £	Over 6 months £	Per week alive £
Costs to the project				
Total project cost	2,849.79	142.66	–	–
Home care assistant	2,373.80	115.96	–	–
Project physiotherapist	24.97	1.17	–	–
Project occupational therapist	9.91	0.57	–	–
Paid helpers	13.30	0.60	–	–
Care manager and project team	329.67	14.84	–	–
Social services department costs				
Total revenue cost	29.46	1.44	115.24	4.43
Total opportunity cost	30.66	1.48	118.10	4.54
Total revenue cost (new arrangements)	36.88	1.78	161.43	6.52
Total opportunity cost (new arrangements)	38.08	1.82	164.29	6.63
Residential care revenue cost	1.38	0.05	46.22	1.78
Residential care opportunity cost	1.46	0.06	48.93	1.88
Day care revenue cost	6.21	0.24	0.80	0.03
Day care opportunity cost	7.34	0.28	0.95	0.04
Home help	19.08	1.04	65.82	2.53
Meals on wheels	2.49	0.10	2.40	0.09
National Health Service costs				
Total revenue cost				
DMH base[a]	842.10	49.68	9,357.73	378.27
Geriatric base[b]	631.46	37.37	5,724.42	231.35
Total opportunity cost				
DMH base[a]	869.70	51.29	9,837.76	397.67
Geriatric base[b]	659.06	38.98	6,204.45	250.75
Hospital costs				
DMH base revenue cost[a]	538.78	31.49	9,293.39	375.79
DMH base opportunity cost[a]	566.38	33.10	9,769.46	395.04
Geriatric base revenue cost[b]	328.14	19.18	5,660.08	228.88
Geriatric base opportunity cost[b]	355.74	20.79	6,136.15	248.13
Medication (at home)	155.17	8.73	12.69	0.49
Community nursing	113.50	6.92	12.85	0.49

Table 9.7 (continued)

	Project cases		Comparison cases	
	Over 6 months £	Per week alive £	Over 6 months £	Per week alive £
Total agency costs				
DMH base[a]	3,748.95	195.39	9,953.00	402.10
Geriatric base[b]	3,538.31	183.08	6,319.69	255.18
Private establishments				
Private residential care	0.00	0.00	6.32	0.38
Private nursing care	5.77	0.22	73.09	3.25
Public expenditure				
Total[c]				
DMH base[a]	5,083.67	259.04	9,838.46	397.70
Geriatric base[b]	4,873.03	246.73	6,205.15	250.78
Pensions and benefits	1,356.33	65.03	286.08	11.37
Social opportunity cost				
Total[d]				
DMH base[a]	5,016.97	255.82	10,492.66	424.15
Geriatric base[b]	4,806.34	243.51	6,859.35	277.23
Housing	291.42	14.13	29.37	1.13
Personal consumption	758.18	36.01	246.47	9.85
Informal carers	171.05	8.21	181.55	7.33

a Long-stay hospital costs at Darlington Memorial Hospital (DMH) level.
b Long-stay hospital costs at geriatric hospital level.
c Includes revenue agency cost elements from earlier in the table.
d Includes opportunity cost elements from earlier in the table.

in receipt of the attendance allowance provided they lived long enough to receive it, but there is no firm evidence of the extent to which this was used to recompense carers. Some carers did say, despite not having been specifically asked, that overall it balanced out as the elderly person reimbursed them.

The costs of care

These analyses present at 1986/7 prices the revenue account costs for the project itself, the social services department, the National Health Service, the private sector of residential and nursing homes, the public purse and society as a whole. The latter covers, in addition, living costs such as food, fuel and housing, the cost of private care and financial costs borne by carers. Table 9.7 shows the costs incurred by these main cost accounts. It also shows the main component parts of these and the total cost to agencies. Costs are presented here both for the overall six-month period and per week alive, which standardise the effect of any difference of survival rates between the groups. A summary of the main total costs with significant group differences, where applicable, is presented in Table 9.8.

The first category, cost to the project, only concerns those cases who received the project service, and it is noteworthy that the majority of the money was spent on the employment of home care assistants, reflecting their importance as the main element of project intervention. Other costs to the social services department were particularly low for project clients, since the project itself provided most of their support. Nonetheless, a small proportion of these people did spend periods of time in residential care, attended day centres and received home help and meals-on-wheels. The revenue cost is not dissimilar to the social services department opportunity cost which, as noted earlier, took account of the discounted future value of capital expenditure. For the comparison group there is necessarily a low cost to the social services department since most individuals spent the whole of the six-month period in hospital care. There were, however, some home help costs caused by short periods spent at home by some individuals and also time spent in residential care, which proved to be greater than that spent by project clients. Under the arrangements introduced in the 1990 National Health Service and Community Care Act, a proportion of board and lodging and care in residential and nursing homes costs is attributable to social services. An estimate of this is shown on Table 9.7 in the totals for the social services department under the new arrangements.

Since the comparison group cases spent most of the cost-monitoring period in hospital, the cost to the National Health Service was higher for comparison group cases, whether considered at the price base of a geriatric hospital or the district general hospital. However, for project clients the National Health Service costs were mainly due to a small number of individuals who spent quite a large amount of the six-month period in hospital or who entered hospital due to illness or for respite care. Unsurprisingly, the other main cost was that of community nursing.

Since it is evident there are marked differences between the types of costs incurred by the comparison group patients (most of whom remained in long-stay hospital care) and the project clients, it is helpful to compare the total agency cost for these groups as a means of providing some idea of their relative care costs. The total agency cost consists of project costs (which were of course nil for the comparison group), social services department costs and National Health Service costs. The National Health Service opportunity costs were used so as to provide an allowance for capital costs which, as explained earlier, were omitted in the revenue accounts. The summary table, Table 9.8, shows that the service costs to the two main agencies and to the project, summed at 1986/7 prices, were approximately £195 per week, compared with £402 in the comparison group, a statistically significant difference

Table 9.8
Summary costs for different parties: price base 1986-87

	Over 6 months			Per week alive		
	Project £	Comparison £	p value	Project £	Comparison £	p value
The project	2,850	–	–	143	–	–
Other SSD (revenue net cost)	29	115	–	1	4	–
Other NHS (5% capital allowance)						
DMH base[a]	870	9,838	–	51	398	–
Geriatric base[b]	659	6,204	–	39	251	–
Total agency cost						
DMH base[a]	3,749	9,953	<0.001	195	402	<0.001
Geriatric base[b]	3,538	6,320	<0.001	183	255	<0.001
Total public expenditure						
DMH base[a]	5,084	9,838	<0.001	259	398	<0.001
Geriatric base[b]	4,873	6,205	<0.001	247	251	ns
Total social opportunity cost						
DMH base[a]	5,017	10,493	<0.001	256	424	<0.001
Geriatric base[b]	4,806	6,859	<0.001	244	277	<0.001

'ns' = not significant.
a Long-stay hospital costs at Darlington Memorial Hospital (DMH) level.
b Long-stay hospital costs at geriatric hospital level.

(p<0.001). Even using the lower unit cost for hospital care, estimated from the costs of the geriatric hospital, the aggregate and weekly cost to agencies is again statistically significantly lower for those individuals receiving the project: a difference of £183 and £255 per week alive (p<0.001). This represents a cost advantage of £72 per week. In part, of course, this is unsurprising since agency costs of community-based care do not allow for the accommodation occupied by elderly people, and therefore provides an incomplete comparison.

The cost of private establishments was greater for comparison group cases. It consisted more often of nursing home than residential care. For project cases, by contrast, much of this nursing care was provided at home.

The public expenditure costs which, in addition to the cost of the care agencies, take account of social security benefits and the cost to the Department of Social Security of private residential and nursing home care, as well as boarding out costs, provide an alternative means of cost comparison. Although indicating a statistically significant difference at the higher cost of hospital care, these indicate only a slight difference between project cases and comparison cases per week alive of £247 and £251, at the lower hospital care rate. The similarity of these sums reflects the higher pension and benefit costs for those living at home. As well as the higher rate of pension, these costs included a very high uptake of attendance allowance for project cases, arranged by the care managers, and greater use of housing benefit. However, the public expenditure costing neglects particularly important areas of cost associated with the provision of community care. In particular, it makes no allowance for the value of housing used by people at home, nor the capital value of National Health Service facilities.

Social opportunity cost provides the most helpful comparison between the two groups, as it includes all of the resources consumed in providing care. As well as considering the cost to agencies with capital elements discounted, this also includes housing, personal consumption and private care costs. The cost of accommodation is particularly salient in costing community care, as a possible effect of enhanced home care may be that elderly people remain in their own homes for longer. Therefore, consideration of the value of housing was necessary in order to make a fair comparison with other forms of care (Challis et al., 1993b). Indeed, housing and personal consumption costs were greater for project clients since they lived at home for a substantial period of the six months, although some comparison group cases did incur housing costs. The costs to informal carers in both groups appeared similar, although the elements which constituted these costs were different for the two groups. Overall it is noteworthy that a difference still remains between project costs and comparison group costs, although this is necessarily narrower than the difference when only the costs of agencies are considered. The lower hospital cost provided a cost comparison of £244 per week alive for project cases and £277 for comparison group cases, a statistically significant difference of approximately £33 per week (p<0.001). This significant difference in cost between the two groups is not surprising, however, due to the comparison of the project service with the provision of long-stay hospital care, which would be expected to be more expensive than other forms of long-term care either at home or in residential care. However, these lower-cost options would have not been a realistic alternative for the majority of clients who received the project service.

It might be suggested that to have provided the comparison group patients with long-stay care in nursing homes would have been a cheaper option than the hospital-based care which they in fact received. This would be to assume that all long-stay care costs were borne at nursing home rates. It would be equally inappropriate to compare actual project care costs in the community with the alternative average institutional care cost. There are three reasons why such assumptions are not valid. First, most elderly patients would require assessment in hospital and possibly some rehabilitation before their discharge to nursing home care. Second, patients would experience episodes of illness and be re-admitted to hospital, possibly incurring the joint cost of a nursing home bed and a hospital bed. Third, if all long-stay beds were closed, hospital unit costs would have to reflect the higher rate of acute care costs and would therefore be closer to the Darlington Memorial Hospital average shown in Table 9.5.

Variations in the costs of care

The analyses in the previous part of this chapter were concerned with the comparison of cost averages for different accounts and components of cost. However, the averages inevitably conceal variations and further analysis is required to develop an understanding of the factors which appear to systematically influence cost. Indeed, an analysis of variation may explain at least as much as a comparison of aggregates. For example, a comparison of average costs ignores the substantial variations of the costs of individuals within care settings. Furthermore, aggregate cost comparisons run the risk of assuming equivalence of effectiveness in two settings and therefore restrict the comparisons to costs. As a consequence, comparisons may be made between not entirely similar patients or groups and some adjustment may be required to compensate for this (Challis, 1992c).

In this section we shall focus upon four different cost elements with differing degrees of comprehensiveness. These are costs to society as a whole, the overall care costs borne by the main agencies, the community care costs borne by those agencies and, finally, that element most under the control of the project care managers, the home care assistants.

The approach to the analysis

Underlying the approach to the analysis was the intention to identify the determinants of cost variation within a production of welfare framework (Davies and Knapp, 1981; Knapp, 1984; Challis and Davies, 1986; Davies and Challis, 1986; Davies et al., 1990). This provides a framework to analyse the relationship between needs, inputs and costs, the characteristics of service users and the effects of services upon them. It thus explicitly brings together the issues of cost and effectiveness. This framework underpinned the studies of care management in Kent and Gateshead (Challis and Davies, 1986; Davies and Challis, 1986; Challis, D.J. et al., 1988a, 1990). The underlying premise of this approach is that variations in costs are determined by client need characteristics, social environment and social support, a person's previous history of care services, their personal characteristics such as age and sex and, finally, the outcomes of care, such as changes in wellbeing over time. Much of the complexity which has to be unravelled in understanding the process of care arises from the interaction of these resource inputs (services) and non-resource inputs (client characteristics) (Challis and Darton, 1990).

Box 9.1 lists the variables which were used in the following analyses. They are categorised within their different domains, the cost-related factors being the dependent variables whose variation the following equations attempt to explain. There are four of these: first, the most inclusive, average social opportunity cost; second, average cost to the main agencies, health and social services; third, average agency costs of care at home; and fourth, the average hours of home care assistant time allocated per client. Each variable was created by dividing the total cost or amount of time over the six-month period by the number of weeks a person was either alive or at home. The order in which the analyses have been presented reflects this process of moving from the most general to the most specific.

The effects of the different independent variables were explored with considerable care. There were four types of independent variable: aspects of care process; health and dependency characteristics; personal characteristics of the elderly person and informal carer; and the outcome indicators. The care process items consisted of measures of length of stay in hospital, location on discharge, the amount of time spent at home, length of survival and payments made to neighbourhood carers. For the measures of number of weeks alive and at home, a quadratic term was also included. This was intended to reflect the possible non-linear relationship between the amount of time a person remains at home and the amount and cost of the care they receive. Thus, on discharge there are inevitably high setting-up costs which would be likely to reduce once the package of care becomes established. However, over time, with the person becoming more dependent, there are likely again to be increasing costs. The indicator of length of stay prior to discharge was very skewed, with the majority of clients having had a length of stay of less than six months, although a small number had markedly greater lengths of stay, of up to five years. The skew in the distribution of this variable was reduced by a logarithmic transformation. The health and dependency items included the presence of a diagnosis of terminal illness, mobility problems, symptomatic health indicators such as breathlessness, activities of daily living, incontinence, indicators of mental health problems and summary indicators from the CAPE BRS (Pattie and Gilleard, 1978). Many of these were examined in different forms of binary division as to whether a particular attribute, such as severe confusion, was present or absent.

Indicators of the characteristics of the elderly person and informal carer included age and the sex of the elderly person, sex and relationship of carer, care tasks undertaken, and indicators of carer burden and stress. A limited number of interaction terms were considered where the creation of new categories could aid explanation. A combination of client sex and relationship of carer to client was examined so that the effect of client sex, carer sex and the nature of the relationship between the two could be more readily under- stood, using indicators such as a male client with a spouse carer.

The outcomes were measures of change in subjective wellbeing or morale (Lawton, 1975; Challis and Knapp, 1980) and quality of care (Challis and Davies, 1986), based upon the initial and follow-up interviews with the elderly

Box 9.1
Variables examined in the cost equations

DOMAIN/VARIABLE	VARIABLE FORM
Cost	
Average agency cost	Cost to the project, other social services revenue and capital costs and geriatric base NHS opportunity costs per week alive, during six months following discharge from hospital.
Average opportunity cost	Cost to the project, other social services opportunity costs, geriatric base NHS opportunity costs, housing costs, personal consumption costs, supplementary benefit board and lodging payments for persons in family placements, costs for private residential homes, costs for private nursing homes and costs to informal carers per week alive, during six months following discharge from hospital.
Average community care cost	Cost to the project, other social services revenue and capital costs and geriatric base NHS opportunity costs, excluding revenue and capital costs for local authority residential homes and geriatric care opportunity costs, per week at home, during six months following discharge from hospital.
Average home care assistant hours	Number of hours of care assistant time received per week at home, during six months following discharge from hospital.
Care process	
Number of weeks alive	Number of weeks alive during six months following discharge from hospital.
Number of weeks at home	Number of weeks at home during six months following discharge from hospital.
Length of stay in hospital	Natural logarithm (base e) of length of stay in hospital (days) prior to initial interview.
Living group on discharge	Living group on discharge: alone, spouse, family, family placement, group home, other.
Cost of paid neighbourhood carers	Amount paid
Health and dependency	
Terminal illness	Diagnosis of terminal illness.
Mobility	Seven categories from ability to walk unaided to chair/bedbound.
Breathlessness	None, moderate, severe.
Risk of falling	None, moderate, severe.
Giddiness	None, moderate, severe.
Sight problems	Can see, partially blind, blind.
Hearing problems	No difficulties, uses hearing aid, some difficulties, very deaf.
Bathing	Whether or not help needed.
Dressing	Whether or not help needed.
Toileting	Whether or not help needed.
Transfer	Whether or not help needed.
Feeding	Whether or not help needed.

Box 9.1 (continued)

Incontinence of urine	Never, sometimes, frequently.
Incontinence of faeces	Never, sometimes, frequently.
Depressed mood	None, mild, moderate, severe.
Confusional states	None, mild, moderate, severe.
Ability to take care of appearance	Almost always, sometimes, almost never.
Dependency summary	CAPE BRS total score.
Physical disability summary	CAPE BRS physical disability score.
Apathy summary	CAPE BRS apathy score.
Communication difficulties summary	CAPE BRS communication difficulties score.
Social disturbance summary	CAPE BRS social disturbance score.

Characteristics of elderly person and informal care

Age of elderly person	Age in years at initial interview.
Sex of elderly person	Male or female.
Carer	Presence or absence of carer.
Sex of carer	Male or female.
Relationship of carer and client	Spouse, not spouse.
Help with rising and retiring	Seven categories from more than once a day to no help needed.
Help with personal care	Seven categories from more than once a day to no help needed.
Check-up visits	Seven categories from more than once a day to no help needed.
Supervision	Seven categories from more than once a day to no help needed.
Help with meals	Seven categories from more than once a day to no help needed.
Help with light housework	Seven categories from more than once a day to no help needed.
Help with soiled linen	Seven categories from more than once a day to no help needed.
Help with tasks outside the home	Seven categories from more than once a day to no help needed.
Providing companionship	Seven categories from more than once a day to no help needed.
Physical ill health of carer	No problems, some problems.
Emotional ill health of carer	No problems, some problems.
Social contact outside home for carer	No impairment, some impairment.
Spare time for carer	Spare time every day, spare time some or no days.
Carer stress	Below or above threshold of malaise inventory.

Outputs

Morale	Change in PGC morale score over six months.
Quality of care	Change in quality of care score over six months.

people. These change measures were examined both as absolute changes and as percentage improvements based upon the initial interviews.

The approach used in these analyses was multiple regression, and a step-wise procedure was adopted. Since the outcome measures, subjective well-being and quality of care, were measures of change over six months, they were dependent upon two interviews with elderly people, and thus this information was only obtained for clients who survived for six months. The main analyses were based upon those cases for whom all information other than the outcome measures was complete, which was between 71 and 75 cases for the different equations as shown on Tables 9.9 to 9.12. Missing data were mainly attributable to the first eleven cases where full interview data were not available and to ten others where a few relevant items were missing. For eight carers, some information on aspects of carers stress was unavailable. For the equation which examined the hours of home care assistant time shown on Table 9.12, the three cases who were discharged to family place-ments were also excluded since they received little or no home care assistant support. Where no follow-up information was available on the outcome measures, the mean value for the variable was included as in other studies (Challis and Davies, 1986; Challis et al., 1990). The assumption underlying this is that other information on these cases, including their costs, is available and there is no reason to suppose that the experience of the care provided for those who died is any different to that of those who survived. Exclusion of cases who died would run the risk of a more partial and possibly biased analysis (Payne, 1977; Little and Rubin, 1987). In the estimation of equations for community services and home care assistant time, the influence of outputs was not explored since both these equations only considered a component part of the total cost, whereas outputs reflected a wider range of cost elements.

Patterns of variation in costs

In these analyses the four cost equations are presented in order of generality from social opportunity costs to hours of home care assistant time. The results are shown in Tables 9.9 to 9.12. There were three types of factor which proved to be significant determinants of variation in cost: aspects of care process, health attributes and informal care. These are discussed below. Given the similar pattern of variables in the equations, the most detailed discussion is for the first equation, that of costs to society.

Costs to society. The best equation which was found to predict costs to society is shown in Table 9.9. This equation explained nearly 80 per cent of the variation in cost. It appeared that the longer a person remained alive after their discharge from hospital over the six-month period, the lower their weekly cost of care. This was a result of a very substantial amount of 'setting-up' activity associated with home support, meaning that usually the first few weeks care after dis-

Table 9.9
Costs to society per week (opportunity costs)

Variable	Coefficient	Std error	t value	p value
Care process				
No. of weeks alive after discharge	-4.26	0.59	-7.19	<0.001
Length of stay in hospital ($\log_e$)	18.20	4.12	4.42	<0.001
Discharge to family placement	-88.66	24.03	-3.69	<0.001
Health				
Severe risk of falling	14.82	8.64	1.72	0.092
Need for help with transfer	58.10	12.40	4.69	<0.001
Frequently incontinent of faeces	49.57	15.99	3.10	0.003
Informal care				
Male client with no carer	55.14	16.40	3.36	0.001
Female client with spouse carer	42.01	12.49	3.36	0.001
Help to transfer by carer, daily	-23.96	11.68	-2.05	0.045
Personal care more than once daily	-39.47	13.68	-2.88	0.006
Meals by carer more than once daily	-37.96	14.27	-2.66	0.010
High carer stress	23.57	10.19	2.31	0.024
Constant	221.12	23.47	9.42	<0.001

F = 18.60
p value < 0.001
R^2 = 0.79
Adj. R^2 = 0.75
Number of cases = 72

charge from hospital were markedly more expensive than subsequent weeks. Factors which contributed to this include a number of home visits by several staff, including care managers, and in many cases a greater amount of home care assistant visits while the person was settling in again at home. Given these higher costs for the first few weeks, it follows that the longer the period of time a person remained at home using services, the longer the period of time over which the setting-up cost could be spread. Furthermore, given that the costing was over a six-month period, for many clients there would not be time for significant deterioration in health status to be reflected in increased levels of care services and consequently greater costs, which might be expected over a longer time period. Unsurprisingly, those elderly people who had been in hospital for longer periods of time prior to discharge proved to be more expensive, reflecting both the additional effort and services required to enable them to return home. Those discharged to a family placement incurred less expense than other clients.

With regard to health indicators, it should be noted that all the elderly people were very dependent and the three factors included — severe risk of falling, need for assistance in transfer, and incontinence of faeces — were indicative of particular extra care demands in an already highly dependent group. The effect of each of these factors was to increase costs since each was indicative of the need for a greater frequency of help. All three of these are elements of what has been described as 'critical interval need' in measuring dependency (Isaacs and Neville, 1976a,b).

Factors associated with informal care also proved to be important determinants of the costs of care. Three factors were important: household structure, the specific activities of the carer and their degree of subjective distress. The effect of the absence of a carer was particularly evident for male clients, rendering their care more costly. Interestingly, female clients with spouse carers were also more costly, indicating the lesser contribution, whether actual or expected, from male carers noted often in the literature (Hunt, 1978; Bebbington and Davies, 1983; Charlesworth et al., 1984). The contribution of carers was particularly evident in certain activities where their input was clearly associated with lower costs. Hence, where a carer assisted with transfer, provided personal care or meals, the costs were lower than otherwise. However, where a carer was experiencing a high level of stress, costs were raised. A number of factors may explain this. First, additional services would be provided to assist carers who were experiencing difficulty, as we have noted in Chapters 4 and 5. Second, carers with high stress levels were likely to be those for whom the services saw most need to offer substitute care and who were likely to withdraw from providing support.

Outcomes did not appear to be sensitive to costs for the clients in Darlington as they had been in the earlier Kent and Gateshead evaluations (Challis and Davies, 1986; Challis et al., 1990). This was partly because the differences were between clients in hospital at first interview and at home at follow up. In hospital settings generally, basic care needs are met reasonably well if perhaps with insufficient sensitivity and privacy. However, the higher order needs, such as morale, may often be met better at home. If anything, the production of welfare approach (Davies and Knapp, 1981; Knapp, 1984; Challis and Davies, 1986; Davies and Challis, 1986; Davies et al., 1990) is less helpful here since the higher cost setting is associated with similar or lower outputs whereas the community-based alternative is necessarily associated with lower costs and also higher outputs. Any relationships found were negative, further suggesting the complex causal relationship between costs and outcomes that exists in health and social care. Thus the improvements in welfare associated with improved health may lead to lower costs and indeed, in a well-monitored service, with lower marginal costs. In practice in the Darlington study, no strong relationship was observed between costs and changes in wellbeing, and what evidence there was for a relationship indicated the negative effect suggested earlier. Our analyses are indicative of a general welfare effect similar across all Darlington clients and variations in levels of care, and therefore cost, appear to be associated principally with variations in client state.

Overall cost to agencies. The equation which most closely fitted the costs borne by the main agencies, health and social services, is shown in Table 9.10. The equation explained about 75 per cent of the variation in cost. The variables included in the equation are very similar to those in Table 9.9, covering care process, health and informal care. As before, length of stay in hospital was associated with higher costs, although a higher number of weeks alive after discharge was associated with lower costs, again reflecting the high setting-up costs of care packages. Family placements again had lower costs. Unsurprisingly, help with transfer and the presence of incontinence of faeces were associated with higher costs due to the greater likelihood of those with such conditions making regular demands upon services. Consequently, the explanation associ-

Table 9.10
Costs to health and social services agencies per week

Variable	Coefficient	Std error	t value	p value
Care process				
No. of weeks alive after discharge	-4.68	0.65	-7.22	<0.001
Length of stay in hospital ($\log_e$)	19.26	4.51	4.27	<0.001
Discharge to family placement	-125.41	26.56	-4.72	<0.001
Health				
Need for help with transfer	59.16	13.71	4.32	<0.001
Frequently incontinent of faeces	52.10	17.68	2.95	0.005
Informal care				
Male client with no carer	67.42	18.12	3.72	<0.001
Female client with spouse carer	45.13	13.72	3.29	0.002
Personal care more than once daily	-41.40	14.98	-2.76	0.008
Meals by carer more than once daily	-37.74	15.26	-2.47	0.016
High carer stress	27.71	11.26	2.46	0.017
Constant	163.49	24.94	6.56	<0.001

$F = 18.18$
p value < 0.001
$R^2 = 0.75$
Adj. $R^2 = 0.71$
Number of cases = 72

ated with their effects is likely to be very similar. With regard to informal care factors, male clients lacking carers and female clients supported by a spouse were again more costly. Provision of personal care and meals by carers was associated with reduced costs. Conversely, high carer stress was associated with higher costs because of the greater demands on services.

In order to take account of the different pattern of funding of residential and nursing home costs after April 1993 when local authorities took over the additional costs of board and lodging, a further equation was estimated reflecting this pattern of costs. The equation proved to be very similar to that shown in Table 9.10, including the same independent variables.

Costs to agencies of community services. The equation which fitted the costs of community services explained 84 per cent of the variation in costs and is shown in Table 9.11. Similar to the previous equations, the explanatory variables came from the three domains of care process, health and informal care. Length of stay in hospital tended again to increase costs, and family placements

Table 9.11
Costs to community services per week at home

Variable	Coefficient	Std error	t value	p value
Care process				
No. of weeks at home after discharge	-12.22	2.80	-4.36	<0.001
No. of weeks at home, squared	0.21	0.09	2.36	0.022
Length of stay in hospital ($\log_e$)	15.47	4.23	3.66	<0.001
Discharge to family placement	-200.82	24.07	-8.35	<0.001
Health				
Need for help with transfer	77.77	12.83	6.06	<0.001
Informal care				
Male client with spouse carer	35.72	15.03	2.38	0.021
Female client with spouse carer	38.53	12.97	2.97	0.004
Help to transfer by carer, daily	-24.26	11.75	-2.07	0.043
Personal care more than once daily	-41.82	13.55	-3.09	0.003
Meals by carer more than once daily	-47.38	14.73	-3.22	0.002
Constant	236.23	25.60	9.23	<0.001

$F = 30.68$
p value < 0.001
$R^2 = 0.84$
Adj. $R^2 = 0.81$
Number of cases = 71

were associated with lower costs, suggesting that it was associated with a lower level of community services. However, for this equation the dependent variable was the cost of care per week at home. Both the length of time at home and its quadratic term entered the equation, the former with a negative coefficient and the latter with a positive term. The joint effect of these two terms suggests that the longer an elderly person remains at home the more the weekly cost declines, reflecting the influence of the initial setting-up costs although this decline decreases slightly over time. Patients needing help with transfer again proved more costly, reflecting the frequency of episodes of help which they would require. There were also some differences in the informal care factors. Clients with spouse carers appeared to have higher costs than others, although male clients were marginally less expensive than female clients. Assistance from carers with transfer, personal care and meals all reduced costs to agencies. Interestingly, high carer stress did not prove to be a significant influence upon community services costs. Given the presence of this factor in the other two equations, it would suggest that carer stress as a cost-raising attribute affects the probability of entry to institutional care rather than the consumption of community services (Levin et al., 1989).

Home care assistant time. Table 9.12 shows the equation for the most specific item of all in these analyses, the allocation of home care assistants' time. The use of hours as the dependent variable in this equation rather than costs is deliberate, since it reflects the primary focus of staff in determining the allocation of this resource. The equation proved to have less explanatory power than the previous ones, explaining about two-thirds of the variation in time allocations. As in the previous equations, three kinds of factor were important: care process, health and informal care. Length of stay in hospital was again associated with higher costs, reflecting the greater care needs and rehabilitative effort required at home for those who had remained in hospital longest. The two health factors which entered the equation were both tasks directly undertaken by home care assistants: need for assistance with bathing and need for help with transfer. As would be expected, both increased the number of home care assistant hours provided. With regard to informal care factors, both the provision of personal care and meals by carers reduced the number of hours of home care assistant time allocated. This clearly reflects a degree of substitution between home care assistants and carers.

Patterns of variation in costs. These analyses have focused upon four different elements of cost, which logically could be influenced by different factors: for example, agency costs, which include hospital care, could be influenced by quite different factors to those which affect amounts of home care assistant time. However, it is interesting to note the high degree of similarity of the variables within each of the four equations, although this is in part due to each equation being built up from the core service which was the provision of care by home care assistants. We have described in detail the most general equation,

Table 9.12
Hours of home care assistant time per week

Variable	Coefficient	Std error	t value	p value
Care process				
Length of stay in hospital (log$_e$)	2.24	0.78	2.89	0.005
Health				
Max. help with bath/dressing	5.56	1.84	3.03	0.004
Need for help with transfer	10.74	2.40	4.48	<0.001
Informal care				
Personal care more than once daily	-8.56	2.28	-3.76	<0.001
Meals by carer more than once daily	-10.54	2.26	-4.67	<0.001
Constant	14.46	3.66	3.95	<0.001

$F = 25.89$
p value < 0.001
$R^2 = 0.65$
Adj. $R^2 = 0.63$
Number of cases = 75

which explains the overall costs to society. As we have noted, there was no occasion where any of the outcome indicators proved to be significant determinants of the variation in costs. Of course, in two of the equations these were deliberately omitted because the analysis was exploring the allocation of particular services or types of service rather than the overall process of care. However, the first two equations — examining cost to society and overall costs to agencies — could have included outcome indicators. Certainly, the evidence in Chapters 7 and 8 suggests that, in general, project clients experienced improvements in wellbeing after their discharge from hospital. One possible explanation for this is that clients were initially interviewed in hospital, a high cost environment, and subsequently interviewed at home, in general a lower cost environment. Paradoxically, therefore, there could be a negative relationship between cost and improved outcomes, the lower cost setting being associated with better outcomes. Had patients been seen at home before receiving project services and then subsequently followed up at home, it is more likely that a relationship between variations in inputs, predominantly community care inputs, and variations in outcomes would be observable.

In the next section the equations are used to analyse the differential costs for clients in different circumstances. This permits us to explore the implications of the patterns of variation in costs which the equations have demonstrated and to try to identify those individuals for whom the community-based approach was likely to prove cost-effective.

Project and comparison groups compared

It was not feasible to estimate equations explaining variations in costs for the comparison group since the majority stayed in hospital throughout the period of the study. However, it is possible to use the equations described in Tables 9.9, 9.10 and 9.11 to estimate the costs of the comparison group as if its members were receiving the services of the project, and thus to compare the costs of the two groups more precisely than simply by comparing average costs, as we have done earlier in this chapter. For each of the three costs — opportunity costs per week alive, agency costs per week alive and community service costs per week at home — the respective equation from Tables 9.9, 9.10 and 9.11 has been used to predict the costs for the comparison group.

For comparison group patients, only the length of stay in hospital and the dependency variables were available. For the purpose of predicting the mean cost for these patients, the values of the remaining variables have been set at the mean values for project clients. The results of these predictions are shown in Table 9.13. It can be seen that, for each of the predictions of the mean cost for the comparison group patients, the predicted mean exceeded both the mean for project clients included in the regression equation and the mean for all project clients. The lower 95 per cent confidence limit for the predicted mean was greater than the means for project clients, with the exception of the mean cost of community-based services for all project clients. However, the mean cost of community-based services for project clients was only included within the 95 per cent confidence interval for the predicted mean due to one outlying case. Therefore, we may conclude that, even with this more sophisticated adjustment to mean costs, the project service remained statistically significantly less expensive for the average patient than the mode of provision offered to the comparison group.

A comparison between the predicted mean costs for comparison group patients, as if they had received project care, with their actual mean costs in mainly hospital care, reveals that the actual agency costs and the actual opportunity cost were significantly higher than the predicted costs. The actual cost to the agencies was £255 per week, compared with an upper 95 per cent confidence limit for the predicted mean cost of £212 per week, and the actual opportunity cost was £277 per week, compared with an upper 95 per cent confidence limit for the predicted mean cost of £271 per week. Thus we may conclude that project care would be less costly for the average member of the comparison group than the hospital-based care which they actually received.

Table 9.13

Mean costs of care per week for project clients and mean predicted costs for patients in comparison area if given project care[a]: price base 1986/87

	Project group		Comparison group		
	Mean cost for all clients £	Mean cost for clients in regression £	Mean cost for all comparison group £	Predicted mean cost £	95% confidence interval[b]
Opportunity costs per week alive	244	240	277	259	247,271
Agency costs per week alive	183	179	255	199	186,212
Community services costs per week at home	189[c]	180	na	196	184,208
Number of cases	101	72/71[d]	113	111	

'na' = not available.

a Mean values of variables for project clients used for variables unavailable for patients in comparison area: weeks alive/weeks at home, discharge to family placement, sex of client and relationship to carer, receipt of informal care, and carer stress.

b Confidence interval for prediction of mean cost.

c Mean cost = £184 per week at home for 100 cases, excluding case with maximum community services cost (£779 per week at home).

d 72 cases for opportunity costs and agency costs, 71 cases for community services costs.

The costs of care of different clients with different need profiles

The three equations in Tables 9.9, 9.10 and 9.11 were used to predict the costs of care using the project service for various combinations of client and carer characteristics and circumstances. Based upon the three types of variables which proved to be significant in the equations — care process, health and informal care — 21 different client types were selected for examination. All were assumed to have been in hospital for 28 days and to have remained at home for at least six months. These ranged from individuals with varied dependency characteristics without carers, and therefore whom would be dependent upon services for nearly all their support, to individuals with spouse or non-spouse carers who might undertake a range of care tasks. The 21 client types are shown in Table 9.14 with the predicted opportunity, agency and community services costs per week, together with the 95 per cent confidence intervals around each estimated cost figure. The confidence intervals shown in Table 9.14 have been calculated to give an overall probability of 95 per cent that all the predictions for the 21 client types would cover the true values for such individuals. The confidence interval for each prediction is wider than if separate 95 per cent confidence intervals were calculated for each individual client type, but gives strong evidence that the predictions cover the true values (Koch, 1977). Some of the lower confidence bounds and, occasionally, the predicted costs, are negative values. This is merely an artefact of estimation and is not the true value of the care costs. This ensures that the probability that one or more confidence intervals do not cover the true value is no greater than 5 per cent, that is, maintaining type I error ('false positives') at 5 per cent, but at the cost of reducing the chance of identifying a true difference between the predicted cost and the true value, that is, increasing type II error ('false negatives').

It can be seen that there is a considerable range of estimated costs. In examining the estimated costs for different client types, the figures in Table 9.14 should be compared to the costs for project clients and the comparison group which are shown in Table 9.13. First, it can be seen that the least expensive types of client were the same for all three cost 'accounts' (types 19, 16 and 10). These cases were those without any of the three cost-raising dependency attributes — risk of falling, need for help with transfer, and incontinence — and who were supported by carers who were not stressed and who undertook a range of care tasks.

Second, for both opportunity costs and agency costs, the rank order of the nine least expensive client types proved to be the same (types 19, 16, 10, 17, 20, 1, 13, 11 and 7). This suggests that broadly the pattern of costs, and factors in the care process likely to influence costs, are broadly similar for the two measures of cost. Most of these cases were supported by unstressed carers who undertook care tasks; for those who did not fit this description, none of the cost-raising dependency attributes was present.

Third, for both the opportunity cost and the agency cost, the most expensive five cases again are in the same rank order (types 6, 9, 5, 15 and 3). All of these cases have two or three of the cost-raising dependency attributes and either no carer, or a spouse carer unable to perform care tasks.

Fourth, the most expensive case for opportunity costs and agency costs (type 6), an elderly male with all three cost-raising dependency attributes and no carer, proved to be only at the mean cost for community services for project cases, £189 per week. One explanation is that such an individual would be expected to have a greater probability of entering hospital or nursing home care and would therefore require hospital or institutional care resources as well as substantial provision of community services.

Fifth, one of the lowest cost types for community services (type 21), a client of either sex with a non-spouse carer, all three dependency attributes, whose carer undertakes care tasks but is stressed, exhibits a similar pattern. Such an individual would be expected to have well below average community service costs, £76 per week, compared with the mean for project clients of £189. However, their expected opportunity and agency costs, of £216 per week and £166 per week respectively, are not far below the mean for project clients. One explanation of this is that while such an individual is coping in the community their service costs are relatively low, but there is a considerable probability of their requiring institutional care, either on an episodic or a permanent basis.

Sixth, one of the most costly cases for community services (type 14), a male client at risk of falling and needing help with transfer, with a spouse carer who is unable to perform care tasks, has an estimated cost of £225 for community services, which is markedly above the mean for project clients of £189. However, the opportunity cost equals the mean of £244 for project clients, and the agency cost of £165 is slightly below the mean for project clients of £183. This would suggest that such an individual, although costly to maintain in the community, is not particularly likely to enter institutional care. There is also likely to be a degree of invisible cross-subsidisation for such a case where assistance nominally provided to the client is also beneficial to a frail spouse carer. This could be described as the generation of positive externalities, where the consumption of services by one individual leads to benefits for another (Knapp, 1984). Such an individual may be compared with a similar person who in addition suffers from incontinence (type 15) whose community service costs are identical but whose opportunity and agency costs are both well above the mean, at £293 and £217 respectively. One explanation is that the presence of this additional dependency attribute would necessitate more health-related interventions and also make continued community care more difficult.

A limited number of cases were sufficiently different from the mean of the project cases to be outside the 95 per cent confidence intervals. As such, these could be said to be significantly more or less costly. Case types 6 and 9, the most expensive, had individual confidence intervals which did not

Table 9.14
Predicted costs of care per week for various combinations of client and carer characteristics: price base 1986/87

Client type, Client sex, carer presence	Client dep.[a]	Care tasks by informal carer[b]	Carer malaise	Opportunity costs per week alive Predicted cost £	95% confidence interval[c]	Agency costs per week alive Predicted cost £	95% confidence interval[c]	Community services costs per week at home Predicted cost £	95% confidence interval[c]
1 Female client, no carer	–	–	–	171	52,290	106	-25,237	112	-9,232
2 Female client, no carer	FT	–	–	244	126,361	165	37,293	189	73,305
3 Female client, no carer	FTI	–	–	293	167,420	217	79,355	189	73,305
4 Male client, no carer	–	–	–	226	100,352	173	35,312	112	-9,232
5 Male client, no carer	FT	–	–	299	174,424	233	95,370	189	73,305
6 Male client, no carer	FTI	–	–	349	217,480	285	141,429	189	73,305
7 Female client, spouse carer	–	No	No	213	89,337	151	14,288	150	24,276
8 Female client, spouse carer	FT	No	No	286	165,407	210	78,342	228	107,349
9 Female client, spouse carer	FTI	No	No	335	203,468	262	117,408	228	107,349
10 Female client, spouse carer	–	Yes	No	112	-13,236	72	-64,208	37	-90,163
11 Female client, spouse carer	FT	Yes	No	184	66,302	131	2,260	114	-4,232
12 Female client, spouse carer	FTI	Yes	Yes	258	128,387	211	69,352	114	-4,232
13 Male client, spouse carer	–	No	No	171	52,290	106	-25,237	147	23,272
14 Male client, spouse carer	FT	No	No	244	126,361	165	37,293	225	102,348
15 Male client, spouse carer	FTI	No	No	293	167,420	217	79,355	225	102,348
16 Male client, spouse carer	–	Yes	No	70	-55,194	27	-108,161	34	-90,158
17 Male client, spouse carer	FT	Yes	No	142	23,262	86	-44,216	112	-7,230
18 Male client, spouse carer	FTI	Yes	Yes	216	91,340	166	31,301	112	-7,230

19 Male or female client, non-spouse carer	–	Yes	No	70	-55,194	27	-108,161	-2	-130,126
20 Male or female client, non-spouse carer	FT	Yes	No	142	23,262	86	-44,216	76	-45,196
21 Male or female client, non-spouse carer	FTI	Yes	Yes	216	91,340	166	31,301	76	-45,196

a 'F' = severe risk of falling, 'T' = dependence in transfer, 'I' = frequent incontinence of faeces.

b 'Yes' = help to transfer at least daily, personal care more than once per day and meals provided more than once per day.

c Confidence interval for prediction of cost for individual.

include the mean opportunity cost for project cases (266,432 and 251,419 respectively), although the overall confidence intervals, shown in Table 9.14, did include the mean opportunity cost for project cases. This suggests that the opportunity cost of providing support for dependent male clients without carers and dependent female clients with spouse carers who do not undertake care tasks is markedly higher than for others. In these data male carers were predominantly spouse carers. Male clients without carers who are dependent are also likely to be markedly more costly to agencies than the average client. Three of the least costly cases (types 10, 16 and 19) had estimated costs whose confidence intervals did not include the mean for both opportunity and community costs. For two of these cases (types 16 and 19) the confidence intervals did not include the mean agency costs. That is to say, these individuals were markedly less costly than the average case. These were characterised by lacking the additional dependency attributes but receiving support from carers who undertook care tasks and were not stressed.

When comparison is made with the actual costs of the comparison group cases, some case types emerge for whom project services would clearly seem to be more cost-effective. This comparison is legitimate since comparison group patients, as long-stay patients, had mostly hospital care costs (91 per cent of total agency costs). Since hospital costs did not vary according to different client characteristics, the mean costs for different individuals would be very similar, making it possible to compare this figure with the different costs predicted from the equations. One-third of the 21 case types had the upper confidence interval of their estimated cost below the control group average costs for agencies. This suggests that for these cases (types 1, 10, 13, 16, 17, 19 and 20) the project service would have been significantly less costly than the hospital-based alternative. These individuals were of relatively lower dependency and had unstressed carers. By contrast, it appears that those with the highest agency costs would be male clients or women with spouse carers. Five of the 21 cases (types 10, 16, 17, 19 and 20) had the upper confidence interval for opportunity costs below the average cost of the comparison group patients, suggesting that these cases would be significantly less costly were they to have received the project service. Again, in general, these cases were of relatively lower dependency within what was a group with high overall dependency or receiving support from an unstressed carer.

Conclusion

To conclude, therefore, it would appear that, whether viewed from the perspective of the agencies, public expenditure or society as a whole, the greater benefits achieved for both elderly people and their carers in the project were at least no more expensive than the alternative provision of hospital care, and the analyses thus suggest that the service model developed in Darlington was capable of providing more efficient long-term care for frail elderly people. That is, greater benefits were obtained for the same or a slightly lower cost. Clearly the cost data only cover a six-month period over which the survival rate varied. However, the cost per week standardises the effects of differential survival rates, which in any case no longer differed after one year. The extent to which such cost profiles endure beyond a six-month period is an important question; however, a follow-up of a care management service over a four-year period suggests that cost patterns remain reasonably constant over a longer time (Chesterman et al., 1988). Furthermore, given the extreme frailty of the individuals in question and therefore their relatively short life expectancy, we can reasonably accept these cost profiles.

The equations which indicate factors influencing variations in cost suggest that a substantial proportion of this could be predicted by three factors: care process; health and dependency; and characteristics of the elderly person and informal care. Using the equations it was possible to compare the cost of care for the average comparison group patient if they were to have received project care with that of project cases. This indicated that the cost of providing project care to these hospitalised individuals would be less than long-stay hospital care. The services of the project appeared to be less costly than hospital care for most of the hypothetical case types analysed. For some this difference was statistically significant. Those who were expected to be substantially more costly than the average project client tended to be males living alone, or were highly dependent females with spouse carers who did not undertake care tasks. Those who were substantially less costly than the project average had relatively lower levels of dependency and received support from un-stressed carers who undertook a range of care tasks.

10 From Project to Mainstream: A Single Agency Service

The Darlington Project, as noted earlier, was a centrally-funded, time-limited intervention whose budget was ring-fenced. The special funding from central government under the Care in the Community arrangements lasted until April 1988. Receipt of the central funding had been contingent upon an agreement that the project would continue with funding by the local agencies although the precise form of this was not made specific. The transition from the status of a special project to a mainstream service has been a major area of concern in the literature on innovation, dissemination and service development (Backer et al., 1986; Fairweather et al., 1974; Ferlie et al., 1989). It is of considerable relevance for two reasons to examine the development of the service after the project phase: first, in the light of the new arrangements for community care arising from the National Health Service and Community Care Act 1990, and the extent to which innovatory services such as the project can contribute to these changes; and second, with the citation of the project in the White Paper *Caring for People* (Cm 849, 1989, para. 3.3.3) as an exemplar of care management, the developments provide evidence of how innovations relate to mainstream services. This chapter traces the process of absorption of the special project into the local service system, examines some of the difficulties that were experienced in so doing, and identifies the changes which occurred. The information for this chapter was gathered from agency reports about the development of the service, researcher interviews with elderly people, participation in meetings before, during and after the changes, and interviews with staff in the service at the point of incorporation into the mainstream, six months later and four years later.

The transition process

As the project phase drew to an end in 1988, and with it the period of central government funding, the discussions of the coordinating group (the joint health and social services group with responsibility for oversight of the project) focused increasingly on the future funding, organisation and management of the service. The project was at that time jointly managed, with staff employed by social services, except for the physiotherapist and occupational therapist. However, the patients receiving project services were people whose long-term care needs would probably otherwise have been met in a hospital or nursing home setting. Concerns about the future of the service were partly related to the characteristics of those who were currently included in the project and the likely characteristics of those who should be future recipients of the service. It was generally seen as desirable to remove the 'perverse incentive' created by the rules of central funding, which was to accept only individuals who had previously been hospitalised. However, this would have meant that new referrals would also come from community sources, such as general practitioners, social services and district nurses, which might have consumed all the resources available. Views of different actors varied according to their perceptions of the effect of a new service upon them.

General practitioners expressed concern at single agency provision, based on the view that elderly people present with social and medical problems, requiring inputs from both agencies. Within the hospital sector, anxieties were expressed by staff of the acute unit (responsible for services such as general medicine and surgery) over future referral procedures and access to the service for current inpatients, reflecting a concern about bed-blocking. Staff of the geriatric service felt that they had reduced their complement of long-stay beds as a consequence of the scheme and saw the need to maintain in full what had become its 'community beds' for those elderly people supported by the project. Hence, the overriding concern of health authority staff was that an influx of referrals from the community would mean that health service funds might be subsidising clients who would normally receive social services care, and therefore that the target group should remain defined as hospital patients. Of course, such a concern would be likely to have been even greater in 1993 after the implementation of the National Health Service and Community Care Act, which, by clarifying responsibilities for long-term care, might unintentionally provide perverse incentives against collaboration in this sphere of activity. The social services had wished to continue a joint service, and also to develop the home help service along some of the directions of the project. However, the social services' major concern was the unmet need of severely disabled elderly people living in their own homes. These two perceived target populations certainly overlapped, but it could not be ascertained by how much. Thus there was an inevitable divergence of goals between the two major agencies, which could not easily be resolved without further funding on a joint basis.

In the short term therefore, the health authority, which faced the most pressing needs arising from a reduction in long-stay beds, was able to continue to fund what was seen locally as a prestigious development due to funding made available from ward closures as a result of the project. Furthermore, it faced a longer-term concern about the possibility of effecting earlier discharge from hospital beds. With the realisation that this new service was to be the sole responsibility of the district health authority, some health staff involved in the planning process expressed concerns about the extensiveness of the care remit, and ways of delineating boundaries were considered. Suggestions included preventing home care assistants from undertaking 'non-nursing tasks', which meant that different tasks would be performed by separate providers on grounds of cost, thus reflecting the higher cost of home care assistants compared with home help or private domestic care. This also reflected administrative boundaries, effectively re-erecting barriers between the relative responsibilities of health and social services on a task basis. Such proposals of multi-service packages might in themselves be quite rational, but had been ruled out in the project as contrary to the philosophy of minimising the number of 'hands-on' care workers, and could be seen as undermining some of the strengths of what had been developed earlier. A monitoring group of health and social services staff was established to guide the project into the new phase and deal with boundary disputes.

Thus, whereas the planning and implementation of the project was characterised by agreement on objectives that could be achieved through cooperation at relatively little cost to either health or social services, the end phase of the project evidenced dissensus and a degree of conflict. These effects are consistent with much of the arguments from literature on inter-organisational behaviour. Exchange theory would suggest that cooperation occurred because each organisation believed that it could achieve its goals more effectively in collaboration than by acting independently (Levine and White, 1961; Aiken and Hage, 1968; Cook, 1977). The joint project arose from the need to acquire central funding through a collaborative development which offered benefits to both parties at relatively little cost. Thus interdependence (Litwak and Hylton, 1962) arose in part from the funding arrangements and could be characterised as a form of 'induced interdependency' (Reid, 1969). One aim of the Care in the Community initiative was to examine models of care which build upon interdependence and shift resources so as to effect the needed response by the social services to a predominantly health service problem, namely, long-stay hospital care. However, as Hudson has observed, 'such an approach may be tenuous and subject to rupture' (1987, p.180). When the central funding ended, there remained little cement to hold the two agencies together. The status of the central funding as joint finance appeared to have led the health authority to perceive it as their money and therefore health as the dominant partner in the relationship. This was reinforced since the financial savings from the bed closures accrued to the health authority so that they were able to finance the continuation of the service and maintain control, thereby ensuring that the impact upon hospital beds would continue. Thus, as the funding arrangements changed, so the balance of apparent costs and benefits to the agencies changed, and the preconditions for interdependence were removed. There remained little basis for exchange since the district health authority both had the resources and stood the risk of bearing the costs if the new service did not meet its goals. Hence an independent strategy must have appeared to be the most efficient and least risky means to achieve their goals. Such a process could be characterised as a move from interagency relationships based upon exchange towards reliance upon patterns of power and dependency (Aldrich, 1976; Schmidt and Kochan, 1977), based more upon bargaining. This was reflected in the representation of the social services in the group which was established to steer the project into the mainstream. Even where the relationship between the two organisations was asymmetrical in terms of power and influence over the project, there was still some compatibility in terms of goals and recognition of the value of continuing dialogue.

After the move from a joint agency to a single agency service occurred, a series of three distinctly different organisational forms emerged, as summarised in Box 10.1. Essentially, the three stages are associated with different ways of handling the care management function. In the first stage this was omitted and assumed to be part of the 'keyworker' role of community health staff. In the second stage, staff were appointed to fill the care manager role, but problems of their 'fit' with existing staff and lack of clarity over their purchasing and providing roles at the micro level made this a less than satisfactory solution. In the third stage, staff who had 'acted up' on an informal basis to fill the care manager gap were acknowledged as performing some aspects of that role, although their need for training in that role remained a source of concern. These changes are examined in more detail below.

The single agency service: stage 1 — the initial new service

Following the move of the service into the health authority, various managerial arrangements and locations were explored. This instability arose partly from major changes occurring in the health service itself, such as the development of the internal market and larger-scale managerial changes within the locality, and also partly from a desire to design the most appropriate form of arrangements for a service providing intensive home care. Among those involved in planning there was considerable debate as to whether the appropriate managerial unit for the service should be the community health unit (covering district nursing and other community health services), reflecting the setting where the service was provided, or the department of geriatric medicine, reflecting the source of the savings for the funding of the service and the unit with most incentive for the continued targeting upon those whom, in the absence of the service, would require hospitalisation. In the event, the service was located in the community unit, permitting close links with district nursing.

Box 10.1

Changes in the structure of the service after the project phase

	PROJECT PHASE	SINGLE AGENCY PHASE		
	Summer 1985 —Spring 1988	Spring 1988 —Autumn 1989	Autumn 1989 —Winter 1991	Winter 1991 — present
Agency management	Joint agency (SSD/NHS)	Single agency (NHS)	Single agency (NHS)	Single agency (NHS)
Employer	SSD	NHS	NHS	NHS
Day-to-day management	Project manager	Health care team leaders	Elderly services manager	Elderly services manager
Care management	Care managers	(Health care team leaders) (District nurses and other staff)	Coordinators	(Elderly services manager) (New service managers)
Home care assistant Management	Care managers	(Health care team leaders) (Clerical officers)	Coordinators	New service managers
Day-to-day administration	Clerical staff	Higher clerical officers	Admini- strative assistants	New service managers and clerical staff
Task specification for home care assistants	District nurses and therapy staff	District nurses and therapy staff	District nurses and therapy staff	District nurses and therapy staff
Client-level work	Home care assistants	Home care assistants	Home care assistants	Home care assistants

Note: Where a responsibility is in brackets, it indicates that it is unclear.

Organisation

As noted, in the spring of 1988 the project became a mainstream service located in the community unit of the district health authority. Its new title was the Intensive Domiciliary Care Service, and all staff were employed by the health service. The aim of the service was described as:

> [T]o offer an intensive multipurpose care service to people in their own homes. The service will achieve this by providing support through home care assistants who are multipurpose workers undertaking personal care tasks, therapeutic tasks on behalf of health and social service professionals, domestic tasks and social tasks (Darlington Health Authority Community Unit, 1988).

The community unit was divided into three geographical areas, and the health care team leader in each sector was the line manager for the service. Plans to transfer the original care managers, who were called service managers, to the health authority, at least on a temporary basis to ease transition, did not materialise due to reasons of cost and staff turnover. The job of organising rotas and payments for home care assistants was given to specifically appointed clerical officers, one of whom had been a home care assistant in the project phase. The steering group report prior to the changes commented thus:

> [W]e will not be employing Service Managers [care managers]. Instead ... three Higher Clerical Officers will undertake those duties of the Service Managers associated with rotas, work allocation, time sheets etc. The other aspects of the Service Manager role will be taken on by the wider Health Care Teams ... This change is in no way meant to imply that the Service Man- ager role has not been a vital part of the Project. It simply recognises the reality of our moving into an established organisation that can take on some of the functions currently being carried out by the Service Managers (Darlington Community Care Project for the Elderly, 1988).

Thus the position of a designated care manager, someone responsible for coordinating a package of care and taking an overview of a client's needs and the effectiveness of services in meeting those needs, no longer existed. As noted in Chapter 5, it had proved possible to delegate some aspects of the care management process, particularly monitoring, to home care assistants, while client circumstances remained stable. This represented a valuable strategy for organising a time-consuming aspect of care management (Department of Health, 1994). However, it is debatable whether this rendered the care manager's role unnecessary.

Those most closely involved — members of the geriatric multidisciplinary team and other staff linked to the project — expressed concern whether effective care coordination and management of the service would occur with these arrangements. However, the expectation was that existing community-based health care staff would act as keyworkers with a responsibility for planning and coordinating care for those elderly people receiving the service in its new form. The transitional plans assumed that the role of the keyworker would include, in addition to all their existing tasks, holding the care plan, progress-chasing the implementation of services involving all relevant professionals, working directly with the client and family, and providing support and guidance to home care assistants. As a keyworker role definition, this extends beyond the normal definition of coordinating the work of the immediate team or service (Ovretveit, 1993).

The existing home care assistants were re-organised into three teams, which were transferred to the three geographically-based teams in the community unit of the health authority. Some problems of different pay and conditions of service emerged as a consequence of transferring home care assistants to nursing auxiliary scales from their previous local authority scales. Home care assistants' contracts were changed from 29 hours per week to 25 hours per week and initially they were paid at a nursing auxiliary rate, which was lower than that paid by social services. However, with a subsequent nurse regrading, these terms improved markedly.

A monitoring group was created with representatives from the acute unit, community unit and social services department to review the operation and effectiveness of the service. Its main functions were to monitor operational relationships between the community unit, acute unit and social services department; to monitor the new assessment and referral procedures; and to monitor the development of the service, in particular costs, caseloads and dependency levels. This reflected the concern about appropriate targeting, which was evident in the documentation prior to the change, but which clearly echoes current concerns nationally about the implementation of community care:

> [T]he Scheme must be seen to continue to have an impact on the Geriatric beds in the hospital ... those patients who might normally be termed 'long-stay' or 'bed-blockers' (Darlington Community Care Project for the Elderly, 1988, appendix C).

Operation in practice

Referral, assessment and review. On a day-to-day basis an assessment and review panel was established to receive referrals, coordinate assessments, make decisions about service allocations, hold reviews and make decisions about termination of the service and transfer to other services. The panel included a consultant geriatrician, a community physiotherapist, a community occupational therapist, a district nurse liaison officer, the higher clerical officers from the service, the former project manager, who had moved to an information/

planning post, the senior home help organiser and a senior social worker. As before, hospital referrals were channelled through a consultant; community referrals had to be channelled through the general practitioner and necessitated a domiciliary visit for initial assessment. Following this, other health practitioners — a physiotherapist, an occupational therapist, and a nurse liaison sister — made assessments which were brought to a subsequent meeting of the panel, when decisions about eligibility were made. After a person was deemed eligible, the higher clerical officer would visit the client and family, introduce the home care assistant, and arrange for health care staff to visit to instruct the home care assistant on the specific care tasks which they had identified. The higher clerical officer would ensure that each client was reviewed by the different health care staff after six weeks and then at six-monthly intervals thereafter, involving the home care assistant in the review meeting. In addition, weekly meetings developed with a geriatrician and staff of the domiciliary care service at the community unit offices to review progress, referrals and consider problems. Although the involvement of the home help organiser and senior social worker retained the link between health and social services, events made the services increasingly separate. For example, no social worker contributed to the assessment. As the home help service was moving away from domestic care towards personal care, it was seen as increasingly important to be specific about the target group for the Intensive Domiciliary Care Service, and also to ensure that transfer from one service to another took place when appropriate. This may have meant that opportunities to interweave the contributions of the two services were more difficult to implement since the services were targeting different groups of clients. In practice, liaison occurred only at the point when a patient was to transfer to the home help service. This meant that responsibility for clients' housework needs became increasingly unclear, since neither agency made this a priority.

In practice, since only health care staff were involved in assessment, there was a tendency to focus more narrowly on health care needs rather than including a broader assessment of social and family needs. With a number of different staff each visiting to make an individual assessment, there was some concern that this could be a daunting experience for a confused or anxious elderly person.

Soon after the new arrangements had been established, the service was extended to include a small number of younger chronically sick clients, who were seen as another potentially relevant client group for this service. This development had occurred at a time when demand from elderly patients had been particularly low. This decision by the community unit management was a source of concern to the geriatric service, since it reduced the number of places for frail elderly people and meant that these places were likely to be committed for a long period of time, given the age and life expectancy of the new clients.

Home care assistants. An early change for the home care assistants was the introduction of uniforms, which produced a mixed response. Some home care assistants gained a sense of status from this, whereas others felt that it ran counter to one of the elements of the project philosophy, which had been to offer individualised care in a relatively informal manner.

After about nine months concerns were expressed by some health care staff that, on occasions, home care assistants were not undertaking the care as instructed, partly reflecting time constraints. The monitoring group attempted to clarify the responsibility of the different health care staff in supervising the performance of home care assistants in particular areas of care. The accountability relationship was to be from home care assistants to the particular health staff on whose behalf they were working, and in the absence of this to the higher clerical officers and their team leader. However, interviews indicated that, from the point of view of the home care assistants, this accountability arrangement remained unclear in practice. They experienced difficulty in getting management decisions made because higher clerical officers were not authorised to make decisions and yet higher managers were inaccessible and too removed from the situation to know the detailed circumstances. This reflected the partial responsibility of each professional for the service; in practice no-one had taken up the care management role and the clerical officers were not permitted to act with much discretion.

During this phase of the operation of the service, some of the consequences of the loss of the care management role became evident. For example, on some occasions home care assistants emerged as advocates on behalf of clients or carers in the absence of anyone else to take on this role. On other occasions, home care assistants experienced problems in coping with difficult situations such as family conflict because they lacked support and guidance. Whereas specific care tasks were the responsibility of identified health care staff, the general support of home care assistants was nobody's role. Consequently, it became the responsibility of the clerical officers.

Care management. Despite the expectation that this role would be taken up by community health staff in addition to their existing functions, in reality, it demanded more than a usual keyworker function. Thus, it is perhaps unsurprising to observe that crucial elements of the care management role were missing, with a consequent effect upon clients.

The loss of the care management role was also evident in the lack of an individual with responsibility to coordinate and maintain care. On occasions, it was unclear who was responsible for taking an overview of the total range of needs. Support to carers was one area where nobody appeared to have a clear definition of role; another was that of advocacy. For example, on one occasion an elderly woman who had suffered several strokes was receiving demanding levels of therapy. The client experienced these as excessively exhausting, yet no-one felt able to take up the client's concern with the therapist, because this was perceived as challenging the therapist's professional expertise. Counselling and support was another area of concern, since no-one appeared to see it as their remit. Thus, in new cases where a carer was somewhat uncertain about the receipt of help, it was not clear that it was anyone's responsibility to explain sensitively the options and discuss the person's ambivalence, so that receipt of the service could be one of the care options considered. Family conflicts which made effective provision of care difficult were yet another source of concern:

> In the case of an elderly woman whose health was deteriorating this led to increasing distress for her caring daughter, who in turn was making intolerable demands on the home care assistants. The situation required careful review, counselling, and provision of respite which the higher clerical officer, despite her best efforts, did not feel in a position to provide.

In cases where the service no longer appeared to be the correct solution, no individual was responsible for organising arrangements such as a transfer to a nursing home:

> At a case conference, a voluntary housing association wished to terminate a client's tenancy on the grounds of reports of increasingly demanding behaviour, which consisted of repeated and unnecessary summoning of the warden. It was decided that the client should be encouraged to consider nursing home care, and the district nurse was selected as the person most appropriate to discuss this with her. One month later, the home care assistant contacted the review panel to say that the elderly woman was still waiting for 'someone' to make arrangements for her to visit a nursing home. After further discussion as to whose role this might be, it was allocated to the higher clerical officer.

Thus, the clerical officers were undoubtedly placed in a difficult position with day-to-day pressure to move significantly beyond the remit of their job descriptions as the organisers of the home care assistants. When a new client was referred for assessment, their formal responsibility was perceived as being limited to identifying available staff within the area. Only when members of the clinical team had made their assessments, and identified that a client was suitable for the scheme was their involvement seen as appropriate. At this juncture they had to meet the client, learn about client needs, find out about available family support, decide which home care assistant to allocate, introduce the home care assistant to the client and decide how much care time to allow. They did not always receive the detailed professional assessments of need and, indeed, were not party to the assessment or instructions given by various health care staff to home care assistants. They were thus reliant on home care assistants to supply this information. Higher clerical officers did not have formal contact with professional members of the multidisciplinary team outside assessment and review meetings. It was expected that, if home care assistants needed advice, information or help in solving problems, they would contact the relevant health care staff directly, and that the clerical officers would not be involved in these contacts. The expectation that theirs was an administrative and organisational role was clear.

In practice, this role appeared to be full of inconsistencies, and the higher clerical officers often had greater levels of responsibility without explicit acknowledgement, or indeed the availability of information and authority to exercise such responsibility effectively. They were often required to support home care assistants, to help them resolve relationship difficulties with clients and carers, to mediate in situations where conflicts arose, and to authorise extra care when needed. They also received out-of-hours calls from home care assistants to re-organise rotas, as well as to provide reassurance and support. From time to time they were required to inform clients of decisions made at review meetings, such as a planned transfer to the home help service or admission to a nursing home, and then make the arrangements. In other cases they tried to alleviate carer stress by arranging day care or providing sympathetic listening time, and they undertook the responsibility of visiting a spouse or other relatives after a client's death to offer sympathy and support as well as arranging to remove aids and equipment which were no longer required. These could often be difficult and stressful situations. Uncertain of whose role it should be to do these tasks or to effect closure of cases, transfer of clients or to refer surviving spouses to other services for support, the higher clerical officers were forced to take on the role. Clearly these demands were beyond the remit of staff employed as clerical officers on the basis of their clerical skills and paid accordingly.

Hence clarity about the role of the higher clerical officers was not evident. Although the team leaders were officially responsible for the recruitment of home care assistants and for dealing with concerns of home care assistants and interprofessional conflicts, in practice they were too removed to tackle these. As a consequence, the higher clerical officers found themselves taking on these roles in the absence of others doing so. In some ways this issue pin-pointed the absence of a care management role, and an internal review of the service in 1989 examined the management of home care assistants to make more effective operation of the service possible.

The single agency service: stage 2 — the introduction of coordinators

The problems identified in the report

The review indicated that the service was not functioning according to the original aims and objectives. It identified five areas of concern with regard to the domiciliary care service: leadership; areas of responsibility and account-ability; coordination of resources; monitoring of care standards; and training and support of home care assistants and carers. To address these concerns it was proposed to bring the clerical officers and home care assistants centrally into the community health unit rather than having each separately responsible to a different team leader. A community care coordinator and assistant, both experienced nurses, were to be appointed to:

> provide the necessary manpower and skills to effectively coordinate the available resources, monitor standards of care and most importantly provide training and support to the home care assistants and to informal carers' (Darlington Health Authority, 1989, p.2).

Many of the areas which the report addressed can be seen as aspects of care management which were omitted in the earlier development. The decision to introduce coordinators arose both from the lack of coordination of care and the separation of the existing clerical officers in three different health care teams. The appointment of specific staff to coordinate care necessarily led to major changes in the roles of the clerical officers. Among other activities, the coordinators took over responsibility for organising rotas. The role of the clerical officers was defined much more as an office-based role, the main function being to support coordinators by processing time sheets and payments. The number of clerical officers was reduced from three to two and they were retitled 'administrative assistants'. At least in the early phase of the coordinator stage, they were not expected either to work on a face-to-face basis with the home care assistants or to undertake client visits. Even the work of organising the rota of care assistants, which included matching client and home care assistant and had been a source of job satisfaction to the clerical officers, was initially seen as the role of the two coordinators. The home care assistants were also located in one central community unit health headquarters rather than within separate health care teams.

The experience of the coordinator service

Despite the difficulties which the clerical officers (now administrative assistants) had been experiencing in their role, the restrictions which the introduction of coordinators imposed upon them appeared to reduce their job satisfaction. Although they had not been expected to undertake much direct face-to-face client-related work, in the absence of others to do this they had done so. Indeed, seeing clients and working with the home care assistants gave them greatest satisfaction in their work. The reduction in this, and the return of their job to a more office-based organisational role, albeit one more consistent with their job description, were features which they did not welcome. Furthermore, the expectation that they should not maintain face-to-face contact with home care assistants and clients placed them uncomfortably in neither a provider role nor an assessor role. Inevitably, therefore, some difficulties were experienced. Gradually, some of the tasks previously undertaken by coordinators reverted back to the administrative assistants. The first activity to return to the remit of the administrative assistants was managing and organising the rotas and time sheets. This was an activity in which they had gained a clear expertise over a long period, enhanced by their knowledge of individual home care assistants. The return of this task to them came closer to producing a separation of functions, akin to the separation of assessment and commissioning from the process of service provision, at the micro level. However, this did not last for more than six months, since by then the senior coordinator had moved to another job. As a consequence, they again undertook some client visiting. When the other coordinator also moved to another job, the administrative assistants again had to undertake all the expected activities as best they could. New appointments were not made to the coordinator posts.

The single agency service: stage 3 — the removal of the coordinator role

About two years after the introduction of the coordinator role, a further management report examined the organisation of the Intensive Domiciliary Care Service (Darlington Health Authority, 1991). This report indicated that the scale of the service was unlikely to experience further development and that activities should be focused principally on maintaining a steady state. In contrast to the earlier report, this report identified the main management activities for the domiciliary care service as relating to the management of home care assistants, including tasks such as managing rotas and booking leave. The report observed that both administrative assistants and their managers were involved in agreeing services with clients and relatives, attending assessment and review meetings, and monitoring the performance standards of home care assistants through visits and feedback from health care staff, and that such duplication was inappropriate. It was also noted that certain activities undertaken only by the manager of the administrative assistants, such as the organisation of training for home care assistants and giving support and counselling sessions, should be undertaken at the level of the administrative assistants themselves. The report proposed that all these activities be returned to the administrative assistants, who would be retitled 'domiciliary care scheme service managers'. The report also recommended that clerical support be given to these individuals and, 'given their expanded role and accountability', further training should be provided to consolidate and develop their first-line manager skills. The coordinator role, which had become increasingly ambiguous, was removed and the two administrative assistants became service managers. However, the recommendation for the implementation of enhanced training, did not occur. Hence the dilemma identified in the first report remained. The need for care management was accepted as a legitimate professional role: however, those performing the role were not provided with the recommended training.

There would seem to be some important lessons in the development of the service for the more general implementation of new enhanced home care services. The dilemmas and problems experienced in Darlington reflect experiences in the development of many other home care schemes. Underlying the discussion of the relative roles and functions performed is a debate that has taken place in local authority home care services over several years. This debate has taken the form of considering the merits and demerits of merging the roles of service management and case management (Goldberg and Connelly, 1982). On the one hand, home care organisers have been frequently under pressure to undertake a range of client-related functions, often attempting to extend their responsibilities, as occurred in the Coventry home help project (Latto, 1982). On the other hand, they face continued service-related pressures to enhance the quality and effective performance of the management of the service. In the day-to-day resolution of these pressures, it is almost inevitable that service management functions — such as recruitment of staff, managing rotas, organising payments, and dealing with sickness — take greater priority than client-related activities. As a consequence, it is the role of monitoring — so crucial to the effective performance of long-term care — that has to be omitted (SSI, 1987), along with other direct work with clients and carers.

The altered arrangements in Darlington had been an attempt to address some of the aspects of the absence of care management by ostensibly separating some of the provider roles from assessor roles (Department of Health, 1990), using coordinators. This is a distinction between, on the one hand, the assessment of an individual's needs and the arrangement and purchase of services to meet them and, on the other, the activity of service provision (Department of Health, 1990, paras 4.5, 4.6). With the loss of the coordinators, the new service managers were once again expected predominantly to bridge the gap. However, the way in which this was meant to be done remained inexplicit. The coordinator approach, although addressing the need for care management and coordination, appeared to blur the distinction between the organisation and provision of home care and the assessment and coordination of a total package of care. Some of the confusion between the coordinator roles and the administrative assistant roles can be seen as relating to this. The removal of the coordinators seemed no longer to address the issues of care management but rather to see the problems in terms of the organisation and management of home care assistants. In the absence of anyone else to fulfil the role of supporting carers and dealing with families and clients, by default these functions were taken up by the new service managers. Indeed, on one occasion they paid for themselves to attend a relevant training course on counselling, recognising the importance of human relations skills, and found this particularly useful in undertaking their jobs. It might have been helpful if the earlier introduction of the coordinator role had broadly located responsibility for client-related activities, such as family support, assessment and monitoring, in the hands of coordinators, and the work with home care assistants, such as recruitment, training and managing rotas, in those of the administrative assistants. The matching of particular home care assistants to the needs of particular clients could have been a joint responsibility. At the micro level this would have offered a solution to the problem of the separation of assessment and provision.

The service after the National Health Service and Community Care Act: current patterns of operation

This chapter has described an evolving service which has changed through time, although a degree of continuity of staffing has acted as a form of organisational cement which has been important in holding the service together. Some of the issues which managers in the health authority have recognised and attempted to grapple with still remain, and are of particular interest since they are more general issues which face the development of many services, particularly in social services.

The aims of the service in 1993 remain broadly similar to those specified in the original project, with the exception that the target population is no longer defined by residence on long-stay wards. Referrals also come from the community and have done since the service moved to mainstream health authority funding. Three aims of the service can be identified: to maintain vulnerable elderly people at home, if that is their wish; to prevent admission to hospital care, where treatment and care can be provided at home; and to reduce length of stay in hospital and permit elderly people to be discharged to their own homes. Unlike what would be expected of many such National Health Service-provided services, rather than offering short-term support and rehabilitation (Townsend et al., 1988), this service provides long-term support.

Service managers. The role of the current service managers can be understood most easily as a kind of home care provider role, principally involving supervising and allocating the time of home care assistants. They are also involved in what amount to boundary clashes when home care assistants, relatives and clients disagree. This may involve discussing matters with their staff and visiting the homes of clients. They each have caseloads of between 20 and 30 cases, with a total budget for an expected group of 51 clients. Their perception of the optimal caseload was about 20, which was the number which emerged in the project phase. Faced with the pressure to perform several roles, it would seem that a clear hierarchy of activities is determined for them by organisational demands. First come the design of the rotas for the home care assistants; second, the organisation of services for new clients; and third, the preparation of wages and time sheets. Administrative necessity means that their provider role, such as organising rotas, must take precedence over more client-related tasks. A similar problem has arisen when home help organisers have been expected to take on social work responsibilities for clients (Goldberg and Connelly, 1982). This must have been reinforced by the fact that, despite the reference to training for the current service managers in the third stage report (Darlington Health Authority, 1991), after the coordinators had left for a variety of reasons this does not appear to have occurred. Anomalies remain in the extent of the service managers' responsibility beyond that of organising and providing home care assistants for particular clients. In terms of linkages, it is difficult to see the service as constituting an extended team, beyond the immediate service managers and their home care assistants, although they are part of a looser network which includes the domiciliary physiotherapist, the domiciliary occupational therapist and one consultant physician specialising in old age.

Home care assistants. The first week's training for new home care assistants includes a day with a physiotherapist, another with an occupational therapist, two days with a district nurse and a session with the continence adviser. They spend the second week with different home care assistants to learn by experience. This reflects the later phases of training for new home care assistants, described in Chapter 5, where training was required as and when new staff were employed. In terms of staff development, the service managers organise training sessions for a group of, say, fifteen home care assistants for a half-day session once a month. These involve a range of professional staff, such as occupational therapists and district nurses, discussing particular activities. The subjects have included dressings, incontinence, hygiene in food preparation and the use of hoists.

Home care assistants still perform the whole range of care tasks, including domestic care, although they are not supposed to do housework. Some clients have private domiciliary help in addition to the home care assistants, although none receives home help from the social services. This reflects the clear separation of health and social care in this service. The range of provision varies in most cases from one visit to three visits per day. The average visit lasts one and a half hours in the morning, one hour at lunch time and between half and one hour at bedtime, although there is considerable variability in the length of visits according to needs and circumstances, which is concealed by averages. Previously, during the project phase, some clients had four visits daily, with the extra visit at teatime.

Where there are issues of liaison with different professionals, such as district nurses, they are usually initiated by the home care assistant, and channelled through the service manager.

Some current concerns

There remain anomalies as to the extent of the service managers' remit beyond their provider role of responsibility for organising the rota and allocating home care assistants to particular clients. The most recent review (Darlington Health Authority, 1991), unlike its predecessor, had not seen this as a contentious area, preferring to focus upon the day-to-day management of home care assistants. In many ways it offered only a limited extension of the roles of service managers by its focus on the immediate management of the home care assistants.

Nonetheless, there remain areas for examination. The responsibility for providing coordinated care is unclear and the care management role remains uncertain. The lack of a person with adequate professional status to negotiate with or arbitrate in disputes about client care and the role of home care assistants remains a problem. There still appear to be turf disputes between professional staff and the service managers, reflecting the perception that to perform these roles with credibility in an organisation requires similar acknowledged professional status for each party. Thus, it is not entirely clear whose role it is to link the home care assistants to therapy and nursing staff, and there is a vacuum in the area of interprofessional negotiation and arbitration of disputes with home care assistants. Inevitably the current service managers, lacking the credentials of professional training, and facing the time constraints of service management, have found difficulty in undertaking direct work with clients and carers. Particularly in the area of quality assurance there is a risk of partial and piecemeal provision, since each professional has the responsibility only for his or her own role. With no individual explicitly responsible for taking a client-centred overview, there is a risk that assessments may become service-oriented. The demands upon the service managers, who had not had either the background experience or the training to fulfil all these roles, have been considerable. The extent to which they have contrived to do so and also develop certain aspects of the service, such as raising funds and providing social activities for the clients of the scheme on their own initiative, is greatly to their credit.

From the clients' perspective there are some anxieties that under the new community care legislation the service might again be provided by the social services, which would mean that they would have to contribute to the costs of the service. Currently, as the service is provided by the National Health Service, it is free. Transfer of clients from the health service to home help provision had raised the difficulty of payment for care in the latter stages of the project, which could never be satisfactorily resolved, being beyond the remit of either health or social services on their own. There is no joint provision to individual clients by the two services.

Overview of the changes

The processes that have occurred have been described in some detail because they reflect some of the concerns in the literature about the implementation of care management. These include the need to differentiate the role of care manager from that of keyworker; and to define the precise role of care management and what it is designed to achieve, and what it cannot. As has been argued elsewhere, care management is no panacea to the problems of delivering effective care, although one important contribution can be more coordinated care (Callahan, 1989; Applebaum and Austin, 1990). However, for care management to be effective its contribution needs to be part of the logic of the service (Davies, 1992; Challis, 1994a,b).

Given health authority objectives, it is clear that targeting of the service needed to reflect the prime concerns of that agency: prevention of long-stay hospital care and effecting discharge from hospital. A joint service would need to find an acceptable way of broadening this target population without excessive loss of focus upon the original group. Such concerns of appropriate targeting of frail elderly people have underlain many services designed to prevent the unnecessary admission to institutional care of elderly people (Kemper et al., 1987).

It is interesting to note that the reports on the Intensive Domiciliary Care Service regularly raised problems about effective quality assurance. This is because, faced with the pressures of providing home care (such as organising staff rotas, payments, recruitment, training and cover), regular visiting and monitoring the adequacy of care are the elements most likely to be neglected (SSI, 1987). Conversely, within the care management approach, quality assurance is designed to be built in through the comprehensive care plan and regular monitoring of individual client care, rather than operating in response to crisis and complaint as in the traditional home care model (Applebaum and Austin, 1990). This distinction between a care management approach and home care approach to quality parallels the distinction between quality assurance and quality control (Common and Flynn, 1992).

The changes which occurred in the development of the Intensive Domiciliary Care Service can be seen as three stages of activity. The first involved moving from the original project care management/client-centred approach to a more service-centred model analogous to the home help service. A second stage reintroduced some elements of care management, although without separating assessment and care management from the provision of services, which might have been logical given the staff resources. In this context, the extra staffing inevitably appeared expensive since duplication occurred. The third stage can be seen as more analogous again to a home care provider unit, except that it gave the managers of the service certain responsibilities for client care which had been vague in the first stage. De facto this recognised the extent to which the newly entitled service managers had attempted to fill a gap. Thus, it would seem that the difficult organisational problems were recognised, and different strategies were devised and deployed to manage the services. However, the pattern of development of the service, and some ambivalence about the respective roles and responsibilities of social services and the health authority, contributed to difficulties in resolving the problems. The changes in provision of community care arising from the implementation of the National Health Service and Community Care Act 1990 provide opportunities to reconsider services such as this, which, by their very nature, cross traditional agency boundaries, and possibly to resolve some anomalies.

The Intensive Domiciliary Care Service and the community care changes

In the light of the National Health Service and Community Care Act, it is clear that a service such as the Intensive Domiciliary Care Service will present an area of continuing negotiation between agencies. There would appear to be at least three issues which emerge from the current operation of the service: the location, both physically and organisationally, of the service; the extent to which the service should be a separate form of provision or part of a wider network; and the scope for linkages with the developing provision of the social services department. Each is considered briefly in turn below.

The location of the service

The service is designed to offer an alternative to long-stay provision for elderly people by supporting them in their own homes, principally by means of its own dedicated home care assistants who undertake a wide range of care tasks. As noted earlier, it is not a short-term, time-limited hospital discharge programme, but instead provides long-term care. As such it is a substantial investment by a health authority into continuing care. However, it is not clearly linked into other related social services and health groups which might be an additional source of support to the staff. As a relatively small-scale initiative serving about 50 people, the equivalent of two long-stay wards, one arrangement might be to link the service more closely with the long-stay provision in the locality, since both are concerned with broadly similar patients. Organisationally this would integrate long-term care for the elderly provided by the health authority, and at a practice level could provide additional support for the service managers from the nursing staff in the long-stay wards, while also providing a degree of continuity for patients who receive respite care. Possible changes in the structure of geriatric services, which are also occurring elsewhere, could contribute to this, perhaps with a new consultant taking more of a responsibility for community-focused work.

The service as part of a wider network

The possible linkages with long-stay care offer one means to link the service with relevant broader networks. There would seem to be no broader home care team with its own group culture beyond the immediate circle of the home care assistants and the service managers. Instead, the service is loosely linked to networks through a consultant in the geriatric service, on the one hand, and through the physiotherapist and occupational therapist to the community health services, on the other. Whereas the hospital-based team can be seen as a tight-knit arrangement, the community-based arrangements are more fluid, with variable membership depending on, say, which district nurse was involved with a particular patient. In such a loose-linked network, the lack of a social worker, reflecting the lack of links with the social services department, can be seen as another difficulty. In terms of the 'tightly-coupled' network (Aldrich, 1979) created between the agencies by the project, such a move to a looser-linked form of collaboration could be seen as one where patient care might be less explicitly organised.

Linkages with the social services

The goals of the service, identified earlier, can be seen as increasingly the province of social services under the new community care arrangements. It could be argued from a health authority perspective that the service offers a generic response to a wide range of needs, some frequently classed as social and others as health. From the client perspective, and ignoring the thorny problem of charges, the desirability of the single worker providing a broad range of tasks is evident, and is accepted as a principle of good practice by the health authority. However, provision of housework remains a problem, as it does for social services when home helps focus more upon personal care activities. There is an overlap between the clients of the service and those receiving home help, and some degree of integration could be beneficial (Barton et al., 1990). If such a service were to be considered for joint commissioning, there would be real problems to be faced in agreeing the funding processes or the financial division between the agencies. Clearly, the targeting arrangements would need reconsideration, reflecting the different concerns of the two agencies, even if the balance of funding between 'health care tasks' and 'social care tasks' could be agreed. Of further relevance is the likely impact of the service on bed-blocking, a major concern for the health authority.

These considerations suggest that joint commissioning in the care of elderly people is most likely to commence in those areas of greatest overlap, least territorial defence by professionals, and therefore the lowest barriers to development. Thus, it is likely to start with activities such as respite care, moving later to discharge schemes, and only later still to more contentious areas such as shared personal care and home support, where the room for dispute is greatest. In these more contentious areas developments may perhaps occur more readily where an agency can singlehandedly act on behalf of both, rather than where there is a continuing dual involvement.

11   Assessment, Care Management and Health Care of Older People

This last chapter brings together the key findings of the evaluation of the project and considers the implications for the wider development of care management. It was part of a family of studies which have examined a particular approach to or model of care management for varied 'at risk' elderly populations in different locations. There were important similarities of findings across the projects which have been reported elsewhere (Challis, 1993; Challis et al., 1993a), and which give added coherence to the model. This chapter is in two parts: the first reviews the main findings of the study, its subsequent development and its service-level impact are reviewed; the second examines the implications for the implementation and development of assessment and care management.

Objectives and outcomes: the main findings

The Darlington Project tackled the problem of providing coordinated intensive support, by addressing the care system as a whole through a simultaneous focus upon four different relevant levels of coordination: coordination of agencies; coordination of interprofessional involvement; coordination of services through a care manager; and coordination and rationalisation of activities through a single care worker. The project was designed to provide home care to physically frail elderly people who would otherwise require long-stay hospital care. It sought to extend the care management approach into a geriatric multidisciplinary team, using multipurpose care workers (home care assistants) to reduce overlap between 'hands-on' care providers. The project team, employed by the social services department, consisted of a project manager, three care managers, and a team of home care assistants. The care managers had to cost the service they provided to clients, working to an average budget of two-thirds of the cost of a long-stay hospital bed. They were members of the geriatric multidisciplinary team, through which all referrals were directed.

The care managers' prime function was, in consultation with the multi-disciplinary team, to assess client need and develop, coordinate and regularly review a package of care, linking together all the necessary resources from a range of providers, both formal and informal. As well as the tasks of monitoring, liaison and coordination, the care managers also had to give a considerable amount of emotional support and advice to elderly people and their families, complementing the activities of informal carers, and to provide support to the home care assistants and resolve conflicts in the care network. During the project it was clear that the care managers created a role which came to be valued and seen as appropriate and necessary by most staff. Each care manager was allocated a budget for their caseload of about 20 clients. A large percentage of this budget was spent on home care assistant time, but resources were also allocated to pay for additional services from members of the community. Home care assistants were instructed by and assisted a variety of different staff, including district nurses, occupational therapists, physiotherapists and speech therapists, as well as the continence adviser, dietician and stoma therapist in an attempt to integrate much of the work of several 'hands-on' providers into the activities of a single care worker. The most frequently performed personal care tasks were toileting, transfer, managing medication, dressing and washing. The most frequent domestic care tasks were housework, cooking and laundry. A comparison of home care assistant activities with those of community nurses, auxiliaries and home helps indicated how the roles of different staff had been successfully bridged.

About two-thirds of the project clients were still in their own homes six months after discharge from hospital, and only three people were in institutional care, the remainder having died during the period. After twelve months, over 50 per cent of those discharged were still at home. Over the first six months project clients were at home for an average of three-quarters of the time, and very little time was spent in any form of institutional care. For indicators of subjective wellbeing, there was a significant improvement in overall morale and a reduction in depression and apathy among the elderly people receiving project services, in contrast to the comparison group. In terms of more practical indicators of quality of care, the project clients had a significantly reduced need for additional care, and there was a significant gain in the number of social activities in which they participated, compared to the long-stay patients.

Carers of project clients carried out significantly fewer care tasks than carers of similarly frail elderly people in the locality, and were significantly less subject to distress associated with the performance of these tasks. Project carers were also significantly less distressed regarding care burdens. Psychological stress, or malaise, was significantly lower for project carers than for those carers whose elderly relative remained in continuing hospital care in the comparison area.

Even using a relatively low unit cost for hospital care, the total cost to the health and social services agencies was £183, compared with £255 for the comparison group, a cost advantage of £72 per week (1986/7 price base). Social opportunity cost figures were estimated as £242 per week for project cases and £277 for the comparison group. The cost of providing project care appeared to be less than that of hospital care for most long-stay patients. Those whose care appeared particularly cost-effective had lower levels of dependency, albeit within a very highly dependent group, and were supported by an unstressed carer.

There were five main objectives specified for the project, as described in Chapter 2. These were:

- The maintenance at home of elderly people who would otherwise have required long-stay hospital care.
- Domestic and caring tasks were to be undertaken by a single worker, the home care assistant, to reduce duplication of effort.
- The quality of care and degree of satisfaction of the elderly people and their carers were to be enhanced compared with long-stay care and standard community services.
- The cost of home care should compare favourably with long-stay hospital care.
- An additional level of care and support at home, which had not previously existed in the locality, was to be provided.

The evaluation suggested that all five criteria were met.

Project-related developments

There is considerable evidence of the immediate impact of the project. In the first instance, it was specifically referred to in the White Paper *Caring for People* (Cm 849, 1989, para. 3.3.3) as an exemplar of the use of care management. Subsequently there have been several developments in the United Kingdom which have been modelled upon the project. The most organisationally similar is a development in the same social services authority (Peebles, 1989). This service, provided by the social services department, is targeted upon elderly people on the margins of hospital and residential care. Eligibility is determined by a team consisting of a consultant physician, senior social worker, nursing sister, occupational therapist and, usually, the relevant general practitioner. A home care manager, employed by the social services within the home care service, is responsible for specialist home care assistants who offer personal and domestic care. As in the Darlington Project, they are supervised by health care staff, such as district nurses where appropriate, for managing such problems as bed sores and changing dressings and colostomy bags. There are also examples of health authorities establishing such a service. In Hertfordshire, a health authority has established an intensive community care scheme with similar care objectives, except that the target group is those who are living at home but require long-term hospital care. Designed for up to 50 clients, the health service employs a care manager with nursing qualifications who assesses need, agrees an individual care programme, and monitors and reviews its effectiveness. Home carers are employed by the social services 'provider unit', are supervised by a home care manager and undertake personal care, home care, nursing and therapy support tasks (South West Herts Health Authority/Hertfordshire Social Care, 1993). There are examples elsewhere too, and in Australia the approach of health care staff training and supporting home care staff has also been noted (DHHCS, 1992) and a study of case management in a geriatric multidisciplinary team (Gray, 1988) has been undertaken.

The development of care management: implementation issues arising from the Darlington study

The Darlington study findings suggest several areas of importance for the future development of assessment and care management in the United Kingdom. Some of these are specifically related to the nature of the project and its linkages with health care, and others more generally to the development of care management regardless of setting. These implementation issues are shown in Box 11.1, and each is discussed in a separate section in the rest of the chapter. They can be divided broadly into two groups. The first concerns processes and operation of care management, and covers issues of assessment,

---

Box 11.1
Implementation issues in the development of assessment and care management

Linking care management, community care and geriatric medicine
   — Assessment and the relevance of geriatric assessment in Australia.
   — Location of care management.

Targeting care management.

The designated care manager role.

The separation of purchaser and provider.

The use of devolved budgets.

Care managers: training, knowledge and skills.

The management of care management.

The pace of development of a new service.

The health and social care divide.

Roles of primary and secondary care services in community care.

Housing and community care.

the location of care management, targeting of care management, the use of designated care managers, the separation of purchaser and provider, and the devolution of budgets. The second set of issues is related to the context within which care management is undertaken, and covers training of care managers, the management of care management, the pace of service development, the separation of health and social care, the relative roles of primary and secondary care services, and the importance of housing. These observations complement the discussion of implementation issues elsewhere (Challis, 1994a,b) and cover some of the key dimensions by which different forms of care management may vary, that were noted in Chapter 2.

Linking care management, community care and geriatric medicine

Assessment and the relevance of geriatric assessment in Australia. Proper assessment of need and good care management were identified as the cornerstone of high quality care in the new community care arrangements in the United Kingdom (Cm 849, 1989). Following the National Health Service and Community Care Act in 1990, local authorities have been made responsible for the assessment of publicly-funded entrants to residential and nursing homes. They are responsible for funding that care or alternative home support with the resources previously allocated from the social security budget for residential and nursing home care, hence the importance of assessment in the allocation of scarce resources. However, it would appear that following the implementation of the community care legislation, assessment may at times exhibit too great a degree of variety, and is often undertaken on a monodisciplinary basis (Department of Health, 1993). Access to a range of multidisciplinary skills is one important determinant of whether such skills are in fact deployed in the assessment of an elderly person, and a group decision may reduce inappropriate variation in assessment due to staff mix differences (Department of Health, 1993). The Darlington Project was specifically designed so that both assessment and screening could take place using the full range of specialist skills. Care managers both contributed to the assessment process and received the contributions of others, providing a degree of continuity from assessment through to care planning and monitoring the adequacy of care. Linkage with the geriatric service was valuable in providing the necessary expertise not only for assessment but also for access to rehabilitation, as described in Chapter 4. However, there remained problems regarding re-assessment since follow-up by the geriatric team could not be formally arranged. The ways in which this was done were inevitably informal, whether in day hospital or in routine outpatient clinics. Immediately after the project became a single agency service, weekly team meetings, which included geriatricians, made these informal arrangements easier. However, this arrangement did not last. Nonetheless, the Darlington approach offered one example of closer involvement of a geriatric service in community care.

In the United Kingdom there is no specified role for geriatric services in the provision of community care. However, the role of geriatric assessment in the community and its impact upon community care have been areas of concern and experimentation elsewhere (Adelman et al., 1987; Dalziel et al., 1992; Thomas et al., 1993). The experience in Australia provides a particularly powerful comparison, where the Aged Care Reforms provide the clearest example of the importance of assessment and the contribution of the geriatric team to this process in community care.

At the beginning of this book, the shared pattern of community care policy changes in many countries (Guillemard, 1993) was noted, involving a move away from institutional care, enhanced home care and improved coordination and care management (Kraan et al., 1991). The Australian experience in many ways exemplifies this trend (Ozanne, 1990). A brief description of this background is necessary to provide a picture of how the changes compare and contrast with those occurring the United Kingdom.

From 1963 there was a dramatic growth in nursing home provision in Australia, when benefit rules were changed, increasing entitlement to support in nursing home care (Department of Community Services, 1986). The lack of substantial alternative provision of home care, coupled with a growing supply of nursing home beds, tended to direct people towards nursing home care, as occurred later in the United Kingdom (Parker, 1987). Early attempts to control this process involved the requirement for the provision of basic medical data for screening. This, however, appears to have met with little success and the McLeay Report (1982) concluded that this had little impact. The outlay on nursing home care increased five-fold between 1972 and 1982 (Howe, 1990). The levels of dependency of elderly people in homes were seen as sufficient for them to live at home with adequate domiciliary care or community support, or in residential settings with less intensive care than currently provided (Howe, 1990).

In the early 1980s, multidisciplinary assessment panels were recommended to improve screening, and the McLeay Report (1982) advocated that assessment be the centrepiece of the new policy. The 1986 Nursing Homes and Hostels Review (Department of Community Services, 1986) recommended the use of mandatory assessment by an approved assessment team as a prerequisite for nursing home admission, and also supported assessment for hostel or residential care. Geriatric Assessment Teams (GATs) were therefore the first element in a policy of 'downward substitution', with hostels (residential homes) and nursing homes in future only taking the frail and more dependent. The policy goal was to enable more elderly people to stay at home and to improve the support of carers, with the necessary funding for additional home-based care coming from both state and Commonwealth sources, through the Home and Community Care (HACC) programme (Commonwealth of Australia, 1989). In addition to this, a graded system of classification of nursing home clients was introduced so that the reimbursement of nursing homes could reflect the dependency profile of their residents. The

Resident Classification Index is a standard measure which provides a means by which the amount of nursing home benefit attached to a particular resident varies according to their assessed need for nursing and personal care. There are five levels, and the nursing and personal care funding element at the highest level is two and one half times that of the lowest level, and it is thereby designed to act as an incentive for nursing homes to admit the more highly dependent residents (DHHCS, 1991). Thus, there would be clear assessment for access to publicly-funded nursing home care, enhanced home care services, and the most frail clients would attract higher levels of reimbursement, thereby giving incentives to nursing homes to accept such individuals.

One possible criticism of the introduction of the assessment process in community care in the United Kingdom is that it can vary according to the individual professionals who are responsible for the assessment (Department of Health, 1993). One advantage of the use of multidisciplinary assessment is that it provides a means for reducing the variability attributable to individual members of staff in reaching a common view. In Australia, standardisation was also achieved by the development of assessment guidelines which provided a framework for team operations. Assessment was given the formal objectives of assisting people to stay at home and ensuring receipt of the most appropriate care for their needs. GATs were given specific goals in undertaking their work (Brown and McCallum, 1991):

- To focus upon the needs and wishes of the assessed persons and their carers.
- To be able to refer to a range of services if institutional care is not deemed appropriate.
- To ensure that service users are involved in the development and management of assessment services.
- To ensure equity of access.

Self-referral was permitted, and although assessment was undertaken at home wherever possible, for many patients this took place in hospital since they were already inpatients. Geriatric Assessment Teams were to undertake a limited element of case management by having one person responsible for ensuring that all aspects of the assessment and follow up were coordinated and making links with general practitioners, hospitals and home care. However, client contact with the GATs tended to be episodic and not long-term (Brown and McCallum, 1991), and their case management activity reflected more a keyworker role as described in Chapter 2. Given their assessment remit, it would have been unrealistic to expect them to undertake a long-term monitoring role. In the UK context, the obvious parallel is the Care Programme in Mental Health (Department of Health, 1990).

Between 1984 and 1987, the pilot Geriatric Assessment Teams in the State of Victoria each developed a specific style shaped by such factors as team size, skill mix and availability of care services (Otis, 1992). In 1988 there were seventeen teams in the state with the number of staff ranging from three to twelve. All had a coordinator, community nurse, social worker and medical officer, and almost all had at least one part-time geriatrician. Geriatric Assessment Teams were located in existing health service facilities, usually geriatric or rehabilitative services, including geriatric centres and acute hospitals (Brown and McCallum, 1991; Otis, 1992). It must be emphasised that the GATs were not a totally new but rather an additional element which included approval of nursing home applications and in some cases involved teams managing waiting lists for institutional care (Gray and Lazarus, 1987). Thus:

> The geriatric assessment program built on existing assessment functions, but it did not replace other forms of assessment. Rather, it formalised the role of assessment in determining access to specific services and, in some cases, provided a specific organisational locus for the new 'gate-keeping' role (Brown and McCallum, 1991, p.7).

The data on the outcomes of the assessment process are of particular interest in terms of how secondary care services may contribute to a policy of downward substitution. Overall, following the implementation of the new policy, between 1986 and 1990 the number of nursing home beds per thousand aged over 70 decreased by nearly 15 per cent, although the number of hostel beds remained constant (Department of Community Services and Health, 1990). Of all the assessments monitored, 43 per cent of clients were recommended for community care and about 22 per cent were recommended for institutional care; 19 per cent were recommended for inpatient treatment; and 16 per cent were recommended for no further action after assessment. But the most crucial effect is the perceived impact of teams, as demonstrated by comparing the reason for referral with the actual recommendation. Table

Table 11.1
Referrals and outcomes: Australian Geriatric Assessment Teams[a]

Recommendation after assessment	Referred for nursing home care %	Referred for hostel care %
Nursing home	55	7
Hostel care	7	55
Inpatient treatment/rehabilitation	13	7
Community care	11	22
Assessment only	14	10
Total	2006	1109

a Adapted from Otis (1992)

11.1 summarises the data from the State of Victoria for elderly people referred for nursing home care and hostel (residential) care in the first six months of 1990 (Otis, 1992). It can be seen that 39 per cent of referrals for residential care and 38 per cent of those for nursing home care were directed for hospital treatment or community support. Another study of the impact of the Geriatric Assessment Teams in Sydney indicated that, of 246 applicants for nursing home care, 98.4 per cent of whom were approved by medical officers for placement (the old system), subsequent re-appraisal by Geriatric Assessment Teams led to approval of only 62.6 per cent (Quartararo and O'Neill, 1990). In Western Australia too, geriatric assessment led to fewer inappropriate admissions than the old placement system (Rhys Hearn, 1990). Work monitoring the effects of the assessment process in Victoria has indicated that there is a clear dependency distinction between settings. Those in nursing homes had the highest level of disability and, although those in residential homes had similar physical care needs to those in community care, they were distinguished by a greater probability of cognitive impairment and absence of a carer (Aged Care Research Group, 1992, 1993b). Reviews have described the development of Geriatric Assessment Teams as very beneficial to the development of geriatric services in general (Ames and Flynn, 1992).

Several studies of geriatric screening suggest that benefits include the detection of previously unrecognised disease and avoidance of inappropriate admission (Rafferty et al., 1987; Kalra and Foster, 1989). In a study in Manchester of 100 referrals accepted for admission to residential care, after geriatric assessment 17 per cent were found to need treatment which could obviate the need for admission (Brocklehurst et al., 1978). Another study in Leicester (Peet et al., 1993) indicated the importance not just of geriatric assessment but also the contribution of geriatric services to continuing management and support of very dependent elderly people. This indicates a more extended role than initial assessment for geriatric services in community care.

This section of the chapter has examined the possible extension of the role of secondary health care services into the arena of assessment in the community care reforms and considered the Australian experience. Of course, one of the benefits of the Darlington Project in its approach to care management was that it located care managers in a geriatric service so that they could have access to a wide range of skills in the assessment of need, not just initially but throughout their involvement with a client. Care management in the Darlington context had an overlapping, but distinctly different, set of functions to the rest of the multidisciplinary team, being focused upon only a subset of those individuals with whom the team was concerned. The next section considers the advantages of a separate but linked care management service within a geriatric team.

Location of care management. A care management service may conceivably be located in a variety of settings, and there are clearly advantages and disadvantages in each (Challis, 1994a,b). Often the model adopted is akin to that of

a social services area team (Department of Health, 1994), while the opportunities of health care settings are less well explored. The Darlington Project offered
one means of establishing linkages between geriatric services and care management, although a number of other approaches have been developed. The
Australian experience again provides a helpful comparison. The policy
developments in Australia with regard to assessment by Geriatric Assessment
Teams and the development of additional home-based care have already been
considered. A third element of change in that country has been the development
of care management through the Community Options Programme which involved 'the testing and evaluation of new and different approaches to planning,
coordination and delivery of services' (Brown and McCallum, 1991, p.6). The
Community Options initiative was accompanied by a series of workshops
throughout Australia (Howe et al., 1990), and the Darlington scheme was
among the models considered at these workshops (Challis, 1990a). A similar
such development was evident in the Australian context of that time, reflecting
the Darlington ideas (Gray, 1988). This located case managers within a well-
established Geriatric Assessment Team based in a purpose-built geriatric
centre.

In the State of Victoria, the Community Options Programme (known locally
as the 'Linkages Projects', based upon the coordinatory functions of care
management), had the additional requirement that Geriatric Assessment
Teams were to be involved in the selection and assessment of clients. This
provided for a link between care management and geriatric services and
makes the experience of these projects particularly relevant to the Darlington
study. Although, in the event, only two out of the eight special projects were
physically located under the auspices of Geriatric Assessment Teams, the link
between care management and the GATs had two objectives (Kendig et al.,
1992):

- to give access to skilled multidisciplinary assessment; and
- to encourage more coordinated and stronger links between community
  care providers and Geriatric Assessment Teams.

As has been noted earlier, similar factors influenced the design of the
Darlington Project. Since the linkage of care management with secondary
health care services is one of the important issues arising from the Darlington
study, it is interesting to examine the evidence from the Australian experience.
There were four main conclusions which emerged from the evaluation of the
Linkages Projects and their relationship to Geriatric Assessment Teams
(Kendig et al., 1992): the development of an additional level of care; varied
assessment practices; varied involvement of case managers in assessment;
and, at times, insufficient involvement of existing care providers in assessment. First, the Geriatric Assessment Teams valued the availability of case
management providing an additional care option at the point of assessment,
similar to the response in the Darlington study. Second, however, there was

considerable variability in Geriatric Assessment Team staff mix, practice and degree of interest in assessing social factors, some of which were critical to case management responses. While variability may also be observed in geriatric services in the United Kingdom (Royal College of Physicians, 1994) it would probably be considerably less marked. Third, the degree of involvement of case managers in the assessment process varied, from full participation to no contribution. In part, this reflected the fact that in only two sites were case managers members of the Geriatric Assessment Team. It was concluded that, if multidisciplinary assessment was required for case management, problems could arise if no-one in the multidisciplinary team was responsible for seeing the assessment through to implementation of the care plan. In the Darlington study this was not an issue, since the care managers were responsible for contributing to the assessment and coordinating the process as well as implementing the necessary care plan. Alternative scenarios to the Darlington model might have included a separation of those making assessments and care plans from those with long-term responsibility (Department of Health, 1994). However, this is unlikely to have resulted in better coordinated care, since difficulties may arise as a result of the separation of responsibilities of hospital and community-based staff in care management, involving transfer of responsibility, while the loss of continuity of work when there are separate assessors has long been discussed (Applebaum and Austin, 1990; Challis, 1990, 1994b, Kendig et al., 1992). Fourth, there was concern that the Geriatric Assessment Teams undertook assessments which did not sufficiently utilise the available knowledge of existing community care providers, nor give them sufficient feedback. A similar observation about assessment practices in the early phase of the community care reforms in the United Kingdom has also been made (Department of Health, 1993). This utilisation of information and feedback was one of the roles undertaken by care managers in the Darlington Project, indicating some of the other possible advantages from locating care management within the geriatric service (Kendig et al., 1992).

Two of the Linkages Projects were located within Geriatric Assessment Teams, and a more detailed study was undertaken of one of these. The Ballarat Linkages study (Charlton et al., 1992) was targeted at elderly people at risk of admission to institutional care. It was linked to the Geriatric Assessment Team through a designated member of staff in that team, who was responsible for maintaining the smooth operational relationship between the Linkages Projects and the assessment team. This was particularly important at the stages of referral and coordinating assessment. Following a referral, all clients were assessed in detail by the GAT in a three-stage process. First, a pre-assessment discussion involved the Geriatric Assessment Team link person, case managers and relevant agencies. This was followed by the second stage: a Geriatric Assessment Team assessment in the client's home. The third stage was a case planning meeting which family members could attend. Case managers were appointed for each client, and care plans were reviewed at six-monthly intervals, with a new Geriatric Assessment Team assessment undertaken after twelve months. The caseloads of the case managers were similar to those in the Darlington Project. The evaluation of this study suggested that it had met the objective of targeting the more dependent, had improved service coordination, provided greater access to and knowledge of services, and increased the number of services received. There was a reduced probability of admission to institutional care in the nine to twelve months following assessment. However, data on quality of life outcomes proved inconclusive (Charlton et al., 1992).

Thus, although there were relatively few case management services located under the auspices of Geriatric Assessment Teams, the mid-term review of the policy (Department of Community Services and Health, 1991) indicated, as had some clinicians (Cole, 1990), that there was further scope for such developments. The national evaluation of the Community Options Programme was even more explicit, suggesting that the closer links between Geriatric Assessment Teams and case managers were beneficial in dealing with incontinence, mobility problems and dementia (DHHCS, 1992): major problems in long-term care, which are three of the four 'giants of geriatrics' (Isaacs, 1981). Interestingly, although the linking of case management with the GATs did not appear to have assisted in incorporating the case management projects into the community care system, as had been anticipated, it did have the important benefit of helping the Geriatric Assessment Teams to become more integrated into the mainstream community care network (DHHCS, 1992). Similarly, within the United Kingdom, there may be comparable opportunities for establishing closer links between care management developments for older people and geriatric services, perhaps by the district health authorities, in conjunction with social services, creating a care management function (Audit Commission, 1992b). However, a crucial difference is that there is a specific defined role for geriatric assessment services in the Australian Aged Care Reforms, namely assessment and screening. By linking with case management this role has been extended so that the 'clinical and diagnostic skills of assessment teams could be more widely used by projects in their assessment and care planning functions' (DHHCS, 1992, p.97). Certainly the relationship between community care, geriatric medicine and other secondary health services is one that merits further investigation.

Targeting care management

Much of the debate on the relative effectiveness of care management services for elderly people in the USA has centred around targeting. Thus, it has been suggested that the failure of a large national series of case management demonstration projects to achieve substitution of nursing home care by home-based care was attributable to problems of targeting (Kemper, 1988; Hennessy and Hennessy, 1990). In the Darlington Project, targeting was managed through the specification of broadly-understood criteria. No dependency scale or similarly formalised criterion was used; rather, clinical decisions about individuals, within specified guidelines, indicated need for long-stay care. Because the patients were either in, or at the point of entry to, long-term care, eligibility was not problematic since the patients were clearly at high risk of admission to institutional care. The use of a geriatric multidisciplinary team, which controls the allocation of patients to its own long-stay beds, for the assessment and screening of community-based referrals, is also likely to ensure that high-risk patients receive project services, since failure to do so will be likely to put pressure upon that geriatric service. However, if a geriatric team undertakes the assessment but has less responsibility for the outcome — for example, where care managers bear costs from local authority budgets — geriatric assessment is likely to necessarily have a more advisory role. Not only is the process of targeting important, but also whether or how it is monitored. Seidl et al. (1983) indicate how a failure to monitor targeting can lead to goal displacement in a community care service. This was not a concern in Darlington, where successful targeting was managed through the multi-disciplinary team. Not only did the geriatric team serve to assess and screen the cases for the service, but it also monitored targeting, both through the group processes of the team meeting and through the membership of clinicians on the interagency monitoring group for the project. However, targeting became more of a concern once the service became open to referrals from the community as well as from hospital. The restrictive targeting imposed by the funding criteria had meant that the difficult task of screening community cases was not an immediate issue. However, targeting concerns probably contributed to some health authority anxieties about a joint service after the central funding period, particularly since the social services department and the health service would identify different priority target groups. In such a context, a monitoring tool — such as the Resident Classification Index used in Australia — would be valuable.

Defining which people are appropriate for care management is a major theme of targeting debate, since not all users of services will require or justify the overhead cost of a designated care manager. It is complicated by the broad definition of care management which has gained currency. The United Kingdom policy document *Caring for People* (Cm 849, 1989) implies that the principles of care management should be applied to all recipients of community care services. It is therefore important, when applying the principles of care management to the care of vulnerable people, to discriminate between the provision of designated care managers for those with severe and complex needs, on the one hand, and more effective organisational procedures for assessment, individual care plans and regular reviews for those with less complex needs, on the other, so that the core tasks are effectively carried out for all other service recipients. This requires the development of new terminology which formally makes the distinction between 'intensive care management' for a limited group and a 'care management approach' across the service system. The definition of the boundary between care management provided through designated care managers and the broader care management approach will inevitably be determined not only by policy definition and need factors, but also by resource factors, such as the availability of trained staff. This definition lies at the centre of the introduction of care management in social care, since it is crucial to its capacity to influence patterns of admission to institutional care. It was identified in the early stages of implementation of community care as an important element in balancing the management of the flow of assessments and reviews (Challis, 1994b; Department of Health, 1994). The care management programmes for elderly people which were able to offer an alternative to institutional care were those which were clearly targeted upon those at high risk of admission (Challis and Davies, 1986; Davies and Challis, 1986; Kemper et al., 1987; Kemper, 1988; Challis et al., 1990; Davies, 1992). In programmes for the chronically mentally ill, a narrow and specific target group definition is associated with reduced institutional care and positive outcomes (Huxley, 1991; Goering and Cochrane, 1992).

The definition of this intensive care management group and the techniques for determining eligibility are therefore critical. However, the implementation of acceptable procedures for ensuring eligibility for care programmes is complex (Shapiro and Tate, 1988; Weissert and Cready, 1989). Measures of functional incapacity are frequently used as eligibility criteria for services (Applebaum and Austin, 1990; Liu and Cornelius, 1991) but such indicators of dependency alone appear to be poor predictors of need for institutional care (Neill et al., 1988; Luehrs and Ramthun, 1991). Capitman (1986) has argued that functional criteria for target group definition need to be supplemented by improved pre-admission screening to identify individuals with short-term risk of nursing home entry. It is clear that the factors which influence levels of utilisation of services are multiple. Brown and McCallum (1991) review some of the main factors, which include living group and social support, activities of daily living, instrumental activities of daily living, medical and health care needs, self-rated health and cognitive impairment. The lack of reliable, valid and efficient indicators of need for institutional care suggests the need to permit discretion within a framework, thereby combining a general eligibility criterion of need for services with the exercise of 'clinical' discretion over which service mode any given individual receives. In the Wisconsin Mental Health Programme (Stein and Test, 1980), where the target population was individuals with chronic mental health problems, neither diagnosis nor severity of illness was seen as a sufficient indicator, although most patients suffered from schizophrenia. Rather, the focus was upon the specific determinants of service mix. Seven criteria were identified: willingness to come for services; medication compliance; need for structured daily activities; ability to self-monitor; frequency of crises; need for professional psychological support; and degree of case management (Stein et al., 1989). Such complexity, which reflects the unique interaction of different facets of need, is not readily susceptible to a simple screening tool without the cost of a low level of specificity (a high proportion of false positives), as encountered in the case management programmes in the United States cited earlier (Kemper, 1988; Hennessy and Hennessy, 1990).

Implementing targeting procedures will always be difficult. Brown and McCallum (1991) conclude that, given the extensiveness and complexity of problems experienced by older people, it is more productive to address these on an individual basis rather than grouping clients on the basis of relatively crude and insensitive indicators. One crucial distinction, implicit in policy but often blurred in practice, is that between the definition of 'high need' and 'high risk of institutional care', at least in the early phases of community care policy development (Davies, 1992). In Darlington, as in other care management schemes, agreed guidelines were devised for referral but, recognising the complexity of circumstances which constitute conditions such as need for institutional care, no rigid pre-entry threshold of dependency was specified and accountability for targeting was monitored post-entry. Clearly such an approach has the advantage of permitting discretion but requires careful monitoring and is potentially subject to dispute. Managerial scrutiny of such decision-making processes is particularly necessary and requires the development of improved information systems, including information on client characteristics (Davies, 1992; Challis, 1994a,b). Thus, the development of mechanisms for achieving effective targeting is likely to be linked with debates about assessment and management.

There is also a long-term concern about targeting which will need to adjust as the community care policies develop. An initial focus upon those who have been inappropriately admitted to residential or hospital care is likely to shift to the extent that the policy is successful and as the binary distinction between institutional and community support is eroded (Challis et al., 1994). There will need to be a move towards defining target groups for intensive services less in terms of their relative risk of admission to institutional care and more in terms of need. This will require considerable investment in screening and assessment capacity to identify the 'high need' individuals (DHHCS, 1992).

The designated care manager role

The project had staff who were designated care managers, whose specific job was to undertake the core tasks of care management for their clients and to allocate the time of home care assistants. In the initial phase after the project, as described in Chapter 10, there were no designated care managers, and existing community health care staff were expected to undertake what was seen as a substantial keyworker role, in addition to their normal work with clients. In the second phase after the project period, 'coordinators' were appointed whose remit included a care management role, and subsequently staff were appointed as 'service managers', although the breadth of their care management responsibilities was unclear. Examining the changing arrangements for undertaking the core tasks of care management permits consideration of the relative merits of different approaches.

Whether care management should be conceived of as a designated job or as an organisational process has been an area of considerable debate since the publication of guidance on assessment and care management (SSI/SWSG, 1991a,b). In the Department of Health monitoring studies of the early implementation of assessment and care management (Department of Health, 1993, 1994), three approaches to care management were evident. Broadly speaking, these were: a designated care manager; care management as a role within an existing job; and a dual role with staff designated to work part-time as designated care manager and part-time as social worker. In an analysis of early developments in Scotland, Buglass (1993) cites three not dissimilar models: a designated care manager; care management as a single agency role within an existing job; and care management as a role within an existing job within a joint health and social care setting. The last of these approximates most closely to the keyworker role which was expected of health care staff in Darlington in the initial period after the project phase.

In Chapter 2, among the defining characteristics of care management, several factors were noted which discriminated this activity from a keyworker role. These were intensity of involvement, breadth of services spanned, and duration of involvement (Applebaum and Austin, 1990). Keyworkers, by contrast, are expected to have a more short-term, less intensive and less extensive range of responsibilities, reflected by factors such as more frequent case turnover. Ovretveit (1993) distinguishes keyworkers from care managers, particularly with reference to a keyworker's narrower breadth of services spanned, usually restricted to their own services. It would have been very demanding for existing community health staff to have fulfilled this role for such a frail client group, with sufficient intensity and duration, along with their existing responsibilities, and difficulties were experienced. As a result, following the first management review of the single agency service, described in Chapter 10, coordinators were appointed to fill the evident gap.

Undoubtedly, the fact that, at times, home care assistants had contributed significantly to some important parts of the care management process, such as monitoring and review, made the removal of the care manager appear possible. However, the partial delegation of tasks did not necessarily mean that the role of designated care manager was irrelevant. The subsequent organisational forms and staffing arrangements considered by the health authority, which was clearly attempting to address this issue, would seem to bear this out. The experience of these different organisational approaches would seem to reinforce the need to discriminate clearly between 'intensive care management' and 'care management as an organisational process' in implementation.

The appointment of a part-time care manager, described in the Scottish study (Buglass, 1993), was not an issue in Darlington, since the project care managers were designated full-time in this role. However, it was found to be an interesting problem in the Social Services Inspectorate's special studies of assessment and care management (Department of Health, 1993, 1994). Staff were unclear about when they were performing different roles and the extent of the shift required of them. In the Gateshead study, where staff attempted to undertake this role it was not successful, and there were evident conflicts. In the Gateshead Health and Social Care Scheme, for a period the community nurse worked part-time as care manager and part-time as nurse and, in order to cope with what she perceived as a major role shift, used her uniform to differentiate both her own expectations and those of others as to her activities (Challis et al., 1990). Working as a care manager on a half-time basis, she changed into her uniform halfway through the week. In the Australian context too, there was an important distinction between full- and part-time case managers. Full-time case management appeared to work well, creating less tension and role conflict for staff, as well as allowing the development of considerable expertise. Part-time staff were often much less accessible, making for difficulties in service coordination. Case managers themselves identified difficulties in the mixed role of part-time case manager and part-time social worker, indicating that there appeared to be insufficient time and too many demands to do both tasks well, or to do all that was expected of a case manager. Also, difficulties arising from conflicts of interest or separating out the two job roles were cited. These difficulties were particularly noted where people added case manager responsibilities to an existing full-time workload with other responsibilities (Kendig et al., 1992).

The separation of purchaser and provider

The Darlington Project was developed before the issue of separating purchaser and provider was central in the health service or in social care. Thus, there was no purchaser/provider separation and, indeed, the different tasks of service management and care management (Challis, 1994a,b) were combined in the responsibilities of the care managers. Since the service became a single agency development, it has been part of a provider unit in the health service. In most social services departments there is an assumption that care management is a purchaser function, although considerable debate exists about precisely where in an organisation such a separation can occur and how it may be operationalised (Department of Health, 1994). There is a need for considerably greater clarity in this area, which is more complex when a service spans health and social care, raising issues of funding and accountability. The kinds of dilemmas and confusion behind the conceptions of purchaser and provider in health and social care are illustrated by the arrangements in Darlington. Here, care managers held budgets, were employed by the social services department and linked to a geriatric service, and were also responsible for the allocation of the time of home care assistants, who were working with health service staff.

The separation of purchaser and provider is seen as an important part of the development of services in the United Kingdom, with care management seen as a purchaser role (Department of Health, 1990, para. 4.5), so as to effect influence upon patterns of service provision. However, the distinction between purchaser and provider is deceptively simple, and different levels of separation may be discerned. At the highest level, there is macro purchasing. Up to the present time, this form of purchasing has been most commonly associated with health authorities contracting with particular providers to provide services for a district or a given area of activity. Similar purchasing procedures may be developed by local authorities, and even care management itself could be purchased on such a basis for particular client groups or for particular areas of the local authority. This process of managing an overall market, and purchasing services to meet the needs of a population within an area, can be distinguished from, at the other end of the scale, the micro purchasing role, whereby care managers individually allocate resources, perhaps through devolved budgets (Department of Health, 1991, para. 1.18). Where health service providers have to interface with social services purchasers, there can be difficulties (Wistow, 1994). For example, some local authorities have developed joint assessment and care management systems with health staff in primary care. However, while the social work staff are defined as purchasers, their health colleagues, undertaking broadly similar roles, are part of a provider unit (Buglass, 1993).

The separation of purchaser and provider roles at the micro level raises more problems than at the macro level, and too rigid a separation may militate against effective work. Some roles and activities span the purchaser/provider divide and blur the superficially clear distinction. The most obvious example is that of counselling and support. Whereas conceptually it might be possible to define supportive counselling as a provider function, in most settings this process, which may involve engaging a person, forming a relationship with them and comprehending the depth of their problems so as to establish the right mix of support and services, proves to be a purchaser function. Indeed, to make such an activity an exclusive provider function would inevitability push care management towards an administrative style of practice (Challis, 1994a,b,c), with a consequent negative reaction by practitioners at the loss of important aspects of their role (Allen et al., 1992; Department of Health, 1994). Not only do the activities of care managers cross boundaries, so also do care providers. In helping a cognitively impaired elderly person, a hands-on carer (provider) might contribute to activities often deemed to be a purchaser's remit, such as assessment, monitoring wellbeing, diet or medication intake, due to their proximity to the elderly person over a considerable period of time, albeit closely supported by a care manager. Hence, at the level of individual care the responsibilities of purchaser and provider are not mutually exclusive, and the inevitable overlap defies neat distinction (Department of

Health, 1991, 1993, 1994). The needs of effective practice do not always lead to organisationally neat solutions, and the nature of the relationship between provider and purchaser has to be explored carefully so that the process of separation does not lead to new problems of inappropriate care. The complexity over what is defined as a service (and therefore a 'provider role') is discussed in the care management guidance (Department of Health, 1991, para. 1.13) and, as a consequence, some schemes have attempted to define limits to activities such as counselling to limit care manager involvement (Pilling, 1988, 1992). One way of viewing the separation is to be clear about the different roles of care management (including casework) and service management, traditionally blurred in agencies, which underpin the functions of purchaser and provider. Another is to look by analogy towards fund-holding general practitioners, who are not simply purchasers but are also actively encouraged to act as providers of certain services, where these appear to be more appropriate than, say, referral to hospital.

Some of these issues arose within the Darlington Project, mainly from the need to define boundaries to the care managers' responsibilities. One concern was the extent to which the care managers were to act as the client's social worker or whether that too was a resource to be brought in by care managers. The care managers themselves were very clear that they were the client's social worker and that whatever social work tasks had to be undertaken — accessing social services resources, counselling, providing support to carers — were their responsibility. Their view was that, since they were the person who knew the client, their carers and their circumstances, and that they were social services staff, this role was logically theirs. As is clear from Chapter 4, this was indeed the case in practice. However, on several occasions, managers discussed the idea of care managers bringing in social workers to undertake particular tasks for clients, as part of the expectation of a purchasing role. Where this involved special skills, such as communication with a person with hearing or visual impairment, or where the social worker was a co-worker in complicated family problems extending well beyond the care of the elderly person, such arrangements were seen as desirable. In other cases, however, it was seen as involving unnecessary duplication of effort. Here lies one of the areas which has bedevilled the development of care management, a sometimes rigid interpretation of the separation of purchaser and provider, a separation which might make a degree of administrative logic, but seriously impedes the practical process of providing necessary care and support in the most effective and efficient ways. The criticisms of such an approach were made by the care managers and, of course, the pursuit of such a model would probably lead to a more administrative form of care management, rather than a clinical one, where the activities of service arrangement and assessment are part of a more holistic approach which includes support and counselling as part of the care manager remit (Challis, 1994a,b,c).

How might the original joint agency Darlington service have operated in a context of separation of purchaser and provider? Of course, this would be contingent upon the form of organisational separation developed, but there are several models. It is a widely-held view that the degree of influence which care managers have over the form and content of services is crucial to the effective implementation of care management. Arnold (1987) has argued that a brokerage model alone is insufficient to have any influence, and Austin (1992), criticising pure brokerage, concludes that, 'case managers who cannot deliver the services they prescribe in their care plans are not very likely to be very effective' (p.11). Dant and Gearing (1990) observe that effective care management requires the care manager to control the supply or availability of services and other resources, and a common conclusion is that care management should be separated from the immediate activity of service provision, to render it client-centred rather than service-focused. One solution might have been to have made the care managers into purchasers, with other staff being responsible for the recruitment and allocation of individual home care assistants, thereby acting as providers. In theory, this would have freed the care managers to concentrate upon their assessment and care planning functions. However, the anticipation and management of potential clashes between different care providers, such as home care assistants and paid helpers or informal carers, would have still been required. There would also have been costs in this separation since it might well have proved more difficult to match specific care assistants to clients, or to delegate some of the monitoring tasks to home care assistants. This task of monitoring by closely involved staff was as important in the Darlington Project as in some of the Australian Community Options projects, and confusion may emerge when the provider staff are responsible to two agencies (Graham et al., 1992). An alternative solution would have been to make the project service into a provider unit, akin to the organisational arrangements adopted by the health authority. This would be a strategy consistent with the aim of reducing the number of 'hands-on' providers as in the original project. Indeed, in some ways this occurred where the interagency coordinating group acted in effect as a purchaser, with the project being accountable for the objectives noted earlier in the chapter. Care managers in such a provider role could be given a budget within which to optimise care mix for individual clients, and purchase care even though not nominally 'purchasers', and the parallel can be made with certain aspects of fund-holding in general practice. However, it could be argued that such an arrangement might provide little incentive to use alternative resources to home care assistants, even when this might be more desirable. The role of management in supervision would therefore be critical in ensuring efficient use of resources.

The use of devolved budgets

The degree of influence over the pattern of service allocation has already been noted as one the determinants of the effectiveness of care management

(DHHCS, 1992). Control over resources is one means of influence and can enable care managers to respond more effectively to the varied individual needs of elderly people (Challis and Davies, 1986; Challis et al., 1990; McDowell et al., 1990). Equally, a care manager lacking control of resources may only make requests to the providers of other services but has relatively little negotiating power to ensure that services are sufficiently responsive to meet clients' needs (Hodgson and Quinn, 1980). Devolution of budgets is one mechanism for giving influence to care managers. However, scale is important. A devolved budget has to be sufficient to cover a substantial proportion of care costs, otherwise it is liable to be used merely for 'topping-up' care or for single and unique items of expenditure. Such 'topping-up' of existing services with individual unique expenditures requires little change in the function of service providers, and is likely to improve individualised care plans only at the margin (McDowell, 1990). More substantial budgets are required for significant influence to be exerted. The Australian review of community options (DHHCS, 1992) indicated that the capacity to purchase individual services was particularly important in rural areas and where it was necessary to produce unique culturally appropriate services for minority groups. There is, however, significant variation in the degree of influence over resource allocation that care managers have been given. This has ranged from pure brokerage, advocacy and negotiation (Pilling, 1988, 1992), through small 'top-up' budgets (Dant et al., 1989), to more substantial budgets close to the full revenue cost of community care (Challis and Davies, 1985, 1986; Challis et al., 1988a, 1989, 1990, 1991a,b).

The Darlington Project care managers had control of resources in two different ways. They were responsible for the allocation of the time of home care assistants, whose wide-ranging care role meant that most care activities were covered, and they could also pay for other inputs such as paid helpers. Given the committed expenditure upon home care assistant time, it was necessary for the care managers to make best use of this before buying other care services. Furthermore, since the project did not run at full capacity for some of the time, there was obviously pressure to use these previously-committed resources first. However, the wide-ranging role of home care assistants meant that the response was less 'service-driven' than might have been the case with a different group of staff. Care managers were able to use their remaining budget to pay for some social activities and additional support for their clients, as was described in Chapter 4. Nonetheless, care managers would have liked more opportunity to experiment with a wider service mix at the margin, to broaden the range of responses they could make to client need. This illustrates a real dilemma in the devolution of budgets: the balance between fixed and flexible expenditure. On the one hand, if too much attention is given to flexible gap-filling and too little to fixed services, then too much of the care manager's time may be spent recruiting people to fill gaps. On the other hand, if too much attention is committed to particular styles of service, then the range of care options is reduced. In effect, this dilemma sharpens further the balance of contracting debate, which is already current in agencies as the wider range of suppliers of domiciliary services develops.

Devolution of budgets was feasible in a project which had its own costing records, developed from similar ones in other care management schemes (Challis and Chesterman, 1985). Formal delegation of responsibility was to the level of the project manager, with care managers able to allocate resources and spend within the guideline of two-thirds of the cost of long-stay hospital care. Such an arrangement for delegation is advantageous when issues of service development are considered. While substantial proportions of the pattern of expenditure need to be sufficiently variable to reflect consumer wishes, not all of a care budget need be devolved to the level of the individual care manager. If a proportion of the budget is top-sliced and held in reserve by a more senior manager, it may be used to tackle issues of equity, by contributing to the care of particularly expensive individuals. It may also be used for aspects of service development, by enabling a more generalised response to problems, such as creating a new service as a response to the similar needs of several clients, which may be more appropriate than a series of individual responses by different care managers. The importance of this service development role, which can amount to another level of purchasing between the macro and the micro, was noted in the review of Australian Community Options programme (DHHCS, 1992).

Care managers: training, knowledge and skills

The care managers recruited for the project were relatively unusual in that they brought a mix of both nursing and social work training and skills to the job. However, since social services have been made responsible for care management in the United Kingdom, there is likely to be a preponderance of social services staff acting as care managers. There have been examples of nursing staff acting as care managers by secondment (Challis et al., 1990), and in the context of the integrated structure of the Northern Ireland Health and Social Service Boards this is more feasible. However, in the rest of the United Kingdom, in the absence of a jointly commissioned service, there are financial disincentives to health authorities to allow nursing staff to act as care managers. For health service providers who see the role overlap, particularly in mental health, mechanisms which are used to monitor nurse productivity also act to restrict the role of nurses in care management (Department of Health, 1994). This is because the monitoring systems focus on direct nurse/patient contacts, whereas one feature of care management is the greater focus upon indirect work, such as service arrangement and liaison (von Abendorff et al., 1994). This is different in other countries, where the debate about the relevant professional group to act as case managers has continued (Kanter, 1987; Roberts-DeGennaro, 1987; Loomis, 1988). The two most likely occupational groups appear to be nurses and social workers (Applebaum and Austin, 1990). Debate about which type of background is suitable is particularly likely in an activity like long-term care which spans the health and social care divide. Unsurprisingly, evidence suggests that there are significant elements of the knowledge and training of each which are relevant. This was the conclusion which emerged in the evaluation of the Community Options Programme in New South Wales (Graham et al., 1992), and is confirmed by the experience of the Darlington Project and the Kent (Challis and Davies, 1986; Davies and Challis, 1986) and Gateshead (Challis et al., 1990) studies. Applebaum and Austin (1990) indicate that:

> social work case managers must have adequate health training to properly serve highly disabled people who commonly experience significant health problems. Similarly, there are important aspects of social work training, such as understanding the structure and availability of the service system and understanding the intricacies of family relations, that are essential to good case management practice. Thus while there is no one profession best suited to perform case management tasks, case managers do need to have training in several important areas (p.159).

They conclude that specific additional skills and experience are required by care managers beyond the standard professional training received by social workers, nurses and other human service professionals. The evaluation of the Linkages Projects in Australia concluded more specifically that case managers require both professional knowledge relevant to working with vulnerable and dependent older people, and an understanding of issues surrounding professional practice in the health and welfare field. This mix of skills and knowledge included:

- 'well developed interpersonal and communication skills;
- good advocacy and negotiation skills;
- good assessment, counselling and general casework skills, combined with a good understanding of, and sensitivity to, family dynamics;
- knowledge of issues associated with ageing;
- knowledge/experience of aged care services and the aged care service system;
- capacity for independent operation, initiative and organisation; and
- good record keeping and case note recording ability' (Kendig et al., 1992, p.131).

Thus, for staff working with older people there are specific training needs (Bergman et al., 1980; Krishef, 1982; Nelson, 1988). Applebaum and Wilson (1988) cited three areas of training as particularly relevant for case managers. First, there was the need to understand health and disability limitations, morbidity and mortality patterns, and mental health needs of clients. The frailty of long-term care clients, with high levels of morbidity and mortality, was seen as posing additional demands for knowledge about health conditions and how these interact with care needs. Second, there was a need to understand the service environment and such contextual elements as the range and type of service providers, eligibility criteria, service unit costs, methods of negotiating with and monitoring providers, working with physicians, and a knowledge of support approaches and services for informal carers. Third and most specifically, there was a need to understand techniques of case management. These include the core tasks of assessment, care planning and ongoing monitoring, approaches to balancing the different case manager roles and methods of time management. A Canadian study offered very similar conclusions (Joshi and Pedlar, 1992), and the evidence from the Darlington Project and the care managers themselves concurs with this. Of the original three, two had both nursing and social work training and experience. Their view was that the experience and knowledge from both were important in their work, although there were skills they still needed to learn. In terms of the three factors above — client knowledge, service system awareness, and techniques of care management — they had acquired knowledge in the first two areas through their previous work and training, but they had to learn about the third as they developed their role. However, since relatively few staff will be trained in both nursing and social work, the importance of the first category of clinical skills should not be overlooked, and special training is desirable (Ivry, 1992), particularly that which involves joint health and social care inputs (SSI, 1991). Hence, the observations of the Audit Commission (1992b) on the importance of areas such as budgeting skills should not obscure the need to focus on a range of practice skills. In the early days of implementation of community care in the United Kingdom, it appeared that where social services departments provided training to staff who were to act as care managers, there was relatively little focus upon the 'clinical knowledge' requirements and a more marked emphasis upon procedural elements (Department of Health, 1994). This is borne out in the evaluation of the Linkages Projects in Australia. Case managers identified their future training requirements as very clearly in the realm of clinical knowledge, particularly counselling and family work, and the understanding and management of dementia and associated problems (Kendig et al., 1992).

The management of care management

The study has suggested that care management needs to be considered as part of a system, as much as at the practice level. This is the more so when the service is designed to link health and social care. Reflecting that system-level concern, the project has been examined at the levels of interagency, interprofessional, service coordination, and client-level care. Project management is particularly important in providing an appropriate environment for the service at the first two of these levels. It is also important in linking problems and concerns at the service coordination and client levels with local policy and interprofessional issues. Although it was noted in Chapter 4 that the service was on a small scale, and that the management overheads required to operate the project would be excessive in a non-experimental service, this is not to deny the significance of the management role. In Chapter 10 it was clear that, following the move to a single agency service, the lack of either a care manager or an immediate manager above that, led to difficulty. This illustrates the area so often omitted in care management literature: the management function. Care management should not be conceived of simply as a field-level activity, but also as a system-level one (Miller, 1983; O'Connor, 1988; Moore, 1990; SSI/SWSG, 1991a).

Interestingly, the national evaluation of the Australian Community Options Programme noted that case management tended to work best in those settings where the service system was reasonably extensive and amenable to flexible patterns of working. Two factors were seen as determining the effectiveness of case management: first, the culture of the service network (whether or not it was client-focused, flexible and committed to community support); and, second, the organisational structure of case management (whether the core tasks were consolidated in a designated worker, the degree of authority the case manager had over the provision of services, and the managerial environment within which this took place) (DHHCS, 1992).

Management of the project was important in establishing the service, in particular in creating the infrastructure arrangements and in dealing with interagency and interprofessional issues of coordinating care. This included acting on behalf of the new service within the service system as a whole, agreeing referral systems, and dealing with 'turf disputes' between professional groups, which are inevitable when a new element enters the service system. At times, the project manager needed to resolve tension in order to maintain good relationships between the project and service providers. However, reshaping the pattern of services in response to client need through care management itself generates conflicts which need sensitive resolution (Kendig et al., 1992). The experience of the role of project management in some of the Australian Community Options projects indicates how the requirements of project management tend to change over time. By the time projects were established and running the main roles of project managers appeared to be:

- overall administration and financial management of the project within guidelines established by the project management committee;
- day-to-day administration and management of the project;
- staff management and support;
- support for case managers and development of their skills;
- advocacy within the service system for the client target group;
- working with the project coordinating committee;
- contributing to the development and planning of services; and

* improving information flow and coordination between local service providers (Kendig et al., 1992).

Two areas which became of increasing importance in the Darlington Project
were the support of care managers and service development. It was noted
in Chapter 4 that the skills required of project managers change as projects
move beyond the planning and initial implementation phase. As the Australian evaluation commented:

> They move from being innovative and exciting positions that are shaping
> a new project to more administrative and project maintenance positions,
> with room for change more at the edges than the central core of the
> project. It is often quite difficult to find people who are skilled and inter-
> ested in both these phases of a project's life (Kendig et al., 1992, p.102).

Similar observations were made about the Care in the Community projects
(Knapp et al., 1992). A contributory factor is the degree of fatigue or 'burnout'
which may occur after the investment of effort in establishing a new service.

It would be easy to see the Darlington Project as passing through these
changes, but, as noted earlier, the importance of the service development
and supervision tasks should not be underestimated. It involves combining
some aspects of the process of 'managerial scanning', forward planning and
problem identification described by Davies et al. (1990), with a client-level
appreciation of factors inhibiting and making more feasible flexible forms of
care. Consequently at the managerial level there will need to be development
of approaches to quality assurance and supervision which differ from much
previous practice. The Department of Health guidance states that:

> Middle managers ... will also have to develop new skills in the promotion
> of a more entrepreneurial approach by practitioners ... important though
> cost consciousness will be it should be balanced by an appropriate con-
> cern for the quality of care that is being provided (SSI/SWSG, 1991b,
> para. 3.29).

The project had its own manual information system based upon assessments of needs, and regular recorded reviews of cases and weekly costings,
based upon record systems from other care management projects (Challis
and Chesterman, 1985). These provided material which could be used for
scanning progress and issues, and for the supervision of care managers. In
addition, the dependency characteristics of the whole project caseload,
throughput and placement outcomes were presented at each interagency
group meeting.

Developing a more outcome focused monitoring approach will be the focus
of much future management activity. Applebaum and Austin (1990) suggest
five broad quality assurance questions that can be pursued once standards
have been agreed and made explicit, and another related to the cost of care

packages has been added. These are:

- How well are eligibility and targeting criteria implemented?
- Are assessments and care plans completed in sufficient time?
- Do service plans meet clients' needs?
- Are service plans actually implemented?
- Are clients and carers satisfied with the care received?
- What is the cost of the package of care provided?

With the addition of questions about cost and service mix, these bear some similarity to the different components of efficiency mentioned in Challis and Davies (1986) and cited in the managerial guidance on care management (SSI/SWSG, 1991b). As part of a quality assurance mechanism, these could be addressed in a number of ways, using a mix of different approaches from routine information to special collections (Barnes and Miller, 1988). First, eligibility and targeting could be monitored by examining data on the characteristics of the population of service users, possibly comparing area variations. This would be part of the monitoring of targeting discussed earlier in this chapter. Independent reviews of a sample of cases would assist in validation, and the use of multidisciplinary assessment could contribute to greater standardisation of judgement. The second question, developing measures of effective response time to assessment and care plans, is dependent upon the formulation of normative standards coupled with regular and independent audit and review of records. In some cases this might be coupled with direct observation of practice. The third question, the extent to which care plans actually meet needs, is obviously an area of professional judgement. One possible approach might be the use of peer review, whether on a home visit or case record basis, and another might be the use of independent audit. Review of care plans by care managers in a group setting could contribute to training as well as audit. A monitoring strategy, used in some US states, involves examining the degree of variation found in care plans. This is based on the proposition that care plans are meant to reflect the wide variety of individual circumstances and, therefore, lack of variety might be indicative of poor quality practice. Questions about service outcome, such as hospital and nursing home placement and subsequent length of stay, length of community tenure and length of service receipt could also act as relevant performance measures. The fourth question, whether or not care plans are in fact implemented, could be monitored by analysis of individual case records, and also by independent audit or review of the system. An example of such an approach using key indicators for long-term care of elderly people is the work undertaken by the Royal College of Physicians and British Geriatrics Society (Hopkins et al., 1992). The fifth question covers the areas of client or carer satisfaction which have always proved problematic for assessment. Surveys of older people have frequently revealed high degrees of satisfaction without generating more substantively useful information. One use of surveys might be on a comparative basis, across time or teams of staff, since the pattern of variation would be a subject worthy of further investigation. Random selection of cases for audit and consumer interview could also be undertaken. Finally, monitoring the cost of service packages and proportions of different elements constituting those costs would provide a picture of the current and trend patterns of commitment to financial support. This could aid forward planning and future purchasing decisions at a strategic level.

There is clearly considerable room for the development of the management of care management, based less on traditional approaches to ensuring procedural adherence and more upon monitoring the outcome of patterns of decisions.

The pace of development of a new service

Throughout its life the project never took on the full quota of cases which had been planned. Despite the expected caseload of 60 clients, representing about 20 cases per care manager, it did not reach that level during the project phase, and in fact for much of the time it operated at about three-quarters' capacity. Although this was a source of concern to many of those involved in the project, it is also a common feature of the development of many projects and is almost certainly shared by many other new services (Challis and Davies, 1986; Challis et al., 1990; Bland et al., 1992). This is probably attributable to a variety of factors:

- *inertia* — slowness of response of actors to new opportunities and patterns of behaviour;
- *unwillingness to use new services* — whether from reasons of fear of the new or hostility to new developments;
- *knowledge* — problems of knowledge among potential referral agents being unaware of the new service's existence;
- *optimism* — the equating of potential cases with accepted cases in the planning process;
- *relevance* — perceptions that the service did not offer what was required; and
- *territory* — concerns that the new service was entering the turf of the potential referrer.

Certainly, the first seemed present in many of the care management projects and in this Darlington was no exception; given the effective referral mechanism through the multidisciplinary team it is unlikely that lack of knowledge was relevant in the slowness of referrals. Similarly, after the early start phase, the publicity undertaken by the service managers with ward staff ensured that the project remained in the forefront of their consciousness. As eligibility criteria have widened from the purely hospital discharge focus of the original funding, and the service has been in existence for a longer period of time, so the demand issue has been less problematic. However, it is noteworthy that many studies, often by the nature of their limited period of funding, have difficulty in recruiting cases at the rate projected, suggesting that the time required to establish a service is greater than that usually allowed. Sometimes this may be attributable to staffing or building delays (Renshaw et al., 1988), although this did not affect the Darlington Project or the other care management initiatives mentioned earlier.

The health and social care divide

As in most countries, the division between health and social care is one which hampers the development of community-based care. The Darlington Project offered a model which could bridge the separation in ways which are compatible with current policy developments. Thus, it provided a clear health contribution to assessment and indicated new roles for secondary services, such as geriatric medicine, by providing an advisory role for health service staff in community care. It provided a potential means for cost-sharing where there were clear overlaps in service provision at the client level and was extending the personal care function of social services home care. There are other examples of secondary services contributing to community-based long-term care. A Scandinavian example is that of hospital-based home care (Beck-Friis et al., 1986). The objective of this service was, as in Darlington, to offer chronically ill patients an alternative to long-term hospital care. The service was funded from re-allocation of funds originally designated for 120 long-term hospital beds. Interestingly, one of the sources of demand for the new service was for terminal care, which also occurred in the Darlington Project. Patients received a mix of services, including respite, day care, home care and a guarantee of hospital back-up offering immediate admission if the need should arise. The Darlington Project provided evening care for putting people to bed until about 10.30 p.m., and night care for periods of illness and terminal care. The Swedish service, unlike that in Darlington, was able to offer regular night care, through two nurses working from 8.30 p.m. to 7 a.m., some of whose work was the equivalent of the evening round in hospital, but also covering such factors as security and safety. Such a service offered a degree of continuity of medical care, with hospital-based physicians working in the community. There are, of course, other models of linkages between geriatric medicine and social care, including the liaison physician arrangement developed in Newcastle over a number of years (Hutchinson et al., 1984). Among the functions of the liaison physicians were assessment of applicants (including hospital patients) for residential care, advice to general practitioners and social services staff on the management and support of elderly people, and advice to residential care staff. Assessment of applicants for residential care was undertaken by a multidisciplinary team at a day hospital. Some evidence for avoidance of inappropriate placement was indicated; slightly under half of the patients seen continued to live in their own homes (Hutchinson et al., 1984).

The Darlington Project was not designed to, and as a single agency service still does not, operate as a discharge service, offering short-term intensive support so that patients may leave hospital earlier. In this way it is quite distinct from short-term, acute-focused, specialised hospital discharge services, of which several examples exist (Townsend et al., 1988; Victor and Vetter, 1988b; Martin et al., 1994). Nonetheless, as was clear in Chapter 10, issues of bed-blocking were a real concern to those planning the development of the service in the health authority. This concern about the relationship of long-term care services to the requirements of the acute sector is by no means peculiar to the locality, or even to the United Kingdom. The dilemma between care management as a means to assist the health service to achieve faster bed turnover and the provision of long-term care was observed in the early monitoring of community care. There is, indeed, some evidence that the objective in some areas for care management was hospital discharge as much as diversion (Department of Health, 1994). It may well be a legitimate overall efficiency goal in the use of scarce and expensive resources, since the largest savings from a policy of 'downward substitution' are likely to arise from substituting home-based care for acute care rather than long-term care (Davies, 1993). In a service such as that in Darlington, a similar effect may ensue. As the health service progressively reduces its complement of long-stay beds, intensive home care may substitute for acute care at the margin, since the opportunity cost of part of the home care provision is an acute bed. However, it is not the avowed goal of the community care reforms to do so, and there is yet again a danger that the powerful acute sector will secure resources from the long-term care services to meet its own efficiency goals. An example of this potential conflict is to be found in Australia, where the concern of the Commonwealth Government has been that the new home care services will divert people from placement in nursing homes, while the state-level governments are concerned to enhance discharge from hospital care. In a very practical sense, however, one report suggested that there were real difficulties in distinguishing between post-acute care and community care for individual patients, particularly when long-term care clients are discharged from hospital (Saunders Report, 1989). The location of care management at the point of entry to acute care, as suggested in the mid-term review of the Australian reforms (DHHCS, 1991), offers one means of managing this problem.

The unclear distinction between health and social care agencies owes more to historical accident and less to rational agency allocation of roles. The future of such an unbalanced system with a remaining unclear role differentiation must still be in doubt. Wistow (1994) suggests that there are three possible approaches to the structuring of interagency relationships: unification; redefinition of roles; and collaboration. The first of these involves the unification of health and social services budgets within a single structure to reduce the risk of cost transfer. The Northern Ireland system of Health and Social Service Boards represents one example of this. The second approach would involve redefining the responsibilities of health and social services as a deliberate act of policy. An interesting example of this is seen in Sweden. Organisational changes have produced a new separation, which draws a distinction between acute and chronic needs, rather than between health and social care (Hokenstad and Johansson, 1990; Johansson and Thorslund, 1991; Thorslund, 1991; Thorslund and Parker, 1994). This has the possible advantage of being more visible and thus more comprehensible to all parties, although boundary problems still emerge. Another such strategy would be an agreement for a single commissioned service from one provider, such as a National Health Service trust, employing staff to cover all aspects of the service funded by both the health service and the social services. There are examples of this developing in the mental health field. The third element of collaboration is important whether or not other changes are made. Wistow (1994) suggests that, even if boundaries are redrawn or agencies are integrated, collaboration will still need to be important at the interprofessional level and more effort should be devoted to achieving this. The service model in Darlington attempted to address this as well as providing structural arrangements for interagency working.

The roles of primary and secondary care services in community care

The project was not situated in a general practice but linked into what is usually conceived as a secondary care setting: geriatric care. As in the development of community care generally, the role of general practice is critical. · There were some anxieties expressed by general practitioners at the commencement of the project that it would lead to additional demands upon them, particularly in terms of emergency and night calls. This appears to be a concern about hospital discharge programmes in particular (Knapp et al., 1992), and community care more generally (Leedham and Wistow, 1992). In Darlington, one study indicated that general practitioners workload in terms of consultation, prescribing and hospital referral rates was considerably higher for patients in nursing homes than for other elderly patients, giving some credence to this anxiety (Andrew, 1988). However, the expectation in much of the guidance and other literature would seem to be that the main role of general practice is in the process of case-finding and initial assessment, particularly in regard to their surveillance role for those over 75 (SSI/SWSG, 1991a; Leedham and Wistow, 1992).

When secondary care provision develops and extends its role into community-based care, there are potential boundary conflicts with primary care. Medical assessment and follow-up for project clients proved to be one such boundary area. As has been noted, it had been hoped that the project would have medical review of its patients at home by the geriatric service. In practice this never materialised, so that where medical review was required it was either the responsibility of the general practitioner in the usual manner, or often the care manager would discuss the patient's needs with the geriatricians to initiate necessary action. The current model of the service, described in Chapter 10, where meetings between the geriatrician and staff running the Intensive Domiciliary Care Service occur at reviews of patients on a six-week and six-month basis makes such a process more difficult to undertake. There has been a longstanding lack of clarity about the degree of medical responsibility for patient care in non-institutional settings which the expansion of secondary services makes more acute, despite the clarification that clinicians cannot be held responsible for all the activities of other staff in teams (DHSS, 1980). These boundary issues have been most common in the field of psychiatry, with such activities as open referral systems designed to assist case-finding or an extended home support role by community psychiatric services. As links between community mental health teams and primary care increase, so the tension between case-finding, through enhanced access, and screening, to focus on the most needy cases, is likely to become more apparent (Onyett et al., 1994). In the care of elderly people, similar conflicts have also been found between nurses in a hospital-at-home scheme (Mowat and Morgan, 1982). Obviously, with the growth of fund-holding, such issues will become more acute and the role of secondary services in the community is not addressed clearly in the United Kingdom community care reforms.

There have been a number of strategies attempting to make more effective linkages between secondary services (for example, psychiatric care, and primary and community care), such as through the development of community teams (Mitchell, 1985; Lindesay, 1991; Dening, 1992). Strathdee and Williams (1984, 1986) suggest three models: first, replacement (where secondary services become the first point of contact); second, throughput (the development of increased referrals to secondary services); third, liaison/attachment, which took three forms. These were: a new team approach (where consultants relate more closely to other primary care staff), consultation (where advice is provided on management), or 'shifted outpatient' (taking place in primary care settings). There have also been experiments linking a range of professional groups to primary care. Marks (1985) examined the role in primary care of psychiatric nurses trained in behavioural therapy, working mainly with phobic or obsessional disorders. The findings were generally positive and a costing analysis indicated that there were gains in more effective use of resources (Ginsberg et al., 1984). Studies have also been undertaken of the role of clinical psychologists in primary care, with some indication of reduction in medication utilisation and problem severity (Earll and Kincey, 1982; Robson et al., 1984). A few examples of team approaches in primary care are available. Jackson et al. (1993) describe a service where a community-based psychiatric team, supported by sessional medical input, was sited in three general practices. Another model is provided by a study of a comprehensive mental health service focusing upon primary care (Falloon and Fadden, 1993). Four multi-disciplinary teams have been integrated with four primary health care teams, share premises and take clinical responsibility for the care of people with mental disorders. Teams therefore consist of general practitioners, mental health therapists and community psychiatric nurses based in practices, linked to 'mental health consultants' — psychiatrists, psychologists, social workers and occupational therapists — all of whom are more scarce in the teams.

The delimitation of boundaries and establishment of linkages between primary and secondary care, which has exercised many in health care, is of equal relevance to social care. Social work attachment to general practice as a means of linking health and social care has been the subject of several studies (Goldberg and Neill, 1972; Cooper et al., 1975; Shepherd et al., 1979; Corney, 1981), with some evidence of positive effects in dealing with family stresses. More recently, there has been interest in the possible link with care management (Challis et al., 1990). Whereas case-finding and local response may be seen as activities aligned with primary care, and therefore where social care should link with primary care, intensive care management, de-limited by its focus upon a narrow and frail group who are likely to be scarce within any one general practitioner's list, is one where linkages might be expected to be made between social care and secondary health care. Which social care activities are most appropriately aligned with primary care, secondary care or both is likely to be a source of experimentation. Certainly, the Darlington Project and the Australian studies discussed earlier indicate that intensive care management can benefit from linkages with secondary care.

Housing and community care

In a hospital discharge scheme, such as the Darlington Project, appropriate discharge is a prerequisite for an effective service. Whereas other projects funded under the Care in the Community Initiative had more explicit housing plans (Knapp et al., 1992), the Darlington Project was predominantly revenue-based. The Darlington service had been planned on the basis of the availability of housing provided by both the local authority and a housing association. In the event, neither materialised due to events beyond the control of those managing the project. Consequently, there was a need to consider an alter-native approach based upon intensive home care for more recent admissions who still retained their accommodation. Nonetheless, a handful of clients were placed in sheltered housing, a limited number of tenancies were obtained in housing association property, boarding-out was organised, and a housing unit was specially adapted. In many ways it was fortunate in that, being a service for elderly people rather than other client groups, there were many people who had entered hospital comparatively recently and had retained their accommodation. On the other hand the lack of housing clearly prevented long-stay patients from entering the project, as was evident from the length of stay of some of the comparison group cases, as discussed in Chapter 7.

Indeed, the decision to focus upon a subgroup of the potentially eligible elderly may have been one that was highly rational even if it had not been forced upon the service by housing scarcity. Despite the funding imperative, it might be questioned whether a service should invest heavily in rehabilitation of existing long-stay patients who have adjusted to the hospital setting and for whom the costs of transition would be very high. Those elderly people who were newly admitted would entail lower investment costs to achieve at least an equivalent quality of life, with less major transitions. This was evident from the cost analysis in Chapter 9, which indicated that those with a greater length of stay would be more costly to support at home and would require more home care assistant time. The lessons from the Wakefield Case Management Project are salutary with regard to housing. This was a care management project designed to move people with moderate to severe learning disability from a long-stay hospital setting into the community. Most of the budget available to case managers was revenue funding for domiciliary services and support. The project could not have direct influence upon the allocation of accommodation. The absence of the commitment of this resource from other agencies meant that few patients could be discharged, and the project was therefore unsuccessful. The experience of this project highlights two factors: first, the importance of clear and realistic expectations of what can be achieved by the introduction of care management; and second, for the management of care management and interagency issues to be addressed if practice is to be effective. In this case, the provision of housing was required before networks of support could be established (Richardson and Higgins, 1990, 1991, 1992). The Darlington Project was never placed in this situation, partly because of the nature of the client group, which had a relatively high turnover rate, so that care managers could focus their efforts, in the main, on those individuals with available accommodation. In the absence of accommodation, difficulties similar to those experienced in the Wakefield project might have been encountered.

There are other issues about the role of housing in the provision of community care. In the future, housing is likely to need to relate more closely to community services if more dependent people are to remain in the community (Cooper, 1988). Housing needs earlier consideration in the provision of community care, not just in demonstration schemes from hospital to new purpose-built environments (Knapp et al., 1992), but as part of the general community care strategy (NFHA/MIND, 1989; Arnold and Page, 1992; Petch, 1994). Indeed, one view is that more institutional models of 'supported accommodation' are the main focus of development due to the availability of funding and benefits with a consequent reduction in the perception of the role of ordinary housing in community care (Clapham et al., 1990). The experience of Scandinavian countries in the development of a range of special housing contrasts with our own. Nevertheless, in the United Kingdom there is a growing overlap between care settings, and many different forms of alternative homes are emerging and may break down the traditional boundaries between institutional and home-based care. Examples include the growing trend, albeit small, towards en suite accommodation in private sector residential homes (Laing & Buisson, 1993), providing something akin to the residential flatlet concept (Willcocks et al., 1987). The breakdown of the almost binary conception of institutional and community care, through the development of more finely differentiated forms of shelter with care, is likely to render more subtle the conception of community care policy (Challis et al., 1994).

Conclusion

This book has described an experiment which attempted to develop care management providing long-term community-based care for frail elderly people, with care managers located as members of a geriatric multidisciplinary team. It was part of a programme of care management studies evaluating aspects of the costs and benefits of different settings and target group definitions within an overall approach. The evidence indicates that there is certainly room for further consideration of such a setting as a base for long-term care, although there would need to be some changes in the pattern of geriatric practice, perhaps reflecting some of the debates within psychiatry, for successful development to take place. Some consideration was therefore given to Geriatric Assessment Teams in Australia, where a clearer role has been defined for geriatric medicine in the development of community care. The role of the multipurpose care worker, suggested in the Griffiths Report (1988), was also examined in some detail in this project. Despite the development in some health authorities of this role, it has not yet developed as it might have done. Both the extension of the role of geriatric medicine in community care and the role of multipurpose care workers — the two linked through care management — are areas which are likely to merit further consideration in the development of the community care system in the next decade and beyond.

In the early phase of development of community care, the focus was, of necessity, upon organisational structures, transfer of funding and procedural systems. The agenda for the subsequent phase will need to examine more closely the health and social care interface, not just at the macro level of joint commissioning or single agency provider agreements, but also at the micro-level issues of practice and how well-established systems and structures, such as geriatric services, may assist the new policy, not just by contributing to more effective targeting through assessment but also by a closer involvement with community-based care.

References

Abrams, P. (1977) Community care: some research problems and priorities, *Policy and Politics*, 6, 125-51.

Acquilla, S. (1986) *Services for the Elderly in the Darlington Health District*, Part II thesis for Membership of the Faculty of Community Medicine, Darlington Health Authority, Darlington.

Acquilla, S., Challis, D.J., Darton, R.A. and Johnson, E.L. (1987a) *Report of the Census of Elderly Patients in Long-Stay Wards in Durham, May 1986*, Discussion Paper 521, Personal Social Services Research Unit, University of Kent, Canterbury.

Acquilla, S., Challis, D.J., Darton, R.A. and Stone, M. (1987b) *Report of the Darlington Day Census, 1986*, Discussion Paper 498, Personal Social Services Research Unit, University of Kent, Canterbury.

Acquilla, S., Challis, D.J., Darton, R.A. and Stone, M. (1987c) *Report of the Darlington Day Census, 1987*, Discussion Paper 550, Personal Social Services Research Unit, University of Kent, Canterbury.

Adelman, R.D., Marron, K., Libow, L.S. and Neufeld, R. (1987) A community oriented geriatric rehabilitation unit in a nursing home, *The Gerontologist*, 27, 143-6.

Aged Care Research Group (ACRG) (1993a) *Aged Care System Study: Eleventh Progress Report*, Lincoln Gerontology Centre, La Trobe University, Melbourne.

Aged Care Research Group (ACRG) (1993b) *Aged Care System Study: Twelfth Progress Report*, Lincoln Gerontology Centre, La Trobe University, Melbourne.

Aiken, M. and Hage, J. (1968) Organizational interdependence and intra-organizational structure, *American Sociological Review*, 33, 912-30.

Aiken, M., Dewar, R., DiTomaso, N., Hager, J. and Zeitz, G. (1975) *Coordinating Human Services*, Jossey Bass, San Francisco, California.

Aldrich, H. (1979) *Organizations and Environments*, Prentice-Hall, Englewood Cliffs, New Jersey.

Allen, I., Hogg, D. and Peace, S. (1992) *Elderly People: Choice, Participation and Satisfaction*, Policy Studies Institute, London.

Ames, D. and Flynn, E. (1992) Dementia services: an Australian perspective, in A. Burns and R. Levy (eds) *Dementia*, Chapman and Hall, London.

Andrew, R.A. (1988) Analysis of a general practitioners work in a private nursing home for the elderly, *Journal of the Royal College of General Practitioners*, 38, 546-8.

Applebaum, R. and Austin, C. (1990) *Long Term Care Case Management: Design and Evaluation*, Springer, New York.

Applebaum, R. and Wilson, N. (1988) Training needs for providing case management for the long term care client: lessons from the National Channeling Demonstration, *The Gerontologist*, 28, 172-6.

Arber, S. and Gilbert, N. (1989) Men: the forgotten carers, *Sociology*, 23, 1, 111-18.

Ardern, M., Mayou, R., Feldman, E. and Hawton, K. (1993) Cognitive impairment in the elderly medically ill: how often is it missed? *International Journal of Geriatric Psychiatry*, 8, 929-37.

Argyle, N., Jestice, S. and Brook, C. (1985) Psychogeriatric patients: their supporters' problems, *Age and Ageing*, 14, 355-60.

Arnold, D. (1987) The brokerage model of long term care: a rose by any other name, *Home Health Care Services Quarterly*, 8, 2, 23-43.

Arnold, P. and Page, D. (1989) *Housing and Community Care: Bricks and Mortar or a Foundation for Action*, School of Social and Professional Studies, Humberside Polytechnic, Hull.

Arnold, P. and Page, D. (1992) *Housing and Community Care: Bricks and Mortar or Foundation for Action?* School of Social and Professional Studies, Humberside Polytechnic.

Audit Commission (1986) *Making a Reality of Community Care*, HMSO, London.

Audit Commission (1992a) *The Community Revolution: Personal Social Services and Community Care*, HMSO, London.

Audit Commission (1992b) *Community Care: Managing the Cascade of Change*, HMSO, London.

Austin, C. (1981) Client assessment in context, *Social Work Research and Abstracts*, 20, 4-12.

Austin, C. (1983) Case management in long-term care: options and opportunities, *Health and Social Work*, 8, 1, 16-30.

Austin, C. (1992) *When the Whole is More than the Sum of its Parts: Case Management Issues from a Systems Perspective*, Paper presented at First International Conference on Long Term Care Case Management, Seattle, Washington.

Backer, T., Liberman, M. and Kuehnel, T. (1986) Dissemination and adoption of innovative psychosocial interventions, *Journal of Consulting and Clinical Psychology*, 54, 111-18.

Bagnall, W., Datta, S.R., Knox, J. and Horrocks, P. (1977) Geriatric medicine in Hull: a comprehensive review, *British Medical Journal*, 2, 102-4.

Ballew, J. and Mink, G. (1986) *Case Management in the Human Services*, Charles C. Thomas, Springfield, Illinois.

Baltes, M. (ed.) (1986) *The Psychology of Control and Aging*, Lawrence Erlbaum Associates, New York.

Barnes, M. and Miller, N. (eds) (1988) Performance Measurement in Personal

Social Services, *Research Policy and Planning*, Special Issue, 6, 2.

Barrett, S. and Fudge, S. (eds) (1981) *Policy and Action: Essays on the Implementation of Public Policy*, Methuen, London.

Barton, A., Coles, O. Stone, M., Dodds, M. and Smith, J. (1990) Home help and home care for the frail elderly: face to face in Darlington, *Research, Policy and Planning*, 8, 1, 7-13.

Bayley, M. (1973) *Mental Handicap and Community Care*, Routledge and Kegan Paul, London.

Bebbington, A.C. (1979) Changes in the provision of social services to the elderly in the community over fourteen years, *Social Policy and Administration*, 13, 2, 111-23.

Bebbington, A.C. and Davies, B.P. (1983) Equity and efficiency in the allocation of personal social services, *Journal of Social Policy*, 12, 3, 309-30.

Bebbington, A.C., Charnley, H., Davies, B.P., Ferlie, E.B., Hughes, M.O. and Twigg, J. (1986) *The Domiciliary Care Project: Meeting the Needs of the Elderly*, Interim Report, Personal Social Services Research Unit, University of Kent, Canterbury.

Becker, G.S. (1964) *Human Capital. A Theoretical and Empirical Analysis with Special Reference to Education*, National Bureau of Economic Research, New York.

Beck-Friis, B., Karlsson, O. and Gustafsson, G. (1986) Hospital-based home care: an example of alternative care in Motala, in W. van den Heuvel and G. Schrijvers (eds) *Innovations in Care for the Elderly*, Uitgeversmaatschappij de Tidjstroom, Lochem-Gent.

Benson, J.K. (1975) The interorganizational network as a political economy, *Administrative Science Quarterly*, 20, 229-49.

Bergman, S., Habib, J. and Tomer, A. (1980) *Manpower in Services for the Aged in Israel*, Brookdale Institute of Gerontology, Jerusalem.

Bergmann, K. and Eastham, E.J. (1974) Psychogeriatric ascertainment and assessment for treatment in an acute medical ward setting, *Age and Ageing*, 3, 174-88.

Bergmann, K., Foster, E.M., Justice, A.W. and Matthews, V. (1978) Management of the demented elderly patient in the community, *British Journal of Psychiatry*, 132, 441-9.

Bessell, R. (1984) The housing needs of frail elderly people, in H. Laming et al. *Residential Care for the Elderly: Present Problems and Future Issues*, Discussion Paper 8, Policy Studies Institute, London.

Billings, A.G. and Moos, R.H. (1981) The role of coping responses and social resources in attenuating the stress of life events, *Journal of Behavioural Medicine*, 4, 139-57.

Bland, R. and Bland, R.E. (1985) *Client Characteristics and Patterns of Care in Local Authority Old People's Homes*, Department of Sociology, University of Stirling.

Bland, R., Hudson, H. and Dobson, B. (1992) *The EPIC Evaluation: Interim Report*, University of Stirling, Scotland.

Blau, P. (1964) Exchange and Power in Social Life, Wiley, New York.

Blazer, D.G. (1982) Social support and mortality in an elderly community population, American Journal of Epidemiology, 115, 684-94.

Bond, J., Brooks, P., Carstairs, V. and Giles, L. (1980) The reliability of a survey psychiatric assessment schedule for the elderly, British Journal of Psychiatry, 137, 148-62.

Bond, M. (1979) New Initiatives in the Care of the Elderly in the Community Arising from the Hillfield's Street Warden Scheme, Coventry Social Services Department, Coventry.

Bond, M. (1980) Women's work in a woman's world, MA Dissertation, Department of Applied Social Studies, Warwick University, Coventry.

Booth, T.A. (1985) Home Truths: Old People's Homes and the Outcome of Care, Gower, Aldershot.

Booth, T.A. (undated) Reasons for Admission to Part III Residential Homes, National Council of Domiciliary Care Services, Norwich.

Borup, J.H. (1983) Relocation mortality research, assessment: reply to the need to focus on the issue, The Gerontologist, 23, 235-42.

Bowling, A. and Browne, P.D. (1991) Social networks, health, and emotional well-being amongst the oldest old in London, Journal of Gerontology, 46,1, S20-S32.

Bowling, A., Formby, J., Grant, K. and Ebrahim, S. (1991) A randomized controlled trial of nursing home and long-stay geriatric ward care for elderly people, Age and Ageing, 20, 316-24.

Bowns, I., Challis, D.J. and Tong, M.S. (1991) Case finding in elderly people: validation of a postal questionnaire, British Journal of General Practice, 41, 100-104.

Brane, G. (1986) Normal ageing and dementia disorders — coping and crisis in the family, Progress in Neuro-psychopharmacology and Biological Psychiatry, 10, 287-95.

Braun, K.L. and Rose, C.L. (1987) Geriatric patient outcomes in three settings: nursing home, foster family and own home, Journal of the American Geriatrics Society, 35, 387-97.

British Columbia Ministry of Health (BCMH) (1992) Case Manager Guidebook, Continuing Care Division, Ministry of Health, Victoria, British Columbia.

Brocklehurst, J., Carty, M. and Leeming, J. (1978) Care of the elderly: medical screening of old people accepted for residential care, Lancet, ii, 141-2.

Brody, E. (1977a) Long-Term Care of Older People: A Practical Guide, Human Sciences Press, New York.

Brody, E. (1977b) Environmental factors in dependency, in A.N. Exton-Smith and J. Grimley Evans (eds) Care of the Elderly: Meeting the Challenge of Dependency, Academic Press, London.

Brodsky, J., Naon, D. and King, Y. (1993) Implications of the Expansion of Home Care Following the Implementation of the Community Long Term Insurance Law, D-204-93, JDC-Brookdale Institute of Gerontology and Adult Human Development, Jerusalem.

Brown, G.W. and Harris, T. (1978) *Social Origins of Depression: A Study of Psychiatric Disorders in Women*, Tavistock, London.

Brown, J. and McCallum, J. (1991) *Geriatric Assessment and Community Care: A Follow-up Study*, Aged and Community Care Service Development and Evaluation Reports No. 1, Australian Government Publishing Service, Canberra.

Buglass, D. (1993) *Assessment and Care Management: A Scottish Overview of Impending Change*, Social Work Research Centre, University of Stirling.

Butler, A., Oldman, C. and Greve, J. (1983) *Sheltered Housing for the Elderly: Policy, Practice and the Consumer*, George Allen and Unwin, London.

Callahan, J. (1989) Case management for the elderly: a panacea?, *Journal of Aging and Social Policy*, 1, 181-95.

Campbell, D.T. and Stanley, J.C. (1966) *Experimental and Quasi-Experimental Designs for Research*, Rand McNally, Chicago, Illinois.

Capitman, J. (1986) Community-based long term care models, target groups, and impacts on service use, *The Gerontologist*, 26, 389-97.

Capitman, J.A., Haskins B. and Bernstein J. (1986) Case management approaches in community-oriented long term care demonstrations, *The Gerontologist*, 26, 398-404.

Challis, D.J. (1981) The measurement of outcome in social care of the elderly, *Journal of Social Policy*, 10, 2, 179-208.

Challis, D.J. (1990) Case management: problems and possibilities, in I. Allen (ed.) *Care Managers and Care Management*, Policy Studies Institute, London.

Challis, D.J. (1992a) The care of the elderly in Europe. New perspectives — social care, *European Journal of Gerontology*, 1, 334-47.

Challis, D.J. (1992b) Community care of elderly people: bringing together scarcity and choice, needs and costs, *Financial Accountability and Management*, 8, 2, 77-95.

Challis, D.J. (1992c) Providing alternatives to long-stay hospital care for frail elderly patients: is it cost-effective?, *International Journal of Geriatric Psychiatry*, 7, 773-81.

Challis, D.J. (1993) Case management in social and health care: lessons from a United Kingdom programme, *Journal of Case Management*, 2, 3, 79-90.

Challis, D.J. (1994a) Care management, in N. Malin (ed.) *Implementing Community Care*, Open University Press, Buckingham.

Challis, D.J. (1994b) Care management: factors influencing its development in the implementation of community care, in Social Services Inspectorate (ed.) *Care Management, Thematic Study Findings*, SSI, Department of Health, London.

Challis, D.J. (1994c) Case management: a review of UK developments and issues, in M. Titterton (ed.) *Caring for People in the Community: The New Welfare*, Jessica Kingsley Publishers, London.

Challis, D.J. and Chesterman, J.F. (1985) A system for monitoring social work activity with the frail elderly, *British Journal of Social Work*, 15, 2, 115-32.

Challis, D.J. and Darton, R.A. (1990) Evaluation research and experiment in social gerontology, in S.M. Peace (ed.) *Researching Social Gerontology: Concepts, Methods and Issues*, Sage, London.

Challis, D.J. and Davies, B.P. (1985) Long-term care for the elderly: the Community Care Scheme, *British Journal of Social Work*, 15, 563-79.

Challis, D.J. and Davies, B.P. (1986) *Case Management in Community Care: An Evaluated Experiment in the Home Care of the Elderly*, Gower, Aldershot.

Challis, D.J. and Ferlie, E.B. (1986) Changing patterns of fieldwork organisation: I. The headquarters view, *British Journal of Social Work*, 16, 2, 181-202.

Challis, D.J. and Ferlie, E.B. (1987) Changing patterns of fieldwork organisation: II: The team leaders' view, *British Journal of Social Work*, 17, 2, 147-67.

Challis, D.J. and Knapp, M.R.J. (1980) *An Examination of the PGC Morale Scale in an English Context*, Discussion Paper 168, Personal Social Services Research Unit, University of Kent, Canterbury.

Challis, D.J. and von Abendorff, R. (1992) *Lewisham Case Management Scheme Report to Management Group*, Discussion Paper 825, Personal Social Services Research Unit, University of Kent, Canterbury.

Challis, D.J., Darton, R.A. and Traske, K.J. (1987) *Darlington Community Care Project: Fieldwork Records Coding Manual*, Discussion Paper 542, Personal Social Services Research Unit, University of Kent, Canterbury.

Challis, D.J., Chessum, R., Chesterman, J.F., Luckett, R. and Woods, R. (1988a) Community care for the frail elderly: an urban experiment, *British Journal of Social Work*, 18 (Supplement), 13-42.

Challis, D.J., Darton, R.A., Johnson, E.L. and Stone, M. (1988b) *Darlington Community Care Project. Questionnaires*, Discussion Paper 476, Personal Social Services Research Unit, University of Kent, Canterbury.

Challis, D.J., Knapp, M.R.J. and Davies, B.P. (1988c) Cost effectiveness evaluation in social care, in J. Lishman (ed.) *Research Highlights in Social Work 8: Evaluation*, 2nd edition, Jessica Kingsley Publishers, London.

Challis, D.J., Darton, R.A., Johnson, L., Stone, M., Traske, K.J. and Wall, B. (1989) *The Darlington Community Care Project: Supporting Frail Elderly People at Home*, Personal Social Services Research Unit, University of Kent, Canterbury.

Challis, D.J., Chessum, R., Chesterman, J.F., Luckett, R. and Traske, K.J. (1990) *Case Management in Social and Health Care: The Gateshead Community Care Scheme*, Personal Social Services Research Unit, University of Kent, Canterbury.

Challis, D.J., Darton, R.A., Johnson, L., Stone, M. and Traske, K.J. (1991a) An evaluation of an alternative to long-stay hospital care for frail elderly patients: I. The model of care, *Age and Ageing*, 20, 236-44.

Challis, D.J., Darton, R.A., Johnson, L., Stone, M. and Traske, K.J. (1991b) An evaluation of an alternative to long-stay hospital care for frail elderly patients: II. Costs and effectiveness, *Age and Ageing*, 20, 245-54.

Challis, D.J., Chessum, R., Chesterman, J.F., Luckett, R. and Traske, K.J. (1992) Case management, in F. Laczko and C.R. Victor (eds) *Social Policy and Elderly People*, Avebury, Aldershot.

Challis, D.J., Chesterman, J.F., Darton, R.A. and Traske, K.J. (1993a) Case management in the care of the aged: the provision of care in different settings, in J. Bornat, C. Pereira, D. Pilgrim and F. Williams (eds) *Community Care: A Reader*, Macmillan, Basingstoke and London.

Challis, D.J., Chesterman, J.F. and Traske, K.J. (1993b) Case management: costing the experiments, in A.P. Netten and J.K. Beecham (eds) *Costing Community Care: Theory and Practice*, Ashgate, Aldershot.

Challis, D.J., Davies, B.P. and Traske, K.J. (1994) Community care: promise, ambition and imperative — an international agenda, in D.J. Challis, B.P. Davies and K.J. Traske (eds) *Community Care: New Agendas and Challenges from the UK and Overseas*, Ashgate, Gower.

Challis, L., Fuller, S., Henwood, M., Klein, R., Plowden, W., Webb, A., Whittingham, P. and Wistow, G. (1988) *Joint Approaches to Social Policy: Rationality and Practice*, Cambridge University Press, Cambridge.

Champion, L.A. (1989) A look at the relationship between life events and vulnerability to depression, *Psychological Medicine*, 20, 154-61.

Charlesworth, A., Wilkin, D. and Durie, A. (1984) *Carers and Services: A Comparison of Men and Women Caring for Dependant Elderly People*, Equal Opportunities Commission, Manchester.

Charlton, F., Arch, M., Carter, M., Humphries, S. and Todd, M. (1992) *Bendigo-Ballarat Linkages Study: A Comparison of Outcomes for Geriatric Assessment Team Clients*, Aged and Community Care Service Development and Evaluation Reports No. 5, Australian Government Publishing Service, Canberra.

Charlton, J., Wallace, M. and White, I. (1994) Long-term illness: results from the 1991 Census, *Population Trends 75*, HMSO, London.

Chartered Institute of Public Finance and Accountancy (CIPFA) (1986) *Personal Social Services Statistics 1984-85 Actuals*, Chartered Institute of Public Finance and Accountancy, London.

Chartered Institute of Public Finance and Accountancy (CIPFA) (1987) *Personal Social Services Statistics 1985-86 Actuals*, Chartered Institute of Public Finance and Accountancy, London.

Chartered Institute of Public Finance and Accountancy (CIPFA) (1988) *Personal Social Services Statistics 1986-87 Actuals*, Chartered Institute of Public Finance and Accountancy, London.

Chesterman, J.F., Challis, D.J. and Davies, B.P. (1988) long-term care at home for the elderly: a four year follow-up, *British Journal of Social Work*, 18, Supplement, 43-53.

Chesterman, J.F., Challis, D.J. and Davies, B.P. (1994) Budget-devolved care management in two routine programmes. Have they improved outcomes? in D.J. Challis, B.P. Davies and K.J. Traske (eds) *Community Care: New Agendas and Challenges from the UK and Overseas*, Ashgate, Gower.

Clapham, D. and Munro, M. (1990) Ambiguities and contradictions in the provision of sheltered housing for older people, *Journal of Social Policy*, 19, 27-45.

Clapham, D., Kemp, P. and Smith S.J. (1990) *Housing and Social Policy*, Macmillan, Basingstoke and London.

Clark, A.N.G. (1983) The history of geriatric medicine, in J.M. Graham and H.M. Hodkinson (eds) *Effective Geriatric Medicine: The Special Work of Physicians in Geriatric Medicine*, Harrogate Seminar Reports 7, DHSS, London.

Clarke, F. (1976) Home care — an alternative to admission, *Health and Social Service Journal*, 86, 4478, 348-9.

Clarke, F. (1979) Hospital caring without walls, *Health and Social Service Journal*, 89, 4634, 309-10.

Cm 849 (1989) *Caring for People: Community Care in the Next Decade and Beyond*, HMSO, London.

Cmnd 1973 (1963) *Health and Welfare: The Development of Community Care*, HMSO, London.

Cmnd 4683 (1971) *Better Services for the Mentally Handicapped*, HMSO, London.

Cmnd 5191 (1973) *Report on the Review of Procedures for the Discharge and Supervision of Psychiatric Patients Subject to Special Restrictions*, (Aarvold Committee), HMSO, London.

Cmnd 6233 (1975) *Better Services for the Mentally Ill*, HMSO, London.

Cmnd 6244 (1975) *Report of the Committee on Mentally Abnormal Offenders*, (The Butler Report), HMSO, London.

Cmnd 8086 (1980) *The Government's White Papers on Public Expenditure: The Social Services*. Reply by the Government to the Third Report from the Social Services Committee, Session 1979-80, HMSO, London.

Cmnd 8173 (1981) *Growing Older*, HMSO, London.

Cmnd 9823 (1986) *Working Together: Education and Training*, HMSO, London.

Coid, J. and Crome, P. (1986) Bed blocking in Bromley, *British Medical Journal*, 292, 1253-6.

Cole, A. (1990) Assessment in the community, in A. Howe, E. Ozanne and C. Selby-Smith (eds) *Community Care Policy and Practice: New Directions in Australia*, Public Sector Management Institute, Monash University, Melbourne.

Coles, O. (1985a) The dependency of old people in residential care: interpreting the trends, *Social Services Research*, 5, 37-66.

Coles, O. (1985b) *Trends in the Characteristics of Residents of Homes for the Elderly: 1977 to 1985. A Comparison of the 1977, 1979, 1981, 1983 and 1985 Day Census Findings*, Social Services Department, Durham County Council.

Collin, C., Wade, D.T., Davis, S. and Horne, V. (1988) The Barthel Index: a reliability study, *International Disability Studies*, 10, 61-3.

Common, R. and Flynn, N. (1992) Contracting for care, *Community Care*, Joseph Rowntree Foundation, York.

Commonwealth of Australia (1989) *Home and Community Care Program National Guidelines*, Australian Government Publishing Service, Canberra.

Cook, K.S. (1977) Exchange and power in networks of interorganizational relations, *The Sociological Quarterly*, 18, 62-82.

Cooper, B., Harwin, C., Depla, C. and Shepherd, M. (1975) Mental health care in the community: an evaluative study, *Psychological Medicine*, 5, 372-81.

Cooper, M. (1988) Linking housing and care, in D. Stockford (ed.) *Integrating Care Systems: Practical Perspectives*, Longman, Harlow.

Corden, A. (1992) Geographical development of the long-term care market for elderly people, *Transactions of the Institute of British Geographers*, New Series, 17, 1, 80-94.

Corney, R. (1981) Social work effectiveness in the management of depressed women: a clinical trial, *Psychological Medicine*, 112, 417-24.

Currie, C.T., Smith, R.G. and Williamson, J. (1979) Medical and nursing needs of elderly patients admitted to acute medical beds, *Age and Ageing*, 8, 149-51.

Dalziel, W.B., Susinski, C.A. and Dalziel, L.M. (1992) Community-based outreach multidimensional geriatric assessment: a clinical and educational model, *Educational Gerontology*, 18, 541-54.

Dant, T. and Gearing, B. (1990) Keyworkers for elderly people in the community: case managers and care coordinators, *Journal of Social Policy*, 19, 331-60.

Dant, T., Carley, M., Gearing, B. and Johnson, M. (1989) *Coordinating Care: The Final Report of the Care for Elderly People at Home (CEPH) Project, Gloucester*, Open University, Milton Keynes and Policy Studies Institute, London.

Darlington Community Care Project for the Elderly (1988) Project Manager's Report, March.

Darlington Health Authority (1989) *Intensive Domiciliary Care Scheme: Service Review*, Darlington Health Authority, Darlington.

Darlington Health Authority (1991) *Intensive Domiciliary Service: Review of Management Arrangements*, Darlington Health Authority, Darlington.

Darlington Health Authority Community Unit (1988) *The Darlington Intensive Domiciliary Service: Monitoring, Assessment, Referral and Review Procedure*, Darlington Health Authority, Darlington.

Darton, R.A. (1984) Trends 1970-81, in H. Laming et al. *Residential Care for the Elderly: Present Problems and Future Issues*, Discussion Paper 8, Policy Studies Institute, London.

Darton, R.A. (1986) *PSSRU Survey of Residential Accommodation for the Elderly, 1981. Characteristics of the Residents*, Discussion Paper 426, Personal Social Services Research Unit, University of Kent, Canterbury.

Darton, R.A. and Wright, K.G. (1992) Residential and nursing homes for elderly people: one sector or two?, in F. Laczko and C.R. Victor (eds) *Social Policy and Elderly People*, Avebury, Aldershot.

Darton, R.A. and Wright, K.G. (1993) Changes in the provision of long-stay care, 1970-1990, *Health and Social Care in the Community*, 1, 1, 11-25.

Davidson, I.A., Dewey, M.E. and Copeland, J.R.M. (1988) The relationship between mortality and mental disorder: evidence from the Liverpool longitudinal study, *International Journal of Geriatric Psychiatry*, 3, 95-8.

Davidson, S.M. (1976) Planning and coordination of social services in multiorganizational contexts, *Social Service Review*, 50, 117-37.

Davies, B.P. (1992) *Care Management, Equity and Efficiency: The International*

Experience, Personal Social Services Research Unit, University of Kent, Canterbury.

Davies, B.P. (1993) Thinking long in community care, in N. Deakin and R. Page (eds) *The Costs of Welfare*, Avebury, Aldershot.

Davies, B.P. and Challis, D.J. (1986) *Matching Resources to Needs in Community Care: An Evaluated Demonstration of a Long-Term Care Model*, Gower, Aldershot.

Davies, B.P. and Knapp, M.R.J. (1981) *Old People's Homes and the Production of Welfare*, Routledge & Kegan Paul, London.

Davies, B.P., Bebbington, A.C. and Charnley, H. with Baines, B., Ferlie, E.B., Hughes, M. and Twigg, J. (1990) *Resources, Needs and Outcomes in Community-Based Care*, Avebury, Aldershot.

Davies, M. (1985) *The Essential Social Worker*, 2nd edition, Gower, Aldershot.

Dening, T. (1992) Community psychiatry of old age: a UK perspective, *International Journal of Geriatric Psychiatry*, 7, 757-66.

Department of Community Services (DCS) (1986) *Nursing Homes and Hostels Review*, Australian Government Publishing Service, Canberra.

Department of Community Services and Health (DCSH) (1987) *Commonwealth Guidelines for Assessment Services*, Australian Government Publishing Service, Canberra.

Department of Community Services and Health (DCSH) (1990) *The Balance of Care: A Framework for Planning, Mid-Term Review of Aged Care Reform Strategy 1990-91*, Discussion Paper 7, Australian Government Publishing Service, Canberra.

Department of Community Services and Health (DCSH) (1991) *Aged Care Reform Strategy: Mid-Term Review 1990-91. Report*, Australian Government Publishing Service, Canberra.

Department of Employment (1987) *Family Expenditure Survey 1986*, HMSO, London.

Department of the Environment (1987) *Housing and Construction Statistics 1976-1986 Great Britain*, HMSO, London.

Department of Health (1990) *Caring for People: Community Care in the Next Decade and Beyond*, Policy Guidance, Department of Health, HMSO, London.

Department of Health (1991) *Implementing Community Care: Purchaser, Commissioner and Provider Roles*, Department of Health/Price Waterhouse, HMSO, London.

Department of Health (1993) *Monitoring and Development: Assessment Special Study*, Department of Health, London.

Department of Health (1994) *Monitoring and Development: Care Management Special Study*, Department of Health, London.

Department of Health (undated) *Residential Accommodation for Elderly and for Younger Physically Handicapped People: All Residents in Local Authority, Voluntary and Private Homes, Year Ending 31 March 1989*, RA/89/2, Department of Health, London.

Department of Health and Social Security (DHSS) (1973) *The Remedial Professions*, HMSO, London.

Department of Health and Social Security (DHSS) (1976) *Priorities for Health and Personal Social Services in England. A Consultative Document*, HMSO, London.

Department of Health and Social Security (DHSS) (1977) *Priorities in the Health and Social Services: The Way Forward*, HMSO, London.

Department of Health and Social Security (DHSS) (1978) *Health and Personal Social Services in England, DHSS Planning Guidelines for 1978/79*, HC(78)12, DHSS, London.

Department of Health and Social Security (DHSS) (1980) *Organisational and Management Problems of Mental Illness Hospitals*, HMSO, London.

Department of Health and Social Security (DHSS) (1981a) *Care in Action. A Handbook of Policies for the Health and Personal Social Services in England*, HMSO, London.

Department of Health and Social Security (DHSS) (1981b) *Care in the Community. A Consultative Document on Moving Resources for Care in England*, DHSS, London.

Department of Health and Social Security (DHSS) (1981c) *Report of a Study on Community Care*, DHSS, London.

Department of Health and Social Security (DHSS) (1981d) *Report of a Study on the Respective Roles of the General Acute and Geriatric Sectors in Care of the Elderly Hospital Patient*, DHSS, London.

Department of Health and Social Security (DHSS) (1983) *Health Service Development: Care in the Community and Joint Finance*, HC(83)6, LAC(83)5, DHSS, London.

Department of Health and Social Security (DHSS) (1986a) *Health and Personal Social Services Statistics for England*, HMSO, London.

Department of Health and Social Security (DHSS) (1986b) *Private Hospitals, Homes and Clinics Registered Under Section 23 of the Registered Homes Act 1984, 31 December 1985, National, Regional and District Summaries*, HMSO, London.

Department of Health and Social Security (DHSS) (1988) *Social Security Statistics 1986*, HMSO, London.

Department of Health and Social Security (DHSS) (undated(a)) *Residential Accommodation for Elderly and for Younger Physically Handicapped People: All Residents in Local Authority, Voluntary and Private Homes, Year Ending 31 March 1986, England*, RA/86/2, Department of Health, London.

Department of Health and Social Security (DHSS) (undated(b)) *Residential Accommodation for the Elderly and for Younger Physically Handicapped People. Local Authority Supported Residents, Year Ending 31 March 1986, England*, RA/86/1, DHSS, London.

Department of Health, Housing and Community Services (DHHCS) (1991) *Aged Care Reform Strategy: Mid Term Review 1990-91*, Australian Government Publishing Service, Canberra.

Department of Health, Housing and Community Services (DHHCS) (1992) *It's Your Choice: National Evaluation of Community Options Projects*, Aged and Community Care Division, Department of Health, Housing and Community Services, Australian Government Publishing Service, Canberra.

Dewey, M.E., Davidson, I.A. and Copeland J.R.M. (1993) Expressed wish to die and mortality in older people: a community replication, *Age and Ageing*, 22, 109-13.

Dexter, M. and Harbert, W. (1983) *The Home Help Service*, Tavistock, London.

DiMaggio, P.J. (1983) State expansion and organisational fields, in R. Hall and R. Quinn (eds) *Organisational Theory and Public Policy*, Sage, Beverly Hills, California.

Disability Alliance (1987) *Poverty and Disabilty: Breaking the Link*, Disability Alliance, London.

Dobrof, R. and Litwak, E. (1977) *Maintenance of Family Ties of Long-term Care Patients: Theory and Guide to Practice*, NIMH Superintendent of Documents, US Government Printing Office, Washington, DC.

Donaldson, C. and Gregson, B. (1989) Prolonging life at home: what is the cost? *Community Medicine*, 11, 200-209.

Duke University Center for the Study of Aging and Human Development (1978) *Multidimensional Functional Assessment: The OARS Methodology. A Manual*, 2nd edition, Duke University Medical Center, Durham, North Carolina.

Dunnachie, N. (1979) Intensive domiciliary care of the elderly in Hove, *Social Work Service*, 21, 1-3.

Dunnell, K. and Dobbs, J. (1980) *Nurses Working in the Community*, HMSO, London.

Durham County Council Social Services Department (1986) *Position Statement 1986*, Durham County Council Social Services Department.

Earll, L. and Kincey, J. (1982) Clinical psychology in general practice: a controlled evaluation, *Journal of the Royal College of General Practitioners*, 32, 32-7.

Emery, F. and Trist, E (1965) The causal texture of human environments, *Human Relations*, 18, 21-31.

Evans, J. Grimley (1983) Care of the elderly in a defined community, in J.M. Graham and H.M. Hodkinson (eds) *Effective Geriatric Medicine: The Special Work of Physicians in Geriatric Medicine*, Harrogate Seminar Reports 7, DHSS, London.

Evans, W.M. and Klem, C.R. (1980) Interorganizational relations among hospitals: a strategy, structure and performance model, *Human Relations*, 33, 315-37

Fairweather, G., Sanders, D. and Tornatzky, L. (1974) *Creating Change in Mental Health Organisations*, Pergamon, New York.

Falloon, R.H. and Fadden, G. (1993) *Integrated Mental Health Care*, Cambridge University Press, Cambridge.

Ferlie, E.B. (1982) *Sourcebook of Innovation in Community Care of the Elderly*,

Discussion Paper 271, Personal Social Services Research Unit, University of Kent, Canterbury.

Ferlie, E.B., Challis, D.J. and Davies, B.P. (1989) *Efficiency-Improving Innovations in Social Care of the Elderly*, Gower, Aldershot.

Fineman, L. (1992) *A Community Care System for the Elderly in Manitoba, Canada*, Paper given at International Symposium on Social Care for the Elderly: Community Care Systems in the Human Services, Tokyo.

Flynn, G. (1987) *The Book of Darlington: Saxon Settlement and Railway Town*, Barracuda Books, Buckingham.

Friedson, E. (1970) *Professional Dominance: The Social Structure of Medical Care*, Aldine, Chicago, Illinois.

Friedson, E. (1984) The changing nature of professional control, *Annual Review of Sociology*, 10, 1-20.

Gibbins, F.J. (1984) High intensity community nursing, in J. Grimley Evans and F.I. Caird (eds) *Advanced Geriatric Medicine 4*, Pitman, London.

Gibbins, F.J., Lee, M., Davison, P., O'Sullivan, P., Hutchinson, M., Murphy, D. and Ugwu, C. (1982) Augmented home nursing as an alternative to hospital care for chronic elderly invalids, *British Medical Journal*, 284, 330-33.

Gilhooly, M. (1984) The impact of caregiving on caregivers: factors associated with the psychological well-being of people supporting a dementing relative in the community, *British Journal of Medical Psychology*, 57, 35-44.

Gilleard, C.J. (1984) *Living with Dementia: Community Care of the Elderly Mentally Infirm*, Croom Helm, Beckenham.

Gilleard, C.J. (1987) Influence of emotional distress amongst supporters on the outcome of psychogeriatric day care, *British Journal of Psychiatry*, 150, 219-23.

Gilleard, C.J., Wilmott, M. and Vaddadi, K.S. (1981) Self-report measures of mood and morale in elderly depressives, *British Journal of Psychiatry*, 138, 230-35.

Gilleard, C.J., Belford, H., Gilleard, E., Whittick, J. and Gledhill, K. (1984) Emotional distress amongst the supporters of the elderly mentally infirm, *British Journal of Psychiatry*, 145, 172-7.

Ginsberg, G., Marks, I. and Water, H. (1984) Cost-benefit analysis of a controlled trial of nurse therapy for neuroses in primary care, *Psychological Medicine*, 14, 683-90.

Glennerster, H. (1983) *Planning for Priority Groups*, Martin Robertson, Oxford.

Goering, P. and Cochrane, J. (1992) *Critical Success Factors for Mental Health Reform: Lessons Learned from Other Jurisdictions*, Clarke Institute Consulting Group, Toronto.

Goldberg, D.P. (1972) *The Detection of Psychiatric Illness by Questionnaire: A Technique for the Identification and Assessment of Non-Psychotic Psychiatric Illness*, Oxford University Press, London.

Goldberg, D.P. and Williams, P. (1988) *A User's Guide to the General Health Questionnaire*, NFER/Nelson, Windsor.

Goldberg, E.M. (1983) Some current and future issues in the social care of elderly people, in Department of Health and Social Security, *Elderly People in the Community: Their Service Needs. Research Contributions to the Development of Policy and Practice*, HMSO, London.

Goldberg, E.M. and Connelly, N. (1982) *The Effectiveness of Social Care for the Elderly: An Overview of Recent and Current Evaluative Research*, Heinemann Educational Books, London.

Goldberg, E.M. and Neill, J. (1972) *Social Work in General Practice*, Allen and Unwin, London.

Golding, R., Lugon, M. and Hodkinson, H.M. (1987) Confirming long-stay status, *Age and Ageing*, 16, 13-18.

Gouldner, A. (1960) The norm of reciprocity: a preliminary statement, *American Sociological Review*, 25, 161-78.

Grad, J. and Sainsbury, P. (1965) An evaluation of the effect of caring for the aged at home, *Psychiatric Disorders in the Aged*, WPA Symposium, Manchester.

Grad, J. and Sainsbury, P. (1968) The effects that patients have on their families in a community care and a control psychiatric service — a two year follow-up, *British Journal of Psychiatry*, 114, 265-78.

Graham, S., Ross, R., and Payne T. (1992) *The Evaluation of Community Options in New South Wales*, Social Policy Research Centre, University of New South Wales, Sydney.

Grant, G. and Nolan, M. (1993) Informal carers: sources and concomitants of satisfaction, *Health and Social Care*, 1, 147-59.

Gray, L. (1988) *Bundoora Linkages Project: Case Management in a Geriatric Team*, Bundoora Extended Care Centre, Melbourne.

Gray, A.M. and Hunter, D.J. (1983) Priorities and resource allocation in the Scottish health service: some problems in planning and implementation, *Policy and Politics*, 11, 417-37.

Gray, L. and Lazarus, R. (1987) A regionalised nursing home placement list, *Community Health Studies*, 11, 120-24.

Green, H. (1988) *General Household Survey 1985: Informal Carers*, HMSO, London.

Greene, J., Smith, R., Gardiner, M. and Timbury, G. (1982) Measuring behavioural disturbance of elderly demented patients in the community and its effects on relatives: a factor analytic study, *Age and Ageing*, 11, 121-6.

Greenwood, R. and Hinings, C.R. (1976) Contingency theory and public bureaucracies, *Policy and Politics*, 5, 159-80.

Gregson, B., Smith, M., Lauder, J. and Bond, J. (1993) *Social Networks and Pre-morbidity Activity Levels of Elderly People Admitted to an Acute Hospital and Outcome at Discharge*, Paper presented at the British Society of Gerontology Annual Conference, September.

Griffiths, R. (1983) *NHS Management Inquiry: Report*, DHSS, London.

Griffiths, R. (1988) *Community Care: Agenda for Action*, HMSO, London.

Guillemard, A.M. (1993) European perspectives on ageing policies, in L. Moreno (ed.) *Social Exchange and Welfare Development*, Consejo Superior de

Investigaciones Cientificas, Madrid.

Haddad, L.B. (1981) Intra-institutional relocation: measured impact on geriatric patients, *Journal of the American Geriatric Society*, 29, 86-8.

Hadley, R. and Hugman, R. (1992) Managing change in a turbulent climate: the experience of a social services department, *Social Work and Social Sciences Review*, 3, 204-26.

Hall, M.R.P. (1982) Risk and health care, in C.P. Brearley (ed.) *Risk and Ageing*, Routledge and Kegan Paul, London.

Hall, R. (1982) *Organisations: Structure and Process*, Prentice-Hall, Englewood Cliffs, New Jersey.

Hall, R. (1986) Interorganizational or interprofessional relationships: a case of mistaken identity?, in W.R. Scott and B.L. Black (eds) *The Organization of Mental Health Services: Societal and Community Systems*, Sage, Beverly Hills, California.

Hall, R. and Quinn, R. (1983) Environments, organisations and policy makers: towards an integrative framework, in R. Hall and R. Quinn (eds) *Organisation Theory and Public Policy*, Sage, Beverly Hills, California.

Hall, R., Clark, J. and Giordano, P. (1977) Patterns of interorganisational relationships, *Administrative Science Quarterly*, 22, 457-74.

Hall, R., Clark, J. and Giordano, P. (1978) Interorganisational coordination in the delivery of human services, in L. Karpik (ed.) *Organisation and Environment: Theory, Issues and Reality*, Sage, Beverly Hills, California.

Hallett, C. and Stevenson, O. (1980) *Child Abuse: Aspects of Interprofessional Cooperation*, Allen and Unwin, London.

Harrington, C. and Newcomer, R.J. (1982) United States: coordinating services to the aged, in M.C. Hokenstad and R. Ritvo (eds) *Linking Health Care and Social Services: International Perspectives*, Sage, Beverly Hills, California.

Harwood, R. and Ebrahim, S. (1992) Is relocation harmful to institutionalized elderly people?, *Age and Ageing*, 21, 61-6.

Health Advisory Service (1982) *The Rising Tide. Developing Services for Mental Illness in Old Age*, National Health Service Health Advisory Service, Sutton.

Health Service Journal (1986) Health management award winners, *Health Service Journal*, 96, 5006, 3 July, 887.

Henderson, A.S. (1981) Social relationships, adversity and neurosis: an analysis of prospective observations, *British Journal of Psychiatry*, 138, 391-8.

Henderson, A.S., Byrne, D.G., Duncan-Jones, P., Scott, R. and Adcock, S. (1980a) Social relationships, adversity and neurosis. A study of associations in a general population sample, *British Journal of Psychiatry*, 136, 574-83.

Henderson, A.S., Duncan-Jones, P., Byrne, D.G. and Scott, R. (1980b) Measuring social relationships: the Interview Schedule for Social Interaction, *Psychological Medicine*, 10, 723-34.

Henderson, A.S. with Byrne, D.G. and Duncan-Jones, P. (1981) *Neurosis and Social Environment*, Academic Press Australia, Sydney.

Henderson, A.S., Grayson, D.A., Scott, R., Wilson, J., Rickwood, D. and Kay, D.W.K. (1986) Social support, dementia and depression among the elderly living in the Hobart community, *Psychological Medicine*, 16, 2, 379-90.

Hennessy, C. and Hennessy, M. (1990) Community-based long term for the elderly: evaluation practice reconsidered, *Medical Care Review*, 47, 221-59.

Hicks, C. (1988) *Who Cares: Looking after People at Home*, Virago, London.

Hillingdon Social Services Department (1974) Recruitment and retention of home helps: a further study, *Clearing House for Local Authority Social Services Research*, 9, 77-96.

Hodgson, J.M. and Quinn, J.L. (1980) The impact of the TRIAGE Health Care Delivery System on client morale, independent living and the cost of care, *The Gerontologist*, 20, 364-71.

Hodkinson, H.M. (1972) Evaluation of a mental test score for assessment of mental impairment in the elderly, *Age and Ageing*, 1, 233-8.

Hodkinson, I. and Hodkinson, H.M. (1981) The long-stay patient, *Gerontology*, 27, 167-72.

Hoenig, J. and Hamilton, M.W. (1969) *The Desegregation of the Mentally Ill*, Routledge and Kegan Paul, London.

Hokenstad, M.C. and Johansson, L. (1990) Caregiving for the elderly in Sweden: program changes and policy initiatives, in D. Biegel and A. Blum (eds) *Ageing and Caregiving: Theory, Research and Practice*, Sage, San Francisco, California.

Hokenstad, M.C. and Ritvo, R. (eds) (1982) *Linking Health Care and Social Services: International Perspectives*, Sage, Beverly Hills, California.

Hopkins, A. (1982) Practical help, *Lancet*, 23 June, 1393-6.

Hopkins, A., Brocklehurst, J. and Dickinson, E. (1992) *The CARE Scheme: Clinical Audit of Long-term Care of Elderly People*, Royal College of Physicians, London.

Horowitz, A. (1985) Sons and daughters as caregivers to elderly parents: differences in role performance and consequences, *The Gerontologist*, 25, 612-17.

Horrocks, P. (1983) Admission and discharge of the elderly patient, in J.M. Graham and H.M. Hodkinson (eds) *Effective Geriatric Medicine: The Special Work of Physicians in Geriatric Medicine*, Harrogate Seminar Reports 7, DHSS, London.

House of Commons (1987) *Hansard*, Issue No. 1429, 123, 79-80.

House of Commons (1992) *Community Care: The Elderly. Volume 1*, Welsh Affairs Committee, Fourth Report, Session 1991-92, HC11-1, HMSO, London.

Howe, A. (1990) Nursing home care policy: from laissez-faire to restructuring, in H. Kendig and J. McCallum (eds) *Grey Policy: Australian Policies for an Ageing Society*, Allen and Unwin, Sydney.

Howell, N., Boldy, D. and Smith, B. (1979) *Allocating the Home Help Service*, Bedford Square Press, London.

Hudson, B. (1987) Collaboration in social welfare: a framework for analysis, *Policy and Politics*, 15, 175-82.

Hunt, A. (1978) *The Elderly at Home*, OPCS, HMSO, London.

Hunter, D.J. and Wistow, G. (1987) *Community Care in Britain: Variations on a Theme*, King Edward's Hospital Fund for London, London.

Hunter, D.J., McKeganey, N.P. and MacPherson, I.A. (1988) *Care of the Elderly*, Aberdeen University Press, Aberdeen.

Hunter, S., Brace, S. and Buckley, G. (1993) The interdisciplinary assessment of older people at entry into long-term institutional care: lessons for the new community care arrangements, *Research, Policy and Planning*, 11, 2-9.

Hutchinson, P., Grimley Evans, J. and Greveson, G. (1984) Linking health and social services: the liaison physician, in J. Grimley Evans and F. Caird (eds) *Advanced Geriatric Medicine 4*, Pitman, London.

Huxley, P.J. (1991) Effective care management for mentally ill people: the relevance of recent evidence from the USA for case management services in the United Kingdom, *Social Work and Social Sciences Review*, 2, 192-203.

Intagliata, J. (1982) Improving the quality of community care for the chronically mentally disabled: the role of case management, *Schizophrenia Bulletin*, 8, 655-74.

Irvine, R.E. (1983) Continuing development of medical care of the elderly, in J.M. Graham and H.M. Hodkinson (eds) *Effective Geriatric Medicine: The Special Work of Physicians in Geriatric Medicine*, Harrogate Seminar Reports 7, DHSS, London.

Isaacs, B. (1971) Geriatric patients: do their families care?, *British Medical Journal*, 4, 282-5.

Isaacs, B. (1981) Is geriatrics a specialty?, in T. Arie (ed.) *Health Care of the Elderly*, Croom Helm, London.

Isaacs, B. and Neville, Y. (1976a) The measurement of need in old people, *Scottish Health Service Studies*, No. 34, Scottish Home and Health Department, Edinburgh.

Isaacs, B. and Neville, Y. (1976b) The needs of old people: the 'interval' as a method of measurement, *British Journal of Preventative and Social Medicine*, 30, 79-85.

Isaacs, B., Livingston, M. and Neville, Y. (1972) *Survival of the Unfittest: A Study of Geriatric Patients in Glasgow*, Routledge and Kegan Paul, London.

Ivry, J. (1992) Teaching geriatric assessment, *Journal of Gerontological Social Work*, 18, 3-4, 3-22.

Jackson, G., Gater, R., Goldberg, D., Tantam, D., Linda, L. and Taylor, H. (1993) A new community mental health team based in primary care: a description of the service and its effect on service use in the first year, *British Journal of Psychiatry*, 162, 375-84.

Jagger, C., Spiers, N.A. and Clarke, M. (1993) Factors associated with decline in function, institutionalization and mortality of elderly people, *Age and Ageing*, 22, 190-97.

Jamieson, A. (ed) (1991) *Home Care for Older People in Europe*, Oxford University Press, Oxford.

Jenkinson, M.L., Potter, J.M. and Hildick Smith, M. (1992) The decline in geriatric long stay beds: who remains?, *Journal of the Royal College of*

Physicians of London, 26, 1, 56-60.

Jerrom, B., Mian, I. and Rukanyake, N.G. (1993) Stress on relative caregivers of dementia sufferers, and predictors of the breakdown of community care, *International Journal of Geriatric Psychiatry*, 8, 331-7.

Johansson, L. and Thorslund, M. (1991) Sweden, in R.J. Kraan, J. Baldock, B.P. Davies, A. Evers, L. Johansson, M. Knapen and C. Tunissen (eds) *Care for the Elderly: Significant Innovations in Three European Countries*, Campus/Westview, Boulder, Colorado.

Jolley, D. and Arie, T. (1978) Organisation of psychogeriatric services, *British Journal of Psychiatry*, 132, 1-11.

Jorm, A.F., Henderson, A.S., Kay, D.W.K. and Jacomb, P.A. (1991) Mortality in relation to dementia, depression and social integration in an elderly community sample, *International Journal of Geriatric Psychiatry*, 6, 5-11.

Joshi, A. and Pedlar, D. (1992) Case managers for seniors: educational needs and opportunities, *Educational Gerontology*, 18, 567-86.

Kahn, A.J. (1974) Institutional constraints to professional practice, in H. Rehr (ed.) *Medicine and Social Work: An Exploration in Inter-Professionalism*, Prodist, New York.

Kahn, A.J. (1975) The mental health system and the future aged, *The Gerontologist*, 15, 24-31.

Kalra, L. and Foster, C. (1989) Assessment of applicants for sheltered housing, *Age and Ageing*, 18, 271-4.

Kaluzney, A.D. and Fried, B.J. (1985) Interorganizational coordination of services to the elderly, in H.T. Phillips and S.A. Gaylord (eds) *Aging and Public Health*, Springer, New York.

Kane, R.L. (1990) *What is Case Management Anyway?*, Long-term Care Decisions Resource Centre, University of Minnesota, Minneapolis.

Kane, R.L., Illston, L.H. and Miller, N.A. (1992) Qualitative analysis of the Program of All-inclusive Care for the Elderly (PACE), *The Gerontologist*, 32, 771-80.

Kanter, J. (1987) Mental health case management: a professional domain? *Social Work*, 32, 461-2.

Kemper, P. (1988) The evaluation of national long term care demonstration: 10. Overview of the findings, *Health Services Research*, 23, 161-73.

Kemper, P., Appelbaum, R. and Harrigan, M. (1987) Community care demonstrations: what have we learned?, *Health Care Financing Review*, 8, 87-100.

Kendig, H., McVicar, G., Reynolds, A. and O'Brien, A. (1992) *Victorian Linkages Evaluation*, Department of Health, Housing and Community Services, Canberra.

Knapp, M.R.J. (1984) *The Economics of Social Care*, Macmillan, Basingstoke and London.

Knapp, M.R.J. (1993) Background theory, in A.P Netten and J.K. Beecham (eds) *Costing Community Care: Theory and Practice*, Ashgate, Aldershot.

Knapp, M.R.J., Cambridge, P., Thomason, C., Beecham, J., Allen, C. and Darton, R.A. (1992) *Care in the Community: Challenge and Demonstration*,

Ashgate, Aldershot.

Koch, G.G. (1977) The interface between statistical methodology and statistical practice (with discussion), *American Statistical Association Proceedings of the Social Statistics Section, 1977*, Part I, 205-18.

Kraan, R.J., Baldock, J., Davies, B.P., Evers, A., Johansson, L., Knapen, M., Thorslund, M. and Tunissen, C. (1991) *Care for the Elderly: Significant Innovations in Three European Countries*, Campus, Frankfurt am Main and Westview, Boulder, Colorado.

Krishef, C.H. (1982) Who works with the elderly? A study of personnel in gerontological setting, *Educational Gerontology*, 8, 259-68.

Laing & Buisson (1993) *Laing's Review of Private Health Care 1993 and Directory of Independent Hospitals, Nursing and Residential Homes and Related Services*, Laing & Buisson, London.

Larder, D., Day, P. and Klein, R. (1986) *Institutional Care for the Elderly: The Geographical Distribution of the Public/Private Mix in England*, Bath Social Policy Papers 10, Centre for the Analysis of Social Policy, University of Bath.

Latto, S. (1982) *The Coventry Home Help Project*, Coventry Social Services Department, Coventry.

Latto, S. (1984) *Coventry Home Help Project: Main Report*, Coventry Social Services Department, Coventry.

Lawton, M.P. (1975) The Philadelphia Geriatric Center Morale Scale: a revision, *Journal of Gerontology*, 30, 1, 85-9.

Leedham, I. and Wistow, G. (1992) *Community Care and General Practitioners*, Working Paper No. 6, Nuffield Institute for Health Services Studies, University of Leeds.

Leff, J. (1993) *Carers*, Paper presented at the Workshop on Economic and Social Appraisal of Hospital and Community Care, January, Royal College of Physicians, London.

Levin, E., Sinclair, I. and Gorbach, P. (1983) *The Supporters of Confused Elderly People At Home: Extract from the Main Report*, National Institute for Social Work Research Unit, London.

Levin, E., Sinclair, I. and Gorbach, P. (1985) The effectiveness of the home help service with confused old people and their families, *Research, Policy and Planning*, 3, 2, 1-7.

Levin, E., Sinclair, I. and Gorbach, P. (1989) *Families, Services and Confusion in Old Age*, Avebury, Aldershot.

Levin, E., Moriarty, J. and Gorbach, P. (1994) *Better for the Break*, HMSO, London.

Levine, S. and White, P. (1961) Exchange as a conceptual framework for the study of interorganizational relationships, *Administrative Science Quarterly*, 5, 583-601.

Levine, E. and Wright, S. (1957) New ways to measure personnel turnover in hospitals, *Hospitals, J.A.H.A.*, 31, 1, 38-42.

Lieberman, M.A. (1961) Relationship of mortality rates to entrance to a home for the aged, *Geriatrics*, 16, 515-19.

Lindesay, J. (ed.) (1991) *Working Out: Setting up and Running Community Psychogeriatric Teams*, Research and Development in Psychiatry, London.

Lindesay, J. and Murphy, E. (1989) Dementia, depression and subsequent institutionalisation — the effect of home support, *International Journal of Geriatric Psychiatry*, 4, 3-9.

Lipsky, M. (1980) *Street Level Bureaucracy*, Sage, New York.

Little, R.J.A. and Rubin, D.B. (1987) *Statistical Analysis with Missing Data*, Wiley, New York.

Litwak, E. (1978) Agency and family linkages in providing neighbourhood services, in D. Thursz and J. Vigilante (eds) *Reaching People: The Structure of Neighbourhood Services*, Sage, London.

Litwak, E. and Hylton, L.F. (1962) Inter-organizational analysis: a hypothesis on coordinating agencies, *Administrative Science Quarterly*, 6, 395-420.

Liu, K. and Cornelius, E. (1991) Activities of daily living and eligibility for home care, in D. Rowland and B. Lyons (eds) *Financing Home Care: Improving Protection for Disabled Elderly People*, Johns Hopkins University Press, Baltimore, Maryland.

Local Government Act 1972 (1972 c. 70) HMSO, London.

Loomis, J. (1988) Case management in health care, *Health and Social Work*, 13, 219-25.

Luehrs, J. and Ramthun, R. (1991) State approaches to functional assessments for home care, in D. Rowland and B. Lyons (eds) *Financing Home Care: Improving Protection for Disabled Elderly People*, Johns Hopkins University Press, Baltimore.

Maguire, P.A., Taylor, I.C. and Stout, R.W. (1986) Elderly patients in acute medical wards: factors predicting length of stay in hospital, *British Medical Journal*, 292, 1251-3.

Marks, I. (1985) Controlled trial of psychiatric nurse therapists in primary care, *British Medical Journal*, 290, 1181-4.

Martin, F., Oyewole, A. and Moloney, A. (1994) A randomised controlled trial of a high support hospital discharge team for elderly people, *Age and Ageing*, 23, 228-34.

McAlpine, C.J. (1979) Unblocking beds: a geriatric unit's experience with transferred patients, *British Medical Journal*, 2, 646-8.

McAlpine, C.J. and Wight, Z.J. (1982) Attitudes and anxieties of elderly patients on admission to a geriatric assessment unit, *Age and Ageing*, 11, 35-41.

McArdle, C., Wylie, J. and Alexander, W.P. (1977) Geriatric patients in acute medical wards, *British Medical Journal*, 4, 568-70.

McDowell, D. (1990) Comments on the Australian situation: a US view, in A. Howe, E. Ozanne and C. Selby-Smith (eds) *Community Care Policy and Practice: New Directions in Australia*, Public Management Institute, Monash University, Victoria, Australia.

McDowell, D., Barniskis, L. and Wright, S. (1990) The Wisconsin Community

Options Programme: planning and packaging long-term support for individuals, in A. Howe, E. Ozanne and C. Selby-Smith (eds) *Community Care Policy and Practice: New Directions in Australia*, Public Sector Management Institute, Monash University, Victoria, Australia.

McDowell, I. and Newell, C. (1987) *Measuring Health: A Guide to Rating Scales and Questionnaires*, Open University Press, Buckingham.

McGurrin, M. and Worley, N. (1993) Evaluation of intensive care management for seriously and persistently mentally ill patients, *Journal of Case Management*, 2, 2, 59-65.

McKay, B., North, N. and Murray-Sykes, K. (1983) The effects on carers of hospital admission of the elderly, *Nursing Times*, 30 November, 42-3.

McLeay, L. (Chair) (1982) *In a Home or At Home: Accommodation and Home Care for the Aged*, Report from House of Representatives Standing Committee on Expenditure, Australian Government Publishing Service, Canberra.

Mental Health Act 1959 (7 & 8 Eliz. 2 c.72) HMSO, London.

Merton Social Service Department (1976) The home help service in the London Borough of Merton, *Clearing House for Local Authority Social Services Research*, 6.

Miller, E.J. and Rice, A.K. (1967) *Systems of Organisation: The Control of Task and Sentient Boundaries*, Tavistock, London.

Miller, G. (1983) Case management: the essential service, in C. Sanborn (ed.) *Case Management in Mental Health Services*, Haworth Press, New York.

Milner, M. (1980) *Unequal Care: A Case Study of Interorganizational Relations in Health Care*, Columbia University Press, New York.

Mitchell, A. (1985) Psychiatrists in primary health care settings, *British Journal of Psychiatry*, 159, 334-40.

Modricin, M., Rapp, C. and Poertner, J. (1988) The evaluation of case management services with the chronically mentally ill, *Evaluation and Programme Planning*, 11, 307-14.

Molnar, J. and Rogers, D.L. (1979) A comparative model of interorganisational conflict, *Administrative Science Quarterly*, 24, 405-24.

Moore, S.T. (1990) A social work practice model of case management: the case management grid, *Social Work*, 35, 444-8.

Morris, L.W., Morris, R.G. and Britton, P.G. (1988) The relationship between marital intimacy, perceived strain and depression in spouse caregivers of dementia sufferers, *British Journal of Medical Psychology*, 67, 231-6.

Morris, R.G., Morris. L.W. and Britton, P.G. (1988) Factors affecting the emotional wellbeing of the caregivers of dementia sufferers: a review, *British Journal of Psychiatry*, 153, 147-56.

Morris, R.G., Woods, R., Davies, K. and Morris, L.W. (1991) Gender differences in carers of dementia sufferers, *British Journal of Psychiatry*, 158 (Supplement 10) 69-74.

Moser, C.A. and Kalton, G. (1971) *Survey Methods in Social Investigation*, 2nd edition, Heinemann Educational Books, London.

Moxley, D. (1989) *The Practice of Case Management*, Sage, Newbury Park,

California.

Mowat, I.G. and Morgan, R.T.T. (1982) Peterborough hospital at home scheme, *British Medical Journal*, 284, 641-3.

Mueller, M. (1975) Economic determinants of volunteer work by women, *Signs*, 1, 325-38.

Mugford, S. and Kendig, H. (1986) Social relations: networks and ties, in H. Kendig (ed.) *Ageing and Families: A Social Networks Perspective*, Allen and Unwin, Sydney.

Müller, H. (1987) Die Anwendung familientherapeutischer Erkenntnisse in der Gerontopsychiatrie als Teilbereich einer ganzheitlichen Behandlung, *Psychiatrische Praxis*, 14, 199-202.

Murphy, E. (1982) Social origins of depression in old age, *British Journal of Psychiatry*, 141, 135-42.

Murphy, E. and Bannerjee, S. (1993) The organisation of old age psychiatry services, *Reviews in Clinical Gerontology*, 3, 367-78.

Murphy, E., Smith, R., Lindesay, J. and Slattery, J. (1988) Increased mortality rates in late-life depression, *British Journal of Psychiatry*, 152, 347-53.

Naon, D., Factor, H. and Primak, H. (1993) *Patterns of Institutionalisation in Israel Before and After the Implementation of the Nursing Care Law*, D-198-93, JDC-Brookdale Institute of Gerontology and Adult Development, Jerusalem.

National Federation of Housing Associations/MIND (NFHA/MIND) (1989) *Housing: The Foundation of Community Care*, National Federation of Housing Associations, London.

National Health Service and Community Care Act 1990 (1990 c. 19) HMSO, London.

National Institute on Community-Based Long Term Care (NICBLTC) (1988) *Care Management Standards: Guidelines for Practice*, National Institute on Community-Based Long Term Care, National Institute on Aging, Washington, DC.

Nationwide Building Society (1986) *House Prices Second Quarter 1986*, Nationwide Building Society, London.

Neill, J., Sinclair, I., Gorbach, P. and Williams, J. (1988) *A Need for Care? Elderly Applicants for Local Authority Homes*, Avebury, Aldershot.

Nelson, G.M. (1988) Personnel and training needs in geriatric social work, *Educational Gerontology*, 14, 95-106.

Netten, A.P. (1993) *A Positive Environment?* Ashgate, Aldershot.

Netten, A.P. and Beecham, J.K. (eds) (1993) *Costing Community Care: Theory and Practice*, Ashgate, Aldershot.

Nissel, M. and Bonnerjea, L. (1982) *Family Care of the Handicapped Elderly: Who Pays?*, Policy Studies Institute, London.

Noelker, L.S. and Wallace, R.W. (1985) The organisation of family care for impaired elderly, *Journal of Family Issues*, 6, 23-44.

Northern Regional Health Authority (1985) *Regional Strategic Plan, 1985-1994*, Northern Regional Health Authority, Newcastle upon Tyne.

O'Connor, G. (1988) Case management: system and practice, *Social Casework*, 69, 97-106.

Office of Population Censuses and Surveys (OPCS) (1976) *Census 1971, England and Wales, Report for the County of Durham as constituted on 1st April 1974*, HMSO, London.

Office of Population Censuses and Surveys (OPCS) (1984a) *Final Mid-1981 and Revised Mid-1971 to Mid-1980 Population Estimates for the Local Government and Health Authority Areas of England and Wales*, OPCS Monitor PP1 84/2, London.

Office of Population Censuses and Surveys (OPCS) (1984b) *Population Projections 1981-2021. Population Projections by Sex, Age and Marital Status for United Kingdom and Constituent Countries, from Mid-1981*, Series PP2 no. 12, HMSO, London.

Office of Population Censuses and Surveys (OPCS) (1988) *Population Projections: Area 1985-2001. Population Projections by Sex and Age for Standard Regions, Counties, London Boroughs and Metropolitan Districts of England from Mid 1985*, Series PP3 no. 7, HMSO, London.

Oktay, J.S., Horwitz, K. and Volland, P.J. (1988) Evaluation of the quality of care and the cost of the Community Care Program, *Adult Foster Care Journal*, 2, 52-71.

Onyett, S. (1992) *Case Management in Mental Health*, Chapman and Hall, London.

Onyett, S., Heppleston, T. and Bushell, D. (1994) A national survey of community mental health teams, *Journal of Mental Health*, 3, 175-94.

Ord, D. and Wade, G. (undated) *Darlington Health Authority: Profile of Services for the Elderly (Including EMI)*, Darlington Health Authority and Durham County Council Social Services Department.

Otis, N. (1992) *Identifying Care Alternatives for Older People: The Victorian Regional Geriatric Assessment Program*, Lincoln Papers in Gerontology 13, Lincoln Gerontology Centre, La Trobe University, Melbourne.

Overall, J.E. and Spiegel, D.K. (1969) Concerning least squares analysis of experimental data, *Psychological Bulletin*, 72, 5, 311-22.

Ovretveit, J. (1986) *Organising Multidisciplinary Teams*, Brunel Institute of Organisation and Social Studies, Brunel University.

Ovretveit, J. (1993) *Coordinating Community Care: Multidisciplinary Teams and Care Management*, Open University Press, Buckingham.

Owens, P. (1987) *Community Care and Severe Physical Disability*, Bedford Square Press, London.

Oxfordshire Social Services Department and Oxford Health Authority (1982) *The Community Care Project for the Elderly: An Exercise in Collaborative Caring, Report of the Project*, Oxfordshire Social Services Department and Oxford Health Authority.

Ozanne, E. (1990) Development of Australian health and social policy in relation to the aged and the and the emergence of home care services, in A. Howe, E. Ozanne and C. Selby-Smith (eds) *Community Care Policy and*

Practice: New Directions in Australia, Public Sector Management Institute, Monash University, Melbourne.

Parker, G. (1990) *With Due Care and Attention: A Review of Research on Informal Care*, 2nd edition, Family Policy Studies Centre, London.

Parker, R.A. (1987) *The Elderly and Residential Care: American Lessons for Britain*, Gower, Aldershot.

Pattie, A.H. and Gilleard, C.J. (1978) Admission and adjustment of residents in homes for the elderly, *Journal of Epidemiology and Community Health*, 32, 212-14.

Pattie, A.H. and Gilleard, C.J. (1979) *Manual of the Clifton Assessment Procedures for the Elderly (CAPE)*, Hodder and Stoughton, Sevenoaks.

Payne, C. (1977) The preparation and processing of survey data, in C.A. O'Muircheartaigh and C. Payne (eds) *The Analysis of Survey Data. Volume 1: Exploring Data Structures*, Wiley, London.

Peebles, R. (1989) Diversion in Durham, *Community Care*, 27 July, Inside, vi.

Peet, S.M., Castleden, C.M., Potter, J.F. and Jagger, C. (1993) Outcome of medical examination for applicants to elderly person's homes in Leicestershire, *Age and Ageing*, 22, (Supplement 2), 5-6.

Perrow, C. (1970) *Organisational Analysis*, Tavistock, London.

Petch, A. (1994) The best move I've ever made: The role of housing for people with mental health problems, in M. Titterton (ed.) *Caring for People in the Community: The New Welfare*, Jessica Kingsley, London.

Pilling, D. (1988) *The Case Manager Project: Report of the Evaluation*, Rehabilitation Resource Centre, City University, London.

Pilling, D. (1992) *Approaches to Case Management for People with Disabilities*, Jessica Kingsley, London.

Plank, D. (1977) *Caring for the Elderly: Report of a Study of Various Means of Caring for Dependent Elderly People in Eight London Boroughs*, Research Memorandum 512, Greater London Council, London.

Platt, S. (1985) Measuring the burden of psychiatric illness on the family: an evaluation of some rating scales, *Psychological Medicine*, 15, 2, 383-93.

Platt, S., Weyman, A., Hirsch, S. and Hewett, S. (1980) The Social Behaviour Assessment Schedule (SBAS): rationale, contents, scoring and reliability of a new interview schedule, *Social Psychiatry*, 15, 43-55.

Platt, S., Hirsch, S. and Weyman, A. (1983) *Social Behaviour Assessment Schedule (SBAS)*, 3rd edition, NFER-Nelson, Windsor.

Public Health Act 1848 (11 & 12 Vict. c. 63) Eyre and Spottiswoode, London.

Quartararo, M. and O'Neill, T.J. (1990) Nursing home admissions: the effect of a multidisciplinary assessment team on the frequency of admission approvals, *Community Health Studies*, 14, 441-9.

Qureshi, H., Challis, D.J. and Davies, B.P. (1983) Motivations and rewards of helpers in the Kent Community Care Scheme, in S. Hatch (ed.) *Volunteers: Patterns, Meanings and Motives*, The Volunteer Centre, Berkhamsted.

Qureshi, H., Challis, D.J. and Davies, B.P. (1989) *Helpers in Case-Managed Community Care*, Gower, Aldershot.

Rafferty, J., Smith, R.G. and Williamson, J. (1987) Medical assessment of elderly persons prior to a move to residential care,: a review of seven years experience in Edinburgh, *Age and Ageing*, 16, 10-12.

Ramsay, F., Horsfall, R. and Rudd, A. (1987) Selection for long-term hospital care, *Age and Ageing*, 16, 301-4.

Reid, W.J. (1965) Inter-agency coordination in delinquency prevention and control, in M.M. Zald (ed.) *Social Welfare Institutions*, Wiley, New York.

Reid, W.J. (1969) Interorganizational coordination in welfare: a theoretical approach to analysis and intervention, in R. Kramer and H. Specht (eds) *Readings in Community Organization Practice*, Prentice-Hall, Englewood Cliffs, New Jersey.

Renshaw, J., Hampson, R., Thomason, C., Darton, R.A., Judge, K.F. and Knapp, M.R.J. (1988) *Care in the Community: The First Steps*, Gower, Aldershot.

Rhys Hearn, C. (1990) Evaluation of the geriatric assessment program in Western Australia, in P. Puliafito (ed.) Proceedings of SYSTED 90 Conference, Bologna.

Richardson, A. and Higgins, R. (1990) *Case Management in Practice: Reflections on the Wakefield Case Management Project*, Working Paper 1, Nuffield Institute for Health Service Studies, University of Leeds.

Richardson, A. and Higgins, R. (1991) *Doing Case Management: Learning from the Wakefield Case Management Project*, Working Paper 4, Nuffield Institute for Health Service Studies, University of Leeds.

Richardson, A. and Higgins, R. (1992) *The Limits of Case Management: Lessons from the Wakefield Case Management Project*, Working Paper 5, Nuffield Institute for Health Services Studies, University of Leeds.

Roberts-DeGennaro, M. (1987) Defining case management as a practice model, *Social Casework*, 68, 466-70.

Robertson, C., Warrington, J. and Eagles, J.M. (1993) Relocation mortality in dementia: the effects of a new hospital, *International Journal of Geriatric Psychiatry*, 8, 521-5.

Robson, M. France, R. and Bland, M. (1984) Clinical psychologist in primary care: a controlled trial and economic evaluation, *British Medical Journal*, 288, 1805-8.

Royal College of Physicians (1977) Medical care of the elderly: report of the working party of the Royal College of Physicians, *Lancet*, 1, 1092-5.

Royal College of Physicians (1994) *The Interface Between Geriatric and General (Internal) Medicine*, Royal College of Physicians, London.

Rubin, S.G. and Davies, G.H. (1975) Bed blocking by elderly patients in general-hospital wards, *Age and Ageing*, 4, 142-7.

Rutter, M., Tizard, J. and Whitmore, K. (eds) (1970) *Education, Health and Behaviour*, Longman, London.

Sainsbury, P. and Grad de Alarcon, J. (1971) The psychiatrist and the geriatric patient: the effects of community care on the family of the geriatric patient, *Journal of Geriatric Psychiatry*, 4, 23-41.

Salvage, A.V. (1985) *Domiciliary Care Services for the Elderly: Provision by Local*

Authority Social Services Departments and Recommendations for their Introduction, Volume 1, Research Team for the Care of the Elderly, University of Wales College of Medicine, Cardiff.

Salvage, A.V. (1986) *Attitudes of the Over-75's to Health and Social Services. Final Report*, Research Team for the Elderly, University of Wales College of Medicine, Cardiff.

Salvage, A.V., Vetter, N.J. and Jones, D.A. (1988) Attitudes to hospital care among a community sample of people aged 75 and older, *Age and Ageing*, 17, 270-74.

Sanford, J. (1975) Tolerance of debility in elderly dependants by supporters at home: its significance for hospital practice, *British Medical Journal*, 3, 471-3.

Sardell, A. (1988) *The US Experiment in Social Medicine: The Community Health Center Program, 1965-86*, University of Pittsburgh Press, Pittsburgh, Pennsylvania.

Saunders, P. (Chairman) (1989) *First Triennial Review of the Home and Community Care Program*, Australian Government Publishing Service, Canberra.

Schmidt, S. and Kochan, T. (1977) Interorganisational relationships: patterns and motivations, *Administrative Science Quarterly*, 22, 220-33.

Schulz, R. and Brenner, G. (1977) Relocation of the aged: a review and theoretical analysis, *Journal of Gerontology*, 32, 323-33.

Scott, W.R. (1981) *Organizations: Rational, Natural and Open Systems*, Prentice-Hall, Englewood Cliffs, New Jersey.

Seeman, T.E., Kaplan, G.A., Knudsen, L., Cohen, R. and Guralnik, J. (1987) Social network ties and mortality among the elderly in the Alameda county study, *American Journal of Epidemiology*, 126, 714-23.

Seidl, F., Applebaum, R., Austin, C. and Mahoney, K. (1983) *Delivering In-Home Services to the Aged and Disabled: The Wisconsin Experiment*, Heath, Lexington, Massachusetts.

Seidman, H. (1970) *Politics, Position and Power: The Dynamics of Federal Organisation*, Oxford University Press, New York.

Seligman, M. (1975) *Helplessness. On Depression, Development and Health*, Freeman, New York.

Seymour, D.G. and Pringle, R. (1982) Elderly patients in a general surgical unit: do they block beds?, *British Medical Journal*, 284, 1921-3.

Shapiro, E. and Tate, R. (1988) Who is really at risk of institutionalisation? *The Gerontologist*, 28, 237-45.

Shepherd, M., Harwin, B., Depla, C. and Cairns, V. (1979) Social work and the primary care of mental disorder, *Psychological Medicine*, 9, 661-9.

Simons, K. and Warburton, R.W. (1980) *A Sensible Service*, Cambridgeshire Social Services Department, Cambridge.

Sinclair, I., Stanforth, L. and O'Connor, P. (1988) Factors predicting admission of elderly people to local authority residential care, *British Journal of Social Work*, 18, 251-68.

Sinclair, I., Parker, R., Leat, D. and Williams, J. (1990) *The Kaleidoscope of Care,*

HMSO, London.

Smith, K.F. and Bengtson, V.L. (1979) Positive consequences of institution-alization: solidarity between elderly parents and their middle-aged children, *The Gerontologist*, 19, 5, 438-47.

Snedecor, G.W. and Cochran, W.G. (1980) *Statistical Methods*, 7th edition, Iowa State University Press.

Social Services Inspectorate (SSI) (1987) *From Home Help to Home Care: An Analysis of Policy Resourcing and Service Management*, SSI, London.

Social Services Inspectorate (SSI) (1988) *Managing Policy Change in Home Help Services*, SSI, London.

Social Services Inspectorate (SSI) (1991) *Training for Community Care: A Joint Approach*, HMSO, London.

Social Services Inspectorate and Social Work Services Group (SSI/SWSG) (1991a) *Care Management and Assessment: Managers Guide*, Social Services Inspectorate and Social Work Services Group, HMSO, London.

Social Services Inspectorate and Social Work Services Group (SSI/SWSG) (1991b) *Care Management and Assessment: Practitioners Guide*, Social Services Inspectorate and Social Work Services Group, HMSO, London.

Social Services Inspectorate and Social Work Services Group (SSI)/SWSG) (1991c) *Care Management and Assessment: Summary of Practice Guidance*, HMSO, London.

South West Herts Health Authority/Hertfordshire Social Care (1993) *Proposal for an Intensive Community Care Scheme*, South West Herts Health Authority, Watford.

SPSS Inc. (1990) *SPSS Reference Guide*, SPSS Inc., Chicago, Illinois.

StatXact (1989) *A Statistical Package for Exact Nonparametric Inference*, Cytel Software Corporation, Cambridge, Massachusetts.

Stein, L. and Test, M.A. (1980) Alternative to mental hospital treatment: I. Conceptual model, treatment programme, and clinical evaluation, *Archives of General Psychiatry*, 37, 392-7.

Stein, L., Diamond, R. and Factor, R. (1989) *A System Approach to the Care of Persons With Schizophrenia*, Mental Health Research Centre, University of Wisconsin, Madison.

Steinberg, R.M. and Carter, G.W (1983) *Case Management and the Elderly*, Heath, Lexington, Massachusetts.

Stephens, M.A.P., Kinney, J.M. and Ogrocki, P.K. (1991) Stressors and well-being among caregivers to older adults with dementia: the in-home versus the nursing home experience, *The Gerontologist*, 31, 217-23.

Stephens, S.A. and Christianson, J.B. (1986) *Informal Care of the Elderly*, Lexington Books, Lexington, Massachusetts.

Strathdee, G. and Williams, P. (1984) A survey of psychiatrists in primary care: the silent growth of a new service, *Journal of the Royal College of General Practitioners*, 34, 615-18.

Strathdee, G. and Williams, P. (1986) Patterns of collaboration, in M. Shepherd, G. Wilkinson and P. Williams, P. (eds) *Mental Illness in Primary Care Settings*,

Tavistock, London.

Sugden, R. and Williams, A. (1978) *The Principles of Practical Cost-Benefit Analysis*, Oxford University Press, Oxford.

Sunderland, N. (1972) *A History of Darlington*, E.J. Morten, Didsbury, Manchester.

Tench, D.W., Benbow, S.M. and Benbow, E.W. (1992) Do old age psychiatrists miss physical illnesses? *International Journal of Geriatric Psychiatry*, 7, 713-18.

Thomas, N. (1988) Evaluative research and the personal social services, in J. Lishman (ed.) *Research Highlights in Social Work 8: Evaluation*, 2nd edition, Jessica Kingsley Publishers, London.

Thomas, D.R., Brahan, R. and Haywood, B.P. (1993) Inpatient community-based geriatric assessment reduces subsequent mortality, *Journal of the American Geriatrics Society*, 41, 101-4.

Thorslund, M. (1991) The increasing number of very old people will change the Swedish model of the welfare state, *Social Science and Medicine*, 32, 455-64.

Thorslund, M. and Parker, M. (1994) Care of the elderly in the changing Swedish welfare state, in D.J. Challis, B.P. Davies and K.J. Traske (eds) *New Agendas and Challenges in Community Care from the UK and Overseas*, Gower, Aldershot.

Tinker, A. (1992) *Elderly People in Modern Society*, 2nd edition, Longman, London.

Tobin, S.S. and Lieberman, M.A. (1976) *Last Home for the Aged*, Jossey-Bass, San Francisco, California.

Townsend, J., Piper, M., Frank, A.O., Dyer, S., North, W.R.S. and Meade, T.W. (1988) Reduction in hospital readmission stay of elderly patients by a community based hospital discharge scheme: a randomised controlled trial, *British Medical Journal*, 297, 544-7.

Twigg, J. (1989) Models of carers: how do social care agencies conceptualise their relationship with informal carers, *Journal of Social Policy*, 18, 53-66.

Twigg, J. (1993) The interweaving of formal and informal care: policy models and problems, in A. Evers and G.H. van der Zanden (eds) *Better Care for Dependent People Living at Home*, Netherlands Institute of Gerontology, Bunnik.

Twigg, J. and Atkin, K. (1994) *Carers Perceived: Policy and Practice in Informal Care*, Open University Press, Buckingham.

United Kingdom Central Council for Nursing, Midwifery and Health Visiting (UKCC) (1986) *Project 2000*, UKCC, London.

Van de Ven, A.H. (1976) On the nature, formation and maintenance of relations among organizations, *Academy of Management Review*, 2, 24-36.

Van de Ven, A.H., Walker, G. and Liston, J. (1979) Coordination patterns within an interorganizational network, *Human Relations*, 32, 19-36.

Victor, C.R. and Vetter, N.J. (1988a) Preparing the elderly for discharge from hospital: a neglected aspect of patient care?, *Age and Ageing*, 17, 155-63.

Victor, C.R. and Vetter, N.J. (1988b) Rearranging the deckchairs on the Titanic:

failure of an augmented home help scheme after discharge to reduce the length of stay in hospital, *Archives of Gerontology and Geriatrics*, 7, 83-91.

von Abendorff, R., Challis, D.J. and Netten, A.P. (1994) Staff activity patterns in community mental health team for older people, *International Journal of Geriatric Psychiatry*, forthcoming.

Wade, B., Sawyer, L. and Bell, S. (1983) *Dependency with Dignity*, Bedford Square Press, London.

Wattis, J. (1988) Geographical variations in the provision of psychiatric services for old people, *Age and Ageing*, 17, 171-80.

Webb, A. (1991) Coordination: a problem in public sector management, *Policy and Politics*, 19, 229-41.

Webb, A. and Wistow, G. (1986) *Planning, Need and Scarcity: Essays on the Personal Social Services*, Allen and Unwin, London.

Weiss, C.H. (1972) *Evaluation Research: Methods for Assessing Program Effectiveness*, Prentice-Hall, Englewood Cliffs, New Jersey.

Weiss, R. (1974) The provisions of social relationships, in Z. Rubin (ed.) *Doing Unto Others*, Prentice-Hall, Englewood Cliffs, New Jersey.

Weissert, G. (1988) The National Channelling Demonstration: what we knew, know now and still need to know, *Health Services Research*, 23, 175-87.

Weissert, W.G. and Cready, C.M. (1989) Toward a model for improving targeting of the aged at risk of institutionalisation, *Health Services Research*, 25, 485-510.

Wenger, G.C. (1986) A longitudinal study of changes and adaptations in the support networks of Welsh elderly over 75, *Journal of Cross-cultural Gerontology*, 1, 3, 277-304.

Wenger, G.C. (1989) Support networks in old age: constructing a typology, in M. Jefferys (ed.) *Growing Old in the Twentieth Century*, Routledge, London.

Wenger, G.C. (1992) *Help in Old Age — Facing up to Change: A Longitudinal Network Study*, Liverpool University Press, Liverpool.

Wenger, G.C. (1994) Support networks and dementia, *International Journal of Geriatric Psychiatry*, 9, 181-94.

Werner, D. (1978) The village health worker: lackey or liberator? in M. Skeet and K. Elliot (eds) *Health Auxiliaries and the Health Team*, Croom Helm, London.

Wickings, I., Coles, J.M., Flux, R. and Howard, L. (1983) Review of clinical budgeting and costing experiments, *British Medical Journal*, 286, 575-8.

Willcocks, D., Peace, S. and Kelllaher, L. (1987) *Private Lives in Public Places: A Research-Based Critique of Residential Life in Local Authority Old People's Homes*, Tavistock, London.

Williams, E.I. and Fitton, F. (1991) Use of nursing and social services by elderly patients discharged from hospital, *British Journal of General Practice*, 41, 72-5.

Williamson, J. (1981) Screening, surveillance and case-finding, in T. Arie (ed.) *Health Care of the Elderly*, Croom Helm, London.

Wing, L. (1989) *Hospital Closure and the Resettlement of Residents: The Case of Darenth Park Mental Handicap Hospital*, Avebury, Aldershot.

Wisconsin Department of Health and Social Services (1992) *Care Management Standards for the Community Options Program: Recommendations from the COP Care Management Standards Development Workgroup*, Wisconsin Department of Health and Social Services, Madison, Wisconsin.

Wistow, G. (1994) Community care futures: interagency relationships — stability or continuing change?, in M. Titterton (ed.) *Caring for People in the Community: The New Welfare*, Jessica Kingsley, London.

World Health Organization (1982) *Activities of the World Health Organization in Promoting Community Involvement for Health Development*, WHO, Geneva.

Wright, F. (1983) Single carers: employment, housework and caring, in J. Finch and D. Groves (eds) *A Labour of Love: Women, Work and Caring*, Routledge and Kegan Paul, London.

Wright, K.G., Cairns, J.A. and Snell, M.C. (1981) *Costing Care: The Costs of Alternative Patterns of Care for the Elderly*, Social Services Monographs: Research in Practice, Joint Unit for Social Services Research, University of Sheffield in collaboration with *Community Care*, London.

Yawney, B. and Slover, D.L. (1973) Relocation of the elderly, *Social Work*, 18 May, 86-93.

York, J.L. and Calsyn, R.J. (1977) Family involvement in nursing homes, *The Gerontologist*, 17, 6, 500-505.

Zarit, J.M. (1982) *Family Roles, Social Supports and their Relationship to Caregivers' Burden*, Paper presented at the meeting of the Western Psychological Association, Sacramento, July.

Zarit, S.H., Todd, P.A. and Zarit, J.M. (1986) Subjective burden of husbands and wives as caregivers: a longitudinal study, *The Gerontologist*, 26, 260-66.

Zucker, L.G. (1988) *Institutional Patterns and Organizations: Culture and Environment*, Ballinger, Cambridge, Massachusetts.

Name Index

Subject Index

Darlington Health Authority, 27, 35,
40-41, 44-45, 60, 284-285, 287-288, 337
Darlington Health Authority
Community Unit, 278, 337
Darlington, history of, 15, 35, 37-40
day care, 7, 37, 47, 79, 85, 93, 122, 216,
237-238, 248, 283, 321
day census, 1, 53, 60-61, 145
Department of Community Services,
298, 338
Department of Community Services
and Health, 300, 304, 338
Department of Employment, 108,
245-246, 338
Department of Health, 17-19, 21-24,
33, 278, 286, 297, 299, 302-303, 306,
308-311, 314, 316, 318, 322, 338
Department of Health, Housing and
Community Services (DHHCS), 99,
149, 296, 299, 304, 307, 313-314, 317,
322, 339-340
Department of Health and Social
Services (DHSS), 2-3, 5-11, 13, 25,
41-45, 49, 53, 153, 156, 164, 244-245,
324, 339
Department of Social Security, 71, 88,
251
Department of the Environment, 241,
338
dependency, 2, 6, 13, 28, 50, 55, 60, 69,
80, 83-85, 128, 151, 160, 162, 164, 169,
178, 182, 193, 196, 198-199, 254-256,
259, 264, 266-267, 270-271, 276, 279,
295, 298, 301, 305-307, 318
depression, 6, 12, 56, 89, 171, 176, 185,
190, 192, 194, 222, 294
dietician, 47-48, 86, 111, 133, 138, 294
Disability Alliance, 340
discharge, 1-3, 5, 8, 19, 22, 28-29,
49-50, 52, 54-55, 57-58, 60, 62, 68-74,
76-77, 79-86, 88-90, 93, 95-96, 100,
107, 110, 114-115, 121-122, 145,
147-149, 151, 157-162, 169, 171, 173,
175, 177-187, 189, 192-196, 198,
200-201, 210, 213-214, 222, 238-239,
242-243, 245, 252, 254-255, 257-261,
263, 265, 275, 287, 290-292, 294, 320,
322-323, 325-326

district nurses, 1-2, 6, 8, 12-13, 41-43,
45-46, 69, 75, 79, 86, 88, 92, 96, 101,
111, 113, 119-121, 123, 133, 135, 146,
156, 158-160, 241, 274, 288, 294-295
Duke University Center for the Study
of Aging and Human Development,
56, 63, 188, 340
Durham, 27, 35, 37-39, 41-46, 52-53,
60-61, 64, 237, 242
Durham County Council Social
Services Department, 27, 35, 42, 45,
336, 340
effectiveness, 9, 21-22, 26, 44, 50-51,
59, 63, 67, 88, 98, 125, 130, 187-189,
253, 278-279, 296, 304, 312, 317
efficiency, 9, 21, 67-68, 70-71, 149, 319,
322
eligibility, 22-23, 67, 280, 295, 305-306,
316, 319-320
falling, 10, 61, 64, 79, 171, 205, 207,
224, 227, 255, 258-259, 266-267, 271
family placement, 71, 179, 192, 255,
257-261, 265
General Health Questionnaire (GHQ),
190
general practitioners, 1-2, 5, 44, 48, 79,
88, 100, 103, 120, 133, 136-137,
145-146, 148, 156, 159-160, 165,
241-242, 274, 280, 299, 311, 321, 323,
325
Geriatric Assessment Team, 298-304,
327
geriatric multidisciplinary team, 1-2,
14, 28-29, 34, 68-70, 75, 98, 149,
157-158, 163, 293, 296, 305, 327
geriatrics, 1, 5-6, 10, 42-44, 68-69,
71-73, 81, 88, 100-101, 103, 145, 148,
150, 158-159, 162, 165, 171, 174, 179,
183, 188, 194-195, 238-243, 248-251,
255, 274, 276, 279-280, 291, 297-298,
300-305, 309, 319, 321, 323-324, 327
Health Advisory Service, 6, 151, 343
Health Service Journal, 34, 343
Hertfordshire Social Care, 296, 355
Hillingdon Social Services
Department, 114, 344
home care assistants, 1-2, 9, 14-15,
25-26, 28-29, 31, 50, 59, 70, 76-90, 92,
94-97, 99-100, 104-134, 137-142, 144,